APPLIED COST and SCHEDULE CONTROL

APPLIED COST and SCHEDULE CONTROL

James A. Bent
James Bent Associates, Inc.
Yardley, Pennsylvania

MARCEL DEKKER, INC.   New York and Basel

Library of Congress Cataloging in Publication Data

Bent, James A., [date]
    Applied cost and schedule control.

    (Cost engineering; v. 3)
    Includes index.
    1. Industrial project management. 2. Cost control.
I. Title. II. Series: Cost engineering (Marcel Dekker,
Inc.); v. 3.
T56.8.B46   658   82-5077
ISBN 0-8247-1654-X   AACR2

MARCEL DEKKER, INC.

270 Madison Avenue, New York, New York 10016

Current printing (last digit):
10 9 8 7 6 5 4 3 2 1

PRINTED IN THE UNITED STATES OF AMERICA

PREFACE

There is the long-stated opinion that actual control is exercised only by project management, where the right of decision is vested, and that a cost-schedule engineer only provides information and has no exercise of control. This is only partly true. A key element for effective control is timely evaluation of potential cost and schedule hazards and presenting them with recommended solutions to project management. This means that the control engineer must be a skilled technician and also able to effectively communicate to management level.

Project control can be defined as the process that

Forecasts and evaluates potential hazards prior to occurrence so that preventative action can be taken

Reviews trends or actual situations to analyze their impact and, if possible, proposes action to alleviate the situation

Provides constant surveillance of project conditions to effectively and economically create a "no-surprise" condition

This book covers the entire life cycle of capital projects and deals with control techniques, methods, and procedures used by owners and contractors for small and large projects. Emphasis is placed on practical approaches and the relationships of a control engineer in the project team. The interface and relationship between project management and staff control engineers are fully explored. Also, the relationship between an owner and a contractor is covered in considerable detail.

This book has been written for both the participating cost-schedule engineer and those engineers and managers exposed to the area of project control, mainly in the area of planning, design, and construction of process plants. The book is intended for both owners and contractors. The book should be of interest to individuals from those companies having established project control procedures and those with a less formal approach. It should be of special interest to those individuals interested in developing new approaches, concepts, and methods in this area. This will be particularly true for the offshore industry (one chapter covers North Sea platforms) and for energy companies (chapters cover synthetic fuels and control of jumbo projects).

It is emphasized that only manual methods are covered in this book. Computer programs are not part of the written material.

As estimating systems vary widely, this book does not cover estimating programs but highlights major requirements of a quality estimate, outlines a detailed estimate review procedure, and covers control and development of an estimate as a project develops.

There are nearly 200 exhibits illustrating method, report format, and project data.

It is my strong contention that systems and procedures do not build projects—*people do.* As such, the relationships of project managers and control engineers are fully explored, as is the relationship between owners and contractors.

I have recommended divisions of work for owners and contractors which avoid duplication of effort and establish a monitoring function for owners and daily control responsibility for contractors.

An American woman living in a remote overseas location was having an electrical installation done by a native electrician. He bothered her so much for instructions that she at last said irritably, "You know what I want—just use your common sense and *do* it!"

The electrician bowed politely and said, *"Madam, common sense is a rare gift of God. I have only a technical education."*

This story illustrates my approach. I have written a book based on many years of firsthand experience on many projects in numerous worldwide locations. Common sense and practical methods are outlined throughout the book and theoretical approaches kept to a minimum. Alternative approaches are reviewed, and, in most cases, a recommended method is suggested.

Application has been my watchword, and I have attempted to structure exhibit, format, and narrative to this concept.

I have added one further concept to this book. In areas of new technology, such as synthetic fuels, coal, uranium, and the offshore industry, I have provided a brief explanation of the subject. I have always found such information helpful in appreciating scope and project conditions as I have moved into new industries.

James A. Bent

ACKNOWLEDGMENTS

My thanks and appreciation to

Mobil Oil Corporation for their enlightened view in encouraging me to
publish many papers on method and procedure while I was in their
employ

My former Mobil colleagues, particularly Hal Siegel, Jack Failla, Bob
Roberts, Barry de Haas, Tony Etheridge, and Sumer Kalsy, for
their technical advice and assistance during my years with Mobil

Bechtel Corporation for their advice on control of jumbo projects

M. W. Kellogg (London) for on-the-job training in construction and
control of subcontracts

Rand Corporation for their chart on cost growth of energy pioneer plants
(Fig. 1.1, Rand Report R-2481-DOE, by E. Merrow, S. W. Chapel,
and J. C. Worthing)

Offshore Engineer (February 1980 issue) for a diagram and information
on the Conoco tension leg platform

My wife Heather and daughter Alison for typing the manuscript and my
sons Roger and Dan for their assistance in the preparation of the
artwork

CONTENTS

COST ENGINEERING

A Series of Reference Books and Textbooks

Editors

FORREST D. CLARK   **A. B. LORENZONI**

Exxon Research and Engineering Company
Florham Park, New Jersey

1. Applied Cost Engineering, *Forrest D. Clark and A. B. Lorenzoni*
2. Basic Cost Engineering, *Kenneth K. Humphreys and Sidney Katell*
3. Applied Cost and Schedule Control, *James A. Bent*

Additional Volumes in Preparation

APPLIED COST and SCHEDULE CONTROL

1

INTRODUCTION TO PROJECT CONTROL

1.1 GENERAL

Philosophical discussions on defining *control* are never-ending. There is the long-stated opinion that actual control is exercised only where the right of decision is vested—in this case, the decision making of the project manager and line supervisors and the establishment of the scope by the design engineers.

It is stated that cost and schedule engineers only provide information and therefore have no exercise of control. This is partly true. Often a staff function does become one of reporting and accounting. However, reporting, trending, and analysis are essential ingredients for forecasting, which, in turn, is an essential ingredient of control.

It is also true that control is minimal where there is little creative analysis and only reporting and accounting.

The fundamental elements of control are the cost estimate and project schedule.

1.2 PLANNING THE PROJECT

One of the most important functions in the life cycle of a project is project planning, especially in the preliminary phases when basic decisions are being made that will affect the entire course of the project. The purpose of project planning is to identify the work that must be done, to gain the participation of those best qualified to do the work, and to develop appropriate project cost and schedule objectives. Sound planning will minimize lost motion and clearly define for all participants— owner, contractor, associated corporate departments, and outsiders— their role in the project. Sound planning will also provide adequate consideration of all project elements and will ensure a proper effort to meet the completion date. See Figure 1.1.

The project manager should personally supervise this effort with the support of business, cost, and schedule specialists. Project planning should consider such items as organization, communication channels, personnel skills, client requirements, the business-political environ-

1

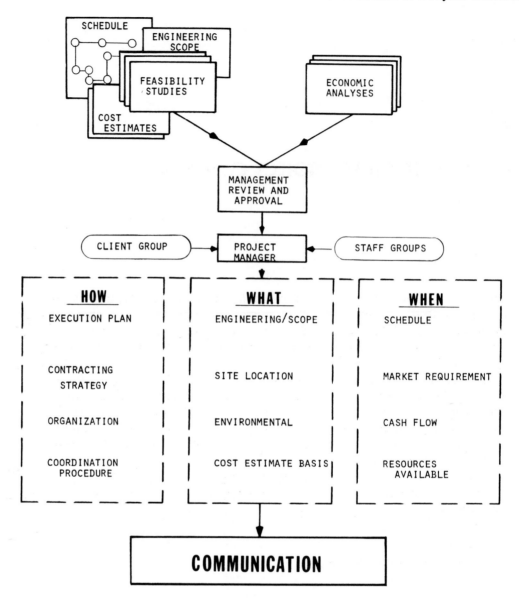

Figure 1.1 Flowchart of planning the project.

ment, project execution strategy, and the drawing up of a plan to set these operations in motion. The project manager should develop a *project coordination procedure* after consulting with the client and others as necessary. This document will identify all principals concerned with the project, define their functions and responsibilities, and indicate appropriate contacts for each. The purpose of the document is to provide an effective basis for coordinating company activity and communications on the project, especially in the early stages of project execution when project scope and other elements are being defined. *Effective communication channels are essential for successful control.*

Who determines the organization, control systems, and resource requirements? Too often, project managers will set up projects without seeking the support, advice, and assistance of staff personnel. On large projects this can be disastrous, particularly for the project control and estimating function. Resource requirements, control systems, and organizational arrangements should be matters of consultation and discussion with staff groups prior to decision by the project manager. This will also ensure that anticipated manpower requirements and resources are adequately reflected in the early conceptual estimates.

Apart from project size, the proposed execution plan and contracting strategy are the most significant elements for determining the control basis and associated organization for the project.

1.3 PROJECT LIFE CYCLE

Figure 1.2 shows the typical phases of a project from an owner's feasibility and front end studies to full implementation by a prime contractor. This typical life cycle is for a large process plant and shows durations of 8 months for a phase I and 33 months for a phase II operation. The durations for the front end vary widely.

There are many possible variations of project life cycles, and this particular configuration is a typical routine of large oil corporations. Many owners use a phased approach rather than a straight-through approach. This provides the owner with less risk on capital investment and also the ability to fully investigate the feasibility and financial viability of multiple projects at the same time.

A phased approach, particularly on large projects, also provides for more control by corporate management as the project is being developed in the feasibility, scoping, and design phases. However, it may add costs and will increase the overall project duration.

The following brief explanations cover the various phases illustrated in Figure 1.2.

Owner front end is the feasibility stage when a design specification is produced by engineering, economic and market evaluations are produced by the affiliate, and a capital cost estimate and schedule are produced by the cost group. The design specification is sometimes produced by a contractor in greater detail than an owner-engineered design specification but not to the detail of a phase I operation. The control basis will be set by overall corporate objectives, mainly in the form of a development budget.

Phase I generally covers conceptual design, process selection, optimization, upgrading of the estimate schedule, environmental-governmental studies, and finalization of the process design. The authorization for funds for the phase II work is then prepared and presented, and when approved, a contractor is selected to carry out the work. The phase I work is carried out by a contractor, normally on a reimbursable basis with a small owner project task force (PTF) in attendance. There are two basic objectives for a phase I operation. For large projects and reconstructions, it provides greater definition of scope, schedule, and cost. On small projects, it provides a design package suitable for lump

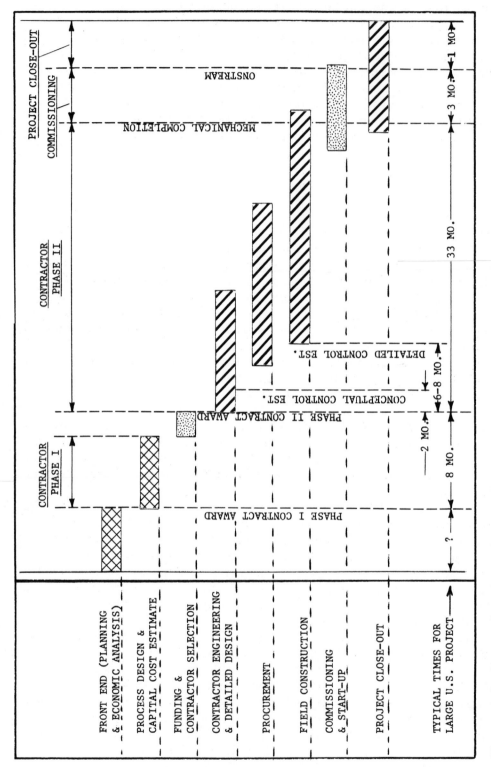

Figure 1.2 Chart of Project life cycle (phased approach).

sum bids. An important element of a phase I operation is providing an execution plan for phase II. The control basis will be the expenditure and cost of the contractor man-hours and a milestone project master schedule.

Phase II is full execution of the project by a contractor. The normal project philosophy is that of a prime contractor with single responsibility for engineering, procurement, and construction. Most large projects are executed on a reimbursable basis with an owner PTF directing and monitoring the work. This will require a complete project control system as outlined in the following chapters.

There are variations of a phase II where engineering and construction responsibilities are split and awarded to different contractors. This is the method usually adopted by utility companies where architect-engineers provide the design and construction contractors manage the field work on a subcontract basis. This approach does not provide a single responsibility, and the designer and constructor can blame each other for errors of design and installation.

As outlined, the phased approach requires different control methods for each phase. A front end (feasibility study), usually carried out within the owner's organization, is authorized by an operating affiliate from its own development budget. As these budgets are developed in 1-year and 5-year cycles, there is rarely a need for detailed cost and schedule control at this stage. Expenditures can range from $100,000 for a small project to $5 million for a very large project.

A contractor phase I, on a reimbursable basis, requires a monthly monitoring of engineering man-hours and associated costs. Controls will be manual expenditure curves and progress measurement of engineering design. Expenditures can range from $1 million for small projects to $20 million for very large projects.

A contractor phase II will require full schedule control for reimbursable and lump sum bases but minimal cost control if on a lump sum basis.

A further variable on control requirements is the question of technology. New technology, such as synthetic fuels and offshore facilities, will generally require additional controls due to the lack of an existing data base. The past decade of the Alaska Pipeline, nuclear power plants, and North Sea platforms has clearly shown that prototype engineering, project size, hostile environments, and lack of data have produced poor cost estimates and schedules. This type of project will generally require a phased approach in order to develop data for a detailed project execution plan.

It cannot be emphasized too strongly that poor cost estimates and unrealistic project schedules can only result in an "out-of-control" project.

1.4 PROJECT EXECUTION PLAN

Figure 1.3 shows the major elements of a project execution plan. This plan is developed during phase I and covers all aspects of scope; associated services; infrastructure; approach to engineering, procure-

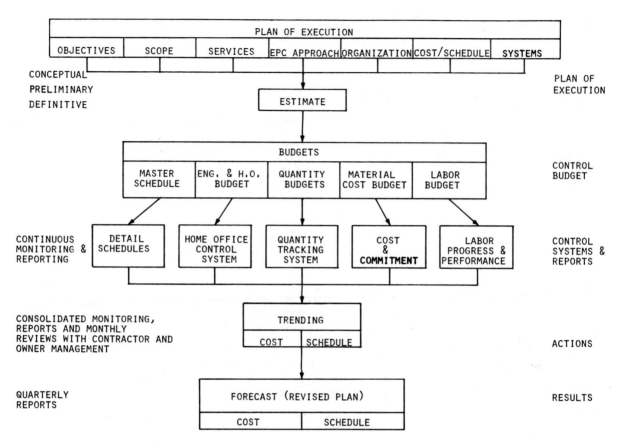

Figure 1.3 Flowchart of project execution plan.

ment, and construction (EPC); resources; organization structure; and project control requirements.

This detailed execution plan is essential for developing a quality control estimate and project schedule. Large overseas projects, with remote job sites, require that the execution plan consider logistics and material handling, local infrastructure and resources, camp facilities, training, expatriate conditions, and national and governmental requirements. A quality execution plan will provide a good estimate, control budgets, detailed schedules, and a breakdown of the project into controllable areas and cost centers. The project organization will be similarly structured, as will trending, control, and reporting systems.

Key Items of Execution Plan

This list is not all-inclusive.

1. *Objectives:* reach agreement with owner on broad objectives
    National engineering and construction content
    Limits of authority
    Community responsibility-town planning

        Public relations: television-press, job site tours

        Contractual relationship-responsibilities

2. *Scope*

        Process decisions-engineering specifications

        Capacity-feedstock and product slate

        Owner products for use during construction

3. *Services:* contractor and owner responsibilities

        Subcontracts

        Procurement

        Commissioning and start-up assistance

        Training: management and craft labor

4. *Engineering, procurement, and construction (EPC) approach*

        Licensers and other third parties

        Location of design offices

        Purchasing, procedures, and practices

        Infrastructure: local area and job site interface

        Project procedures

        Workweek for engineering and construction

        Contractor employee conditions and procedures

        Preassembly-modularization

        Constructibility analysis

        Labor relations and recruiting strategy

        Construction equipment plan-rigging studies

        Construction preplanning: path of construction, field
           facilities

5. *Infrastructure*

        Camp: messing and personnel facilities

        Local resources: banks, postal, religious, etc.

        Transportation: job site and local area

        Rest and recreation

        Security

6. *Organizations*

        Size and complexity: integration and project management

        Breakdown of project: cost and management

        Engineering and construction management

        Third-party integration

        Owner organization: relationship with contractor

        Organizational development (OD)

        Communication system

        Matrix, task force, and functional considerations

        Decision process: delegation, strategic, tactical

7. *Cost and schedule*

        Resource evaluation: manpower and manufacturing

        Control estimate-work breakdown structure

        Project control system

        Trending systems-quantity control

        Schedule milestones and owner interfaces

        Long lead items

        Logistics and material handling

        Environmental, governmental regulations and permits

   8. *Systems*
         Manual versus computer
         Owner requirements
         Level of detail and distribution
         Flexibility requirements: contraction and expansion
         Frequency of reports
   9. *Auditing system*
         Terms of reference
         Evaluations and reports
         Procurement and financial
         Documentation
  10. *Procurement*
         Worldwide operation
         National requirements
         Purchasing procedures and strategy
         Centralized buying-field purchasing
         Owner approvals
         Negotiation practices
  11. *Subcontracting*
         Content: work category and contract type
         Organization and control requirements
         Prequotation meetings
  12. *Material control*
         Material takeoff: control and reporting
         Freight consolidation
         Marshaling yards
         Job site controls
         Weather protection and maintenance
         Documentation
  13. *Project rundown and demobilization*
         What to control and at what point
         Level of control and reporting
         Personnel demobilization
         Material surplus program

1.5 CONTRACT STRATEGY

The current market environment plus the project cost and schedule
objectives will generally determine the contracting strategy. Lump
sum work is generally the most efficient method; however, a well-
defined engineering package and stable market conditions are essential. There are several alternatives for the reimbursable project, and
a phased approach, though lengthy, can reduce the financial risk of
a straight-through project.

Lump sum (fixed price) bids are expensive to produce, and contractors are not anxious to pursue this course without a reasonable
expectation of success. A poor owner definition can cause a low contractor estimate, resulting in continuous claims and extras by the

contractor. It can also result in a large contingency being applied by the contractor.

Under lump sum contracts, control of time and money is the primary concern of the contractor, as his performance directly affects his profits. Here, the owner is concerned with checking the contractor's compliance with project requirements, evaluating cost extras, and periodically analyzing the project schedule.

Under most cost-plus contracts, however, the contractor has limited incentive for controlling time and money beyond professional responsibility. In such cases, the owner is more deeply involved in the project control function than on lump sum projects. Here, owner personnel must supervise closely the contractor's preparation of the definitive cost estimate and control system. This is necessary to ensure that the estimates and evaluations are prepared for facilities that are adequate to the owner's needs and to provide the owner with a better insight and understanding of the reliability and accuracy of the contractor estimates.

Target cost and schedule incentives can produce improved performance. However, the owner thereafter faces a contractor program to inflate the cost target with high estimates of engineering changes and extras.

A fixed fee, based on a percentage of the total cost, can reward poor performance. The higher the cost, the greater the fee.

Omnibus-type fees for portions of engineering and construction can result in the lack of necessary services. A fee for engineering can result in lack of optimization, poor design, overgenerous specifications, and poor equipment engineering, resulting in high-priced equipment. Material costs are reimbursable. Similarly, a fee for construction equipment can result in excessive use of labor, leading to higher labor costs and schedule extension. Labor costs are reimbursable. A fixed fee for construction management can result in lack of supervision and services, particularly if construction conditions change from those anticipated.

These problems can be magnified with projects on a "fast-track" approach where there is a greater element of the unknown.

1.6   THE CONTROL ESTIMATE

Most owners develop an estimate at the front end and feasibility stage. This conceptual estimate would generally fall in the ±30% accuracy level and would be based on cost-capacity curves or equipment and bulk ratio breakdowns.

This estimate could be updated as the design is developed, or the control could be transferred to the contractor's estimate, which is probably being developed on a different basis. Using the contractor's estimate will generally produce a greater sense of commitment and responsibility by the contractor. Whichever estimate is used to control the project costs, it is not recommended that the contractor

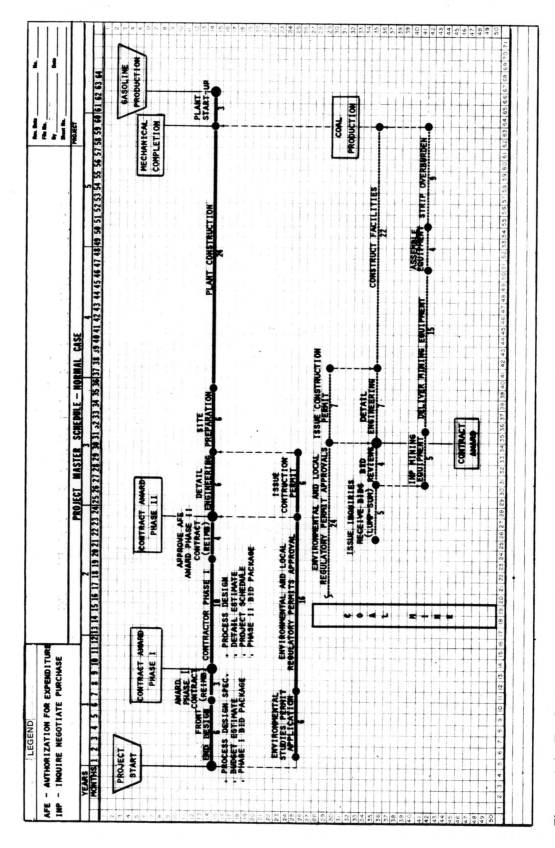

Figure 1.4 Typical summary schedule.

10

be forced to structure his estimate to the same work breakdown and account codes of the owners.

1.7 THE PROJECT SCHEDULE

In addition to a conceptual estimate, an overall schedule is developed by the owner at the front end of a project. This schedule is developed on a summary basis as scope and execution plans are still in a preliminary stage. As the project develops, it is recommended that daily control and detailed planning be transferred to the contractor's scheduling operation. Overall monitoring of the contractor's schedules and planning operation should be maintained by the owner.

This early schedule provides the time basis for the estimate and presents to management an overall program showing the major decision points. At this stage, it is vital that this information be easily and clearly communicated to management.

The best format for this summary schedule is a time-scaled network. It will provide an excellent picture of time and the major phases and dependencies of the project. From a technical viewpoint, time-scaled networks are inefficient as they can require considerabl rework and redrafting, but from a communication viewpoint, they are outstanding.

Figure 1.4 is a typical example of a summary schedule. This schedule, of a synthetic fuel plant, shows a phased approach, the major scope elements of a process plant and a coal mine, environmental requirements, contracting decision points, mechanical completion, and plant start-up.

With an adequate scheduling data base, the following significant information can be easily developed with this schedule:

Escalation midpoints for material and labor
Progress curves for engineering and construction (phase II)
Manpower histograms for engineering and construction (phase II)
Owner manpower and project team requirements

Activity durations are determined by judgment, past experience (data base), or a combination of both.

1.8 A PROJECT CONTROL ORGANIZATION

Figure 1.5 illustrates a typical organization for project control. It is recommended that the project control section be part of the project management division, whereas estimating and its associated functions can be a separate group.

The project control section would have three main project support groups and one staff support group: cost control and scheduling

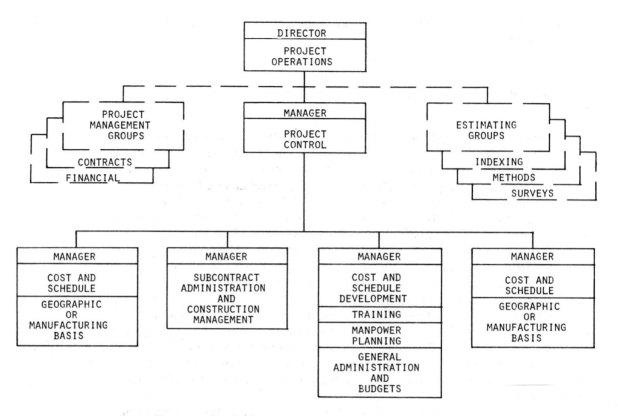

Figure 1.5 Typical project control organization.

support groups organized on a geographic or manufacturing basis; a central group for methods development, training, and manpower planning; and a specialist group to handle subcontract administration and construction management.

Rotational assignments and career development objectives should ensure the movement of personnel through the project control and project management groups. This would improve manpower utilization, provide greater training opportunities, and increase individual skill levels.

Personnel in the cost and schedule support groups should be trained to handle both cost and schedule work. Capability in both functions would be beneficial for providing home office "suitcase" services and also personnel for control manager positions.

Due to the high work load, large projects would require separate functions of cost and scheduling.

A significant organization problem of project management and a staff project control group is the "we and they" attitude. When the project control group is part of the project management division, the we and they attitude is greatly reduced. In addition, the "audit image" is also reduced.

Alignment in project management divisions can sometimes stifle independent and adverse evaluations by project control personnel.

2

A CONTROL ENVIRONMENT

2.1 GENERAL

Without question, *it is the project manager's responsibility to create an environment which will enable control to be exercised.* This means the project manager will seek counsel, accept sound advice, and stretch control personnel to the extent of their capability.

A key element for effective control is timely evaluation of potential cost and schedule hazards and presenting them with recommended solutions to project management. This means that the control engineer must be a skilled technician and also able to effectively communicate to management level. Sometimes, a skilled technician's performance is not adequate because he or she is a poor communicator. *Technical expertise will rarely compensate for lack of communication skills.* As in all staff functions, the ability to "sell" a service can be as important as the ability to perform the service. Project teams are usually brought together from a variety of "melting pots", and the difficulty of establishing effective and appropriate communications at all levels should not be underestimated. In this regard, the project manager is responsible for quickly establishing a positive working environment where the separate functions of design, procurement, construction, and control *are welded into a unified, cost-conscious group.* Project managers who relegate the control function to a reporting or accounting function are derelict in their duties.

Project control can be defined as the process that

Forecasts and evaluates potential hazards prior to occurrence so that preventive action can be taken

Reviews trends or actual situations to analyze their impact and, if possible, proposes action to alleviate the situation

Provides constant surveillance of project conditions to effectively and economically create a "no-surprise" condition

2.2 TASK FORCE VERSUS FUNCTIONAL ORGANIZATION

The question of a functional organization versus a task force approach is a much debated subject. It is the writer's opinion that a task force

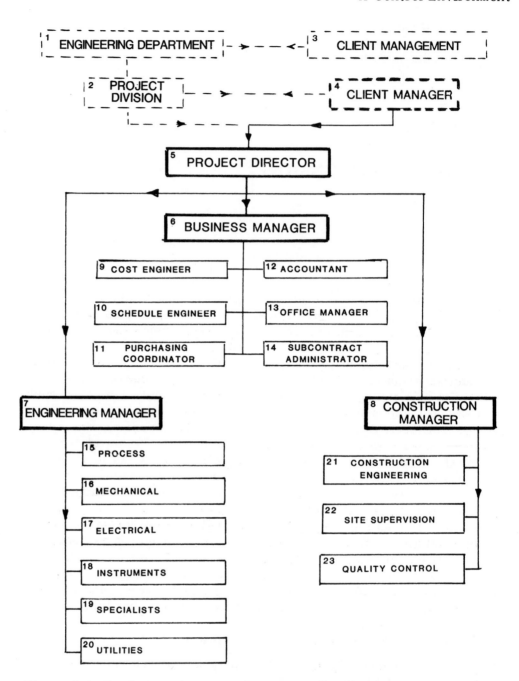

Figure 2.1 Typical project task force organization.

approach is more efficient for large projects, whereas the functional
organization can be adequate for small projects. The task force approach
produces a greater concentration of resources and fewer levels of management, as the reporting line to the functional departments becomes
one of personnel allocation and advice rather than direction.

Many owners now use task forces to monitor contractor performance.
Some contractors are of the opinion that this approach increases sche-

dule durations and project costs. However, in today's volatile market-
place with associated contractor reluctance to bid on a lump sum basis,
owners believe task forces are necessary and that they make a clear,
positive contribution to meeting owner objectives. In addition, owner's
project control expertise, in many instances, is equal to contractor's
capability.

Figure 2.1 illustrates a typical owner task force organization. This
shows an owner operation with a central engineering department having
responsibility for the corporation capital project program. The operating company, or client group, is responsible for funding the project
and, in a sense, hires the central engineering department to manage
the project. This requires that the project director have two reporting
lines: functional line to the engineering project division and a financial
line to the client manager.

This dual relationship can cause conflict. This occurs most often
when the client manager attempts to manage the project director in a
functional project business. The most common situation of conflict is
when the client manager works directly with the contractor.

The focal point for instructions to the contractor must be through
the project director and then flow from the owner task force to the
contractor organization. The owner and contractor must structure their
task force organizations to harmonize. The better the coordination and
communication of owner and contractor personnel in this joint task force
operation, the greater the prospect for successful project execution.

Systems and procedures do not build projects. People do.

2.3 OWNER-CONTRACTOR RELATIONSHIPS

A significant feature of a successful project control operation is the
relationship between contractor and owner personnel. One item in the
initial phase of a capital project is the *screening* and *qualifying* of
contractor's prior to contract award. During this activity, owner control requirements can be clearly explained, and an implementation program can be obtained from the contractors being evaluated. Some
owners have a formal system for evaluating contractors.

After contract award, the reality of the implementation program will
be tested during detailed discussions in setting up a mutually acceptable
system. These should be conducted in a spirit of equal partnership.
*The owner control specification will be the basis of discussions on con-
trol organization, procedures, systems, and controls.* These early reviews can prevent later system changes, costly reorganizations, and
personnel reassignments. Such discussions should be promptly followed
by meetings with the contractor's engineering, procurement, construction, and project services groups to verify mutual understanding and
acceptance of a common approach to planning, scheduling, and cost
control. At this stage, the discussions must necessarily be brief and to
the point. Everybody is busy. But they are essential to ensure that the
contractor's control system meets the owner's requirements.

Detailed planning, scheduling, and cost control are the contractor's responsibility, and it is his or her responsibility to see that they are efficient operations, effectively utilized. This is an equal partnership operation.

Apart from estimating systems, many owners have established control data such as the following:

1. Engineering man-hours per piece of equipment and man-hours per drawing
2. Construction man-hours per work category
3. Standard engineering and construction productivity profiles
4. Standard engineering and construction progress profiles
5. Overall milestone durations and dependent relationships
6. Standard procurement and subcontract relationships
7. Typical man-hour expenditure curves
8. Typical material commitment curves
9. Standard engineering discipline relationships
10. Home office and construction indirect relationships
11. Standard engineering and construction all-in rate profiles
12. Typical breakdown of engineering by discipline and section
13. Typical breakdown of construction by craft and prime account
14. Domestic and worldwide productivity factors
15. Typical manpower buildup and rundown
16. Construction manpower density-productivity curves
17. Domestic and worldwide labor and material escalation rates

Data, as indicated above, enable owners to check a contractor's estimates and continuously monitor performance through all phases of a project. Many contractors have invested heavily in the development of performance evaluation and review techniques (PERTs) and critical path method (CPM) techniques and control systems. In spite of this investment, and the resulting sophisticated systems with their associated heavy running costs, owners continue to comment on the poor execution of the contractor project control function. In turn, contractors complain that owners do not clearly identify their project objectives, change their minds regarding scope (causing costly recycles of engineering), and are often disorganized. A major complaint by contractors is that owners monitor their activities too closely. It is essential that an owner's cost and schedule representatives refrain from continuously getting into "too much detail." This, invariably causes an adverse relationship. Contractors should be allowed freedom of action and an occasional error.

There are two significant procedures which attempt to clearly establish the detailed working relationship of owner and contractor: the coordination procedure, outlined in Chapter 1, which covers organizational and functional relationships, and a *document action schedule*, which specifies the owner involvement in all documents produced by the contractor. This covers engineering drawings, specifications, inquiry packages, bid tabulations, purchase orders, subcontracts, and all control and reporting documents. When too tight a level of approval is im-

posed by the owner, it can result in additional costs and lengthening
of the schedule.

A major complaint by owners is in contractor scheduling. Rarely
does the owner encounter a contractor's performance where the
planning, scheduling, and control of engineering, procurement, and
construction phases are effectively bound into one system. Too often,
rigid departmentalization of contractors has forced owners' representatives to act as catalysts and coordinators to achieve efficient execution.

Overdepartmentalization is evident when separate groups of a contractor's organization operate to an appreciable degree to the exclusion
of the interests of associated groups and departments. In particular,
owners experience too many instances where engineering design, procurement, project, and construction departments act as separate companies. Corporate politics sometimes are allowed to override project objectives and the true long-range objectives of the engineer-contractor.
Unless engineering, procurement, and construction groups operate as a
team, with differing functions but common objectives, project execution
will be inefficient and costly.

All contractors emphasize in sales presentations the unified application of their resources to the owner's project. Departmental flexibility
and coordination are stated as being strengths of the company organization. In practice, the owner too often finds that planning, scheduling,
and control are exercised only within compartmented contractor departments. While it is highly desirable that individual departments and departmental sections participate in the setting of schedules, and in controlling these schedules, overall progress scheduling and control are
the owner's prime concern. For this reason, final schedule authority
must rest in a strong, active project management, supported by adequate staff schedule personnel.

Alternatively, owners sometimes find scheduling operations consoli-
dated in autonomous groups, the output of which is voluminous but
unused. If the engineer-contractor is to meet the owner's objectives,
and in the long run his or her own objectives, the output of planning
and scheduling groups must be both usable and used by the project team.

2.4 AN INTEGRATED SYSTEM

Like any control function, effective project control requires that all
efforts be fully integrated; that status be fully and accurately reported;
that costs, programs, and engineering scope be compared against
budget estimates, schedules, and specifications (the norms); and that
the loop be closed either by modifying and correcting the control system or by changing the control methods. This cycle of events is
necessary and should be continual for successful project execution.
The owner's interest and participation in these events will vary from
project to project and depends primarily on the type of project contract.
In short, for effective project control, a project team (not an individual)

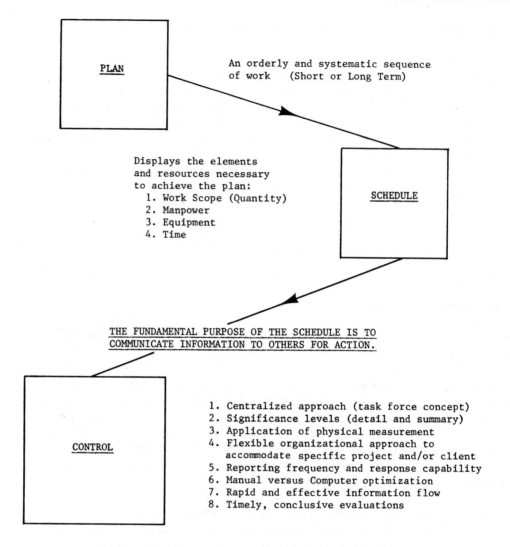

The following text appears within the figure:

PLAN

An orderly and systematic sequence
of work   (Short or Long Term)

Displays the elements
and resources necessary
to achieve the plan:
1. Work Scope (Quantity)
2. Manpower
3. Equipment
4. Time

SCHEDULE

THE FUNDAMENTAL PURPOSE OF THE SCHEDULE IS TO
COMMUNICATE INFORMATION TO OTHERS FOR ACTION.

CONTROL

1. Centralized approach (task force concept)
2. Significance levels (detail and summary)
3. Application of physical measurement
4. Flexible organizational approach to
   accommodate specific project and/or client
5. Reporting frequency and response capability
6. Manual versus Computer optimization
7. Rapid and effective information flow
8. Timely, conclusive evaluations

EFFECTIVE CONTROL TECHNIQUES WILL SHOW TREND PERFORMANCES
SO THAT EARLY REMEDIAL ACTION CAN BE TAKEN.

(REPORTING AND ACCOUNTING AFTER THE FACT IS NOT A CONTROL TECHNIQUE!)

Figure 2.2   Planning, scheduling, control—an integrated system.

must concentrate on anticipating and detecting deviations from project
norms and then take full and timely action to handle such deviations.
Project norms should be revised only when it is absolutely certain that
they are beyond achievement; *however, prompt reports should indicate
deviations as they become apparent,* even though no immediate action is
taken.

Figures 2.2 and 2.3 illustrate major elements of integrated scheduling
and cost control systems.

Figure 2.2 is a flowchart indicating the elements necessary for an
integrated schedule system. It is the writer's opinion that owners and

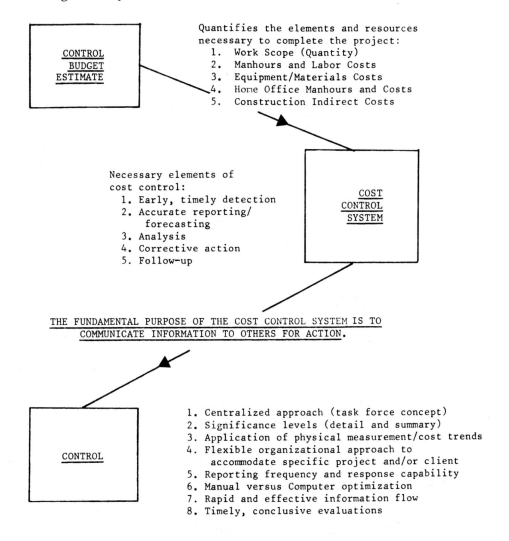

Figure 2.3 Cost control—an integrated system.

contractors need to achieve fully integrated and coordinated control systems along these general lines. To do so will require in many instances a thorough rethinking of schedule-related operations and upgrading of personnel. In some instances, judicious "head knocking" is going to be required to call attention to outmoded practices and attitudes and failures to conform to stated management policies.

Figure 2.3 is a flowchart indicating the elements necessary for an integrated cost control system. The major items are a quality estimate (based on quantities), an effective trending system, and qualified personnel working on a task force basis.

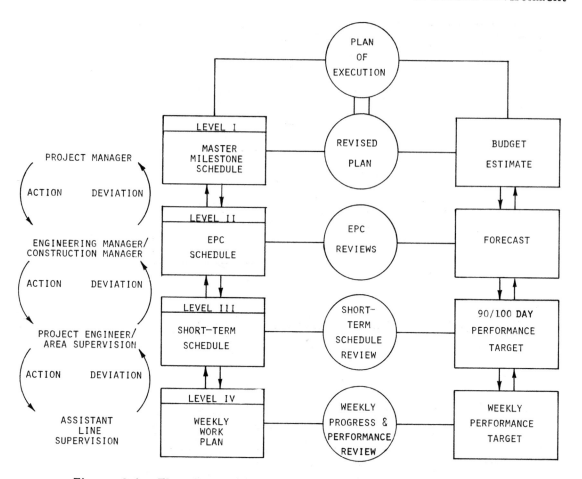

Figure 2.4 Flowchart of management information system.

2.5 COMMUNICATION: MANUAL OR COMPUTER

Figure 2.4 is a flowchart of a typical management information system, or, in other words, the operating levels of the project control system. Again, the key word is communication.

The project control system must generate summary and detailed information for different levels of management. Information must be current, timely, and accurate. This flowchart shows four levels of detail, which are typical for most large projects.

Information is generally a combination of computer programs and manual reports. It is difficult to conclude that computer programs are better than manual systems. There are obvious advantages with the computer, but many systems prove ineffective due to the tremendous level of detail.

Scheduling systems with tens of thousands of activities are rarely effective. Alternatively, it is very time-consuming to produce a detailed field progress report without a computer program.

Each project and each contractor operation should be thoroughly investigated for application of a computer approach to project control.

As most owners work in a monitoring role, it is unlikely that owners would need their own extensive computer program for control purposes.

2.6 OWNER REVIEW OF CONTRACTOR CONTROL SYSTEM

On large projects, soon after contract award, a team should be established to review, in detail, the contractor's cost and schedule system, organization, and assigned personnel. The purpose is to recommend to the project manager a complete project control system for the project. The team should be led by a senior member of the home office control group and consist of task force and staff cost and schedule personnel. As this review will take 4-6 weeks, the addition of home office personnel is generally necessary as the work load of the project-assigned personnel is very heavy at this time. The team leader must be very experienced in order to understand and handle the complete range of a contractor's project control operation. Hence, a supervisor from the home office is generally required.

Personnel should be nominated by the manager of project control and a timed, execution plan presented to the project manager for approval prior to commencement of the work.

Specific objectives of this review are the following:

1. Investigate the project control systems and organizations of the prime contractor, joint venture, or management contractors and prepare a recommended total project control system. *The investigation should be based on maximizing the use of existing contractor systems and resources. Changes should be minimal, and only significant deficiencies should require modification.* Should a contractor system or organization have significant deficiencies, it is recommended that the contractor modify his or her system by supplementing it with the appropriate owner procedure and formats. However, it is important that changes be kept to a minimum and that the contractor be permitted full use of procedures and methods with which he or she is familiar.
2. Prepare a detailed report covering the investigation and recommendation.
3. Prepare a schedule for the implementation of the preceding recommendations, extending to the point where the control system is fully operational.
4. Present the plan and recommendation to the owner and contractor executive management to obtain full understanding and endorsement by management at an early stage in the project.

2.7 IMPLEMENTATION SCHEDULE: PROJECT CONTROL SYSTEM

It is essential to establish a quality project control system at the earliest possible date. As an aid to meeting this objective, it is recommended

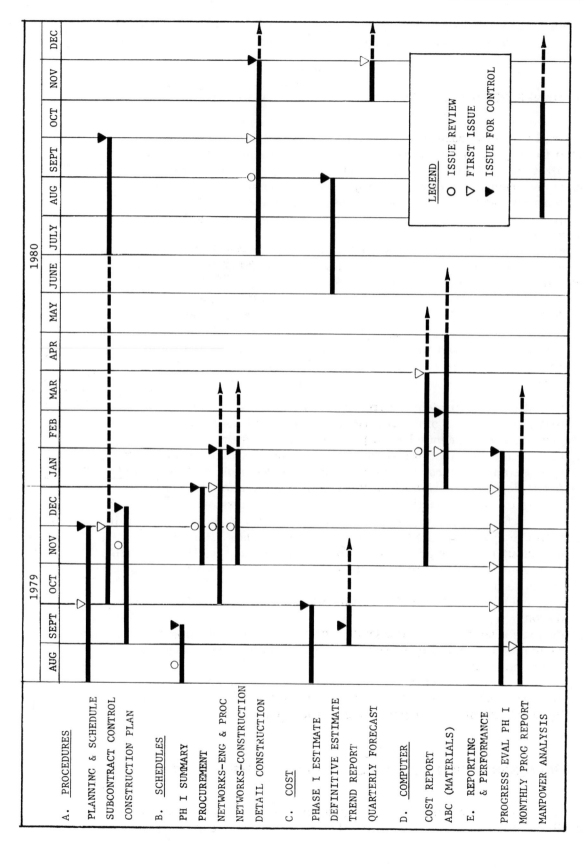

Figure 2.5   Control system implementation schedule.

that a detailed *implementation schedule* be prepared showing the completion dates agreed upon by the contractor. This schedule should be developed in summary and detailed form and will outline all facets of the proposed control system, showing deadlines for completion and personnel allocations for the work.

The contractor should list and provide *duration estimates* for all procedures such as schedules, reports, estimates, computer programs, organization charts, etc., which constitute the overall project control system. It is suggested that a flowchart(s) showing the major elements of the system be prepared by the contractor. The contractor should provide schedules and details of resource for completion of the project control system.

This owner review and preparation of the associated implementation schedule can be a frustrating time for contractors. It could be doubly so if owner personnel lack experience and the contractor has to spend considerable time in education as well as explanation. The process is time-consuming and could require the time of key contractor control personnel who are already heavily engaged in the project.

However, this is the time for contractors to fully explore owner control requirements, provide effective and detailed explanations of their systems, accept obvious improvements, and defend "poor" programs which they believe are effective and which they have "proved out" on projects.

Owners should have a *minimal-change* policy, and contractors should encourage owner personnel to live up to this policy.

Figure 2.5 illustrates a segment of a typical implementation schedule. This schedule should cover major categories of procedures, schedules, cost, computer programs, measurement, and reporting. It should be updated weekly or biweekly for progress and status.

2.8 JUMBO PROJECTS

A significant aspect of project work in the 1970s has been the increasing size and complexity of projects. Major examples are the Trans-Alaska pipeline, offshore platforms in the North Sea, gas-gathering facilities in the Middle East, the Sasol synthetic fuel plant in South Africa, and the Syncrude Tar Sands plant in Alberta. These are termed *jumbo* or *mega* projects.

New and changing technology, a hostile environment (Alaska and the North Sea), construction on a massive scale, plus the minimum of experience and data provided the background to estimating, planning, and scheduling of these facilities.

The oil industry was breaking new technological barriers in terms of size and complexity of production facilities. The resultant first-generation jumbo projects experienced a considerable degree of last-minute innovation and were built without full scope definition and little appreciation of offshore construction. Because of the urgent need to bring these facilities on-stream, companies were tackling many of the problems during the construction and installation stages. Therefore, cost and schedule overruns were common occurrences.

It was not until about 1976 that realistic criteria and appropriate techniques had been developed to control these very large and complex projects. It was discovered that current concepts and practices of functional and task force organizations were not very effective. In particular, a task force with centralized decision making was not adequate. Management layers stretched out communication channels and decision making.

The following size parameters give a general breakdown of projects into small, medium, large, and jumbo:

	Small	Medium	Large	Jumbo
Engineering man-hours	100,000	600,000	1,500,000	6,000,000
Engineering manpower	100	200	400	1,000
Construction man-hours	500,000	4,000,000	8,000,000	50,000,000
Construction	400	1,500	3,000	10,000
Construction staff	50	150	500	1,000
Schedule (months) (detailed engineering to completion of construction)	25	30	35	50-60

Comparing the jumbo projects of the 1970s with conventional plants, the major lessons learned were the following:

1. A decentralized approach to place decision making as close to the work as possible.
2. The need to combine owner and contractor project teams into one operating unit.
3. The reduction of management layers so that decentralized project teams could communicate quickly with overall project management.
4. The increased effect that basic organization changes can have on a very large project.
5. The importance of leadership, as opposed to managerial skills, in an effective project management organization.
6. The increased importance of a quality execution plan prior to the start of detailed engineering, procurement, and construction (phase II). The execution plan is to provide a base for the estimate as well as a plan for executing the project.
7. Greatly increased influence of governmental agencies and joint venture partners.
8. Inadequacy of the existing data base and the assumptions of size effect. It is possible that the traditional *scale effect*, where increased size and units reduce unit costs, does not apply on jumbo projects. Pioneer projects are likely to experience unit cost increases as their technology advances. Extreme caution must be exercised in scaling

up capacity/cost ratios of conventional plants for jumbo projects requiring new technology and prototype engineering.

The following comments further amplify a new approach to a jumbo project.

2.8.1 Decentralization

During phase II, the project should be divided into major cost centers, to an approximate value of ±$200 million, each with its own budget, schedule, and complete project organization. Jumbo projects would then have 15-20 such individual cost centers.

Decision making should be by the individual project organization, constrained only by its budget and schedule and objectives set by the central project management group. The central project group would be responsible for coordination of resources and common services, overall cost and schedule objectives, and interfaces with client, corporate, and government groups.

Cost, schedule, procurement, and engineering specialists of the individual project group would report directly to their project manager and functionally to the specialist manager of the central group. They would receive their day-to-day direction from their project manager and technical guidance from the functional manager of the central group.

Phase I (conceptual process design) and the commissioning and start-up phases should be organized on a central project group basis. As the major decisions of a phase I operation are comparatively few, mainly process design and selection, execution plan, and contracting strategy, the decision-making process should be in the hands of a few people. Similarly, construction at the 95-98% point will move into the commissioning and start-up phase. This requires the reuniting of the individual projects for a common approach to start-up and operations.

2.8.2 Owner-Contractor Partnership

An adversary or stand-alone relationship between an owner and contractor will add costs and extend the schedule on jumbo projects. The amounts of money are large. Decision making requires greater evaluation and analysis. Fast decision making requires that the owner and contractor work as a team during the evaluation process to prevent loss of time, with major reviews and presentations. As most jumbo projects are built on a "fast-track" basis, fast decision making is essential if the schedule is to be achieved.

Continuous agreement at working levels between the owner and contractor will generally require owner personnel additional to the traditional levels of the past.

Even though there will be a united team approach, it is vital that the contractor be allowed to freely operate at the daily working level.

A new concept is the completely integrated owner-contractor project team, where owner personnel may have supervisory and subordinate roles. The major problems of this approach are questions of contractor responsibility, professional pride, personnel relationships, and proprietary information. The concept has much to offer and is one that deserves considerably more study, analysis, and development.

2.8.3 Organization Changes

The need for organizational and procedural changes can be recognized and the problem reduced with an organizational development (OD) group. This group would be established to unblock decision-making bottlenecks and improve inadequate procedures. Its objective would be to constantly monitor and evaluate organization, communication, procedures, and methods. This function requires specialized personnel with experience to cover all phases and functions of the project.

Due to the wide range of experience required, it is probable that two groups would be required: one group for the home office covering engineering and procurement and a second group for the field covering construction. About four to six personnel, at peak, would be required for an effective OD group.

2.8.4 Leadership Versus Managerial Skills

"People skills" are essential in the management and control of jumbo projects. With task forces ranging in size from 500 to 1000, the importance of people skills cannot be overemphasized. It is possible that leadership skills are more important than managerial skills. Personnel motivation is an essential ingredient of a successful project team.

2.8.5 Control Estimate

As a quality estimate is vital to the project control effort, an owner-contractor team should be established to develop the estimate. This will provide continuous working agreement on such significant elements as escalation, productivity levels, unit rates, work breakdown structure, control areas, and individual cost centers.

A detailed estimate could be produced about 12-16 months after the phase II contract award and would probably require 40 contractor and 10 owner personnel. With this approach, management review and approval could take 1 week instead of the months of review and reconciliation which is the more normal case.

2.8.6 Planning and Scheduling

The size of the activity network is not the major consideration. The quality of the weekly construction program is the main concern. Construction man-hours will be in the range of 40-100 million. With peaks of 10,000-15,000 men, a quality weekly work program is absolutely essential.

It is likely to be a manual system and should be based on quantities, unit man-hour rates, and varying productivity adjustments and be reconciled against the objectives of the overall schedule. Productivity goals should be preplanned and then reported against on a weekly basis. (See Section 5.31 for detailed information on method and format.)

2.8.7 Quantity Control

The quantity control technique is rarely used. On jumbo projects, where the amounts of money are so large, a quantity tracking system is essential for effective cost control. Appropriate *bulk quantities* (earth, concrete, piping, etc.) should be selected and tracked, by a random sampling technique, from the process design of phase I through the detailed engineering of phase II.

2.8.8 Rundown Control

The rundown control method is rarely used in present-day project work. Again, due to size, this is an essential technique for jumbo projects. As engineering and construction commence their rundown (about 80% complete), individual budgets, schedules, and manpower histograms should be developed to separately control the remaining work. (See Section 6.44 for further details.)

2.8.9 Governmental Agencies and Joint Venture Partnerships

Many of today's jumbo projects have governments as a partner. Governmental regulations and agencies and partner and joint venture relationships add a further dimension that must be recognized by planning, scheduling, and cost effort.

Governmental energy companies may require *preferred purchasing* (buying in the host country), extensive training programs for supervisory staff and craft labor, and the development of an infrastructure local to the project job site.

Joint venture partners require a vote in major decisions. This takes time. Major purchases can require approval of partners prior to purchase. Again, this takes time. Periodic review and presentations can be required by partners. This takes effort and costs money.

All the preceding aspects should be carefully considered when developing the project execution plan and schedule.

Figure 2.6 vividly illustrates the effects of problems outlined in the opening paragraph of this subsection. This study (R-2481-DOE) by the Rand Corporation for the U.S. Department of Energy shows final costs versus initial feasibility estimates for many jumbo projects. As can be seen, the cost growth is 200-300% due to either bad estimates, poor performance, or a combination of both. Major changes causing significant

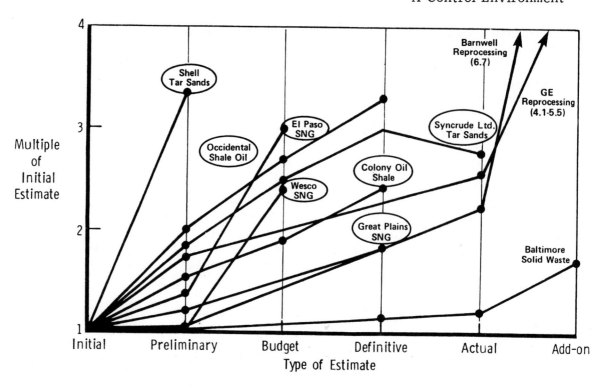

Figure 2.6   Jumbo projects—chart of cost increases in constant dollars
(by project). (From E. Merrow, S. W. Chapel, and J. C. Worthing.
*A Review of Cost Estimation on New Technologies. Implications for Energy
Process Plants*, Rand Report R-2481-DOE, Rand Corporation, July 1979.)

cost additions can be classed as poor performance. Concern is being expressed that current estimates for jumbo synthetic fuel projects will
follow the patterns shown in Figure 2.6.

2.9 PROJECT LEVELS OF CONTROL AND REPORTING

Levels of control and reporting vary widely in the industry. They can be
dependent on the following:

Recognition, understanding, and need for control
Company commitment to control
Personnel resources and capability
Size and complexity of projects
Owner-contractor contractual arrangements
Owner-contractor control relationship-expertise
Acceptance of cost control
Cost effectiveness of control

Most major contractors have comprehensive project control systems.
However, very few owners have a similar capability, or even detailed

control specifications which would enable contractors to thoroughly understand owners' project control requirements.

As outlined in Section 2.7, an early, effective project control program is an essential requirement. It is difficult to achieve this objective on reimbursable projects if owners are not able to specify, in detail, their requirements. Even on lump sum projects a similar approach is necessary, as effective planning, scheduling, and progress measurement should be an owner requirement. Apart from an adequate change order procedure, cost control reporting is the contractor's sole responsibility on lump sum projects.

Figure 2.7 lists typical project control requirements for the following project categories:

Feasibility study (0-10,000 engineering hours)
Small-size project (10,000-100,000 engineering hours)
Medium-size project (100,000-500,000 engineering hours)
Large-size project (500,000-1,500,000 engineering hours)

In an attempt to quantify project size, engineering man-hours have been allocated to these categories. *This can only be a guide as project size is dependent on the size of the company.*

It is generally recognized that as project size increases, additional control procedures are necessary. Obviously, control for control sake should be avoided. Typical examples of costly and inefficient control systems are very large activity network programs, duplication of effort by owner and contractor on reimbursable projects, and some governmental reporting procedures.

The outlined control procedures are divided into the major phases of a project. They are additive as the project category increases in size. A small project would require the items listed in categories 1 and 2 of Figure 2.7. Similarly, a large project would require all the listed items. The listed methods and procedures are found in this book.

2.10 MANPOWER PLANNING: ENGINEERING DEPARTMENT

One of the more difficult areas of project control is in-house company planning of engineering personnel. The major uncertainty, causing difficulty, is forecasting the amount and type of future project work. The difficulty is usually greater for owners.

The contracting industry has two major considerations: an annual estimate of the owner's capital projects program and an assessment of its ability to obtain a share of that work.

The owner's engineering department can face the following:

Amount of feasibility studies
Technical service requirements
Methods development and technical research
Actuality of probable or anticipated projects

PROJECT LEVELS OF CONTROL & REPORTING – REIMBURSABLE PROJECTS

FOR THE DESIGNATED PROJECT SIZE, THE OUTLINED TECHNIQUES, REPORTS AND PROCEDURES ARE ADDITIVE TO THE PREVIOUS LEVEL. LUMP SUM PROJECTS WOULD REQUIRE MOST OF THE SCHEDULING PROCEDURES. SEE PROJECT CONTROL MANUAL FOR DETAILS OF METHOD AND PROCEDURE.

PROJECT	OVERALL	ENGINEERING	PROCUREMENT	CONSTRUCTION	SUBCONTRACTS
1. FEASIBILITY (10,000 ENG. HOURS)	SUMMARY SCHEDULE EXECUTION PLAN ESTIMATE COST REPORT MONTHLY REPORT	PROJECT MASTER SCHEDULE MANHOUR CURVE MANHOUR RATE CURVE MANPOWER HISTOGRAM	DELIVERY LEAD TIMES LOGISTICS EVALUATION	SITE SURVEY SOIL REPORT	LICENSER PACKAGES
2. SMALL PROJECT (100,000 ENG. HOURS)	TREND REPORT PROJECT STATUS REPORT • ENGINEERING • MATERIAL COMMITMENT • CONSTRUCTION CONTINGENCY RUNDOWN CURVE CASH FLOW CURVE	DISCIPLINE SCHEDULE (MILESTONES) ENGINEERING MANHOUR CURVE HOME OFFICE MANHOUR CURVE BID EVALUATION PROGRAM	P.O. COMMITMENT REGISTER MATERIAL STATUS REPORT OVERALL COMMITMENT CURVE ($) VENDOR DWG. REPORT	PRE PLANNING PROGRAM MANFORCE REPORT THREE MONTH SCHEDULES CONSTRUCTION PROGRESS BARCHART (OVERALL) MANPOWER HISTOGRAM OVERALL MANHOUR CURVE OVERALL RATE CURVE	OVERALL SCHEDULES (BY SUBCONTRACT) PROGRESS/STATUS REPORT (BY SUBCONTRACT) SUMMARY COST REPORT
3. MEDIUM PROJECT (500,000 ENG. HOURS	CONTRACTORS EVALUATION PROGRAM DETAILED CONTROL SPECS. TASK FORCE APPROACH COMPUTER SCHEDULING PROGRAM COORDINATION PROCEDURE EXTRA WORK / CHANGE ORDER PROCEDURE	ENGINEERING CHANGE LOG MATERIAL REQUISITION CURVE DOCUMENT AND ACTION SCHEDULE PROGRESS MEASUREMENT PROGRAM (DISCIPLINE) • QUANTITIES / HOURS • PROGRESS CURVES • MANPOWER CURVES • PRODUTIVITY CURVES FRONT END SCHEDULES (3 MO.) DWG. SCHEDULES H.O. EXPENSE EXPENDITURE CURVE ($)	EQUIPMENT COMMITMENT CURVE ($) BULK MATERIAL COMMITMENT CURVE ($) MATERIAL REQUISITION CURVES INSPECTION – EXPEDITING REPORTS	FIELD ESTIMATE (QUANTITIES) CONSTRUCTION AREA PROGRESS BARCHARTS WEEKLY WORK PROGRAM PROGRESS MEASUREMENT PROGRAM • QUANTITIES/HOURS • PROGRESS CURVES • MANPOWER CURVES • PRODUCTIVITY CURVES STATUS REPORT • PROGRESS • PRODUCTIVITY • MANPOWER INDIRECTS EXPENDITURE CURVE ($) STAFF SCHEDULE EQUIPMENT SCHEDULE BACKCHARGE REGISTER COST REPORT	SUBCONTRACT COMMITMENT CURVE ($) SUBCONTRACT PREPARATION SCHEDULE UNIT PRICE SUBCONTRACTS • COST REPORT • QUANTITY REPORT • PERFORMANCE EVALUATION • PROGRESS CURVE • MANPOWER HISTOGRAM
4. LARGE PROJECT (1,500,000 ENG. HOURS)	CONTRACTORS SCREENING PROGRAM PROJECT CONTROL IMPLEMENTATION SCHEDULE WEEKLY MANFORCE REPORT	ACCOUNT REQUISITION CURVES PIPING DESIGN PROGRAM DRAWINGS TRACKING CURVES (P&I's) (FOUNDATIONS) (ISOMETRICS) QUANTITY TRACKING PROGRAM RUNDOWN CONTROL PROGRAM • DRAWINGS • MANHOURS • DATES • MANPOWER • PROGRESS • PRODUCTIVITY PUNCH LISTS	ACCOUNT COMMITMENT CURVES ($) ACCOUNT REQUISITION REPORT CRITICAL PURCHASING LIST MATERIAL DELIVERY HISTOGRAM SURPLUS MATERIAL REPORT	WORK UNIT TRACKING CURVES • EARTHWORK • CONCRETE • PIPING AREA STATUS REPORTS STAFF MANHOUR & RATE CURVE EQUIPMENT MANHOUR RATE PROFILE FIELD OFFICE EXPENSE EXPENDITURE CURVE ($) INDIRECT MANHOUR AND RATE CURVE RUNDOWN CONTROL PROGRAM • MANHOURS • MANPOWER • PROGRESS • PRODUCTIVITY PUNCH LISTS	INDEPENDENT BID ANALYSIS PROGRAM SENSITIVITY ANALYSIS PERFORMANCE CURVE AND REPORT

Figure 2.7   Chart levels of control-reporting.

Many owner central engineering departments act as nonprofit
service companies to operating divisions of the corporation. As such,
their work load is largely dependent on the capital projects program
of the operating divisions. It is not too difficult to assess technical
service requirements, methods development, and technical research
based on past experience, but assessments of feasibility studies and
capital projects depend on factors often outside the control of the engineering department:

Quality of corporate strategic planning program
Corporate financing
Project economic viability
Communication channels with operating divisions
Relationships with operating divisions
"Project charter" of engineering department
Image-credibility-capability of engineering department.

Even though there can be many uncertainties in work load, one
thing is certain: Quality evaluations of work load and associated manpower planning are essential—particularly with the current shortfall of
engineers and the industry prediction that the shortfall will increase
for the long term.

The following exhibits outline a systematic approach to engineering
manpower planning.

2.10.1 Planning by Individual

Individual planning is the lowest level of detail. Not only does it provide an assessment of manpower needs to meet a projected workload;
it also provides a program of career development for each engineer.

Figure 2.8 illustrates a 3-year plan for project services personnel
(estimating, cost control, scheduling). This shows feasibility work,
project assignments (home office and task force), methods development, rotational assignments, transfers, replacements, and recruiting
requirements. This should be a *dynamic document* as conditions-
requirements can quickly change. The control sheet should be constantly updated and issued monthly.

It is recommended that all section personnel "plans" be evaluated
and summarized by the project services group into a monthly engineering department manpower report. It is probable that this would be
a computer-based program so as to provide overall manpower reports
by individual listing, project assignments, feasibility work, sections,
etc.

As manpower plans are only as good as assessments of work load, it
is vital that work projections be evaluated each month. This requires
close liaison-coordination among project, engineering, construction,
and project services groups to ensure that current and future work
assessments are adequate.

COLOR CODE: HOME OFFICE   PROJECT ASSIGNMENT   TRANSFER OUT

Activity **PROJECT SERVICES** | Staff Assignments and Personnel Planning   PAGE: ____ DATE: ____

NAME	SCHEDULE			REMARKS
ESTIMATING				
1. EVANS	GEN. ABC PHASE I. XYZ FEASIBILITY	TASK FORCE (XYZ) COST CONTROL	GENERAL EST'G.	
2. DAVIES	GENERAL ESTIMATING • BUDGETS • FEASIBILITY			
3. JONES	A.F.E ESTIMATING			
4. WILLIAMS	METHODS DEVELOPMENT / PRODUCTIVITY FACTORS / LABOR & MATERIAL ESCALATION	TRANSFER TO SCHEDULING		
COST CONTROL				
5. PRICE	TASK FORCE	TRANSFER TO PROJECTS		
6. BENNETT	"SUITCASE" PROJECTS 103/201/430	XYZ PROJECT TASK FORCE		
7. GRAHAM	"SUITCASE" PROJECTS 120/180/250/310			
SCHEDULING				
8. ROBERTS	FEASIBILITY SCHEDULES & "SUITCASE" PROJECTS		TRANSFER TO DESIGN	
9. JENKINS	FEASIBILITY SCHEDULES & "SUITCASE" PROJECTS	XYZ PROJECT TASK FORCE		
10. LONGDEN	METHODS DEVELOPMENT / FEASIBILITY SCHEDULES			
RECRUITING				
11. COST ENGINEER	RECRUIT TRAINING GENERAL COST CONTROL ('SUITCASE) TASK FORCE			TO REPLACE PRICE
12. ESTIMATOR		RECRUIT TRAINING GENERAL ESTIMATING		TO REPLACE WILLIAMS
13. SCHEDULER		RECRUIT TRAINING GENERAL SCHEDULING		TO REPLACE ROBERTS
14. ESTIMATOR	RECRUIT TRAINING GENERAL ESTIMATING			TO REPLACE EVANS
	JAN FEB MAR APR MAY JUN JUL AUG SEPT OCT NOV DEC **1980**	JAN FEB MAR APR MAY JUN JUL AUG SEPT OCT NOV DEC **1981**	JAN FEB MAR APR MAY JUN JUL AUG SEPT OCT NOV DEC **1982**	

Figure 2.8   Staff assignments and personnel planning report.

USE CONTINUATION SHEET FOR REST OF SCHEDULE →

PROJECT NUMBER	MANHOURS			MANHOURS FOR PAST SIX WEEKS						MAN-WEEKS TO GO	WEEKLY SCHEDULED MEN		
	BUDGET	FORECAST	TO DATE	5	6	7	8	9	10		JAN	FEB	MAR
	2	3	4							11	12	13	14
1													

ENGINEERING DEPARTMENT – MANPOWER PLANNING

TOTAL ABOVE PROJECTS

MISCELLANEOUS PROJECTS

DEVELOPMENT WORK

TOTAL MANHOURS

TOTAL MEN AVAILABLE

TOTAL MEN REQUIRED

Figure 2.9 Personnel planning–by-project report.

2.10.2 Planning by Project

The planning-by-project report format is primarily used by contractors as it concentrates on project manpower allocations.

Figure 2.9, usually a computer report, assesses manpower allocations and requirements based on budget man-hours, the man-hour forecast, man-hours to date, the schedule, and man-hour allocations for the past 6 weeks. Only 3 months of the schedule are shown, and continuation sheets would provide requirements for the complete schedule. Columns 5-10 show man-hours expended for the past 6 weeks and also provide a base to assess the viability of future requirements. The computer program will take the man-hour forecast, to-date man-hours, schedule, and hourly workweek assessment and forecast the weekly scheduled manpower requirement. The bottom two lines show the men required against the men available, and the difference provides the necessary recruiting program.

This particular report illustrates an overall engineering manpower report. A similar report could be produced for each section.

2.10.3 Planning by Work Category

Figure 2.10 illustrates a report format generally used by owners. It is similar to the previous contractor project report but has additional categories: probable projects, feasibility studies, technical service, etc. Also, it separates technical from nontechnical, managers, and secretaries. Obviously, some managers are technical. But the report provides a continuous assessment of the number of managers to engineers and the relationship of technical to nontechnical. Both relationships need to be evaluated for an efficient operation. This report shows an annual plan. Additional years could be developed based on the quality of the individual plan cycle.

As previously stated, assessments for feasibility studies and probable projects can be difficult. The outlined numbers illustrate a large, international operating company having a central engineering department of some 300 engineers. Evaluation of these manpower relationships should bear in mind that detail drafting and other services can be outside contracts. A typical relationship of draftspersons to engineers can be about 3.5 to 1.

This report should be issued monthly and would undoubtedly be derived from a computer program.

2.10.4 Planning by Section

Figure 2.11 is a report for the company previously illustrated (Figure 2.10). Whereas the previous report showed manpower by work category, this report shows manpower by section. The construction group is part of the project management groups.

ENGINEERING DEPARTMENT – MANPOWER PLANNING – WORK CATEGORY

NOTES:
1. DRAFTING IS OUTSIDE CONTRACT.

% FIGURES ARE AS OF MIDYEAR
AS OF MARCH

CODE	WORK CATEGORY	%	ANNUAL PLAN											
			J	F	M	A	M	J	J	A	S	O	N	D
	TECHNICAL PERSONNEL													
	CURRENT AFE PROJECTS	48	188.7	197	197	192.1	188.6	180.4	184.1	183.3	181.1	179.4	159.6	159.6
	PROBABLE PROJECTS	5	0	0	0	1	3.3	18.6	26.6	35.3	41.8	44.3	55.4	55.6
	FEASIBILITY STUDIES	12	43.2	43	43	43.5	44.6	44.8	45.8	46	46.1	46.1	45.3	44.9
	TECHNICAL SERVICE	4	14.2	14.2	14.2	14.2	14.2	14.2	14.2	14.2	14.2	14.2	14.2	14.2
	TECHNICAL METHOD DEVELOPMENT	12	42.8	42.8	43.8	43.8	43.3	43.4	43.6	43.5	43.5	43.5	43	43
	START UP / OPERATIONS	1	2	2	2	2	2	2	2	2	2	2	2	2
	SUB TOTAL TECHNICAL	82	290.9	299	300	296.6	296	303.4	316.3	324.3	328.7	329.5	319.5	319.3
	MANAGERS & SECRETARIES	7	27.2	27.2	27.2	27.2	27.2	27.2	27.2	27.2	27.2	27.2	27.2	27.2
	OTHER INDIRECTS (SERVICES ETC.)	11	42.9	42.9	42.9	42.9	42.9	42.9	45	43	43	43	43	43
	MISCELLANEOUS	0	0	0	0	0	0	0	0	0	0	0	0	0
	REQUIRED TOTAL	100	361	369.1	370.1	366.7	366.1	373.5	386.5	394.5	398.9	399.7	389.7	389.5
	ACTUAL PAYROLL		319	327										

Figure 2.10   Personnel planning—by-work category report.

ENGINEERING DEPARTMENT – MANPOWER PLANNING – BY SECTION

NOTES:
1. DRAFTING IS OUTSIDE CONTRACT.

% FIGURES ARE AS OF MIDYEAR
AS OF MARCH.

CODE	SECTION	%	ANNUAL PLAN											
			J	F	M	A	M	J	J	A	S	O	N	D
	EMPLOYEE RELATIONS	1	4·5	4·5	4·5	4·5	4·5	4·5	4·8	4·9	4·9	5	5	5
	PROCUREMENT	1	4·2	4·4	5	5·3	5·7	4·8	4·7	4·8	5·4	5	5·2	5·4
	PROJECTS – U.S. REFINING & CHEMICAL	5	14·6	15·9	15·9	16·7	17·3	19·7	19·8	20·1	21·4	20·8	19·7	20·1
	– OVERSEAS R & C	6	17·6	18·3	17·6	17·4	17·3	21·7	23·4	24·7	24	23·2	23·2	22·6
	– MIDDLE EAST	3	9·5	9·5	9·5	9·5	9·5	9·5	9·5	9·5	9·5	9·5	9·5	9·5
	– OFFSHORE / SYNFUELS	12	45·2	45·2	45·2	46	45·8	46·2	46·1	45·2	44·3	44·3	44·3	44·3
	PROJECT SERVICES (EST'G. / COST & SCHED.)	11	40	40	40·5	40·5	40·5	40·5	42·5	44·3	46	47	45	45
	CONTRACTS	1	4·5	4·5	4·5	4·5	4·5	4·5	5·5	5·5	5·5	5·5	5	5
	GENERAL SERVICES (NON TECH.)	5	22·4	22	21·9	21	21	20·2	22·4	23·5	21·6	21	21	21
	PROCESS ENGINEERING	14	52·6	55·8	55·8	54·5	52·7	53·2	48·8	49·2	48·3	48·7	46	45
	FACILITIES ENGINEERING	26	93·3	96·1	98·2	94·8	94·7	97	104·5	108·8	114·1	115·6	111·2	117·3
	OFFICE & PLANT SERVICES	5	17·7	17·7	17·7	17·7	17·7	17·7	17·8	17·8	18	18·1	18·2	18·3
	OVERSEAS ENGINEERING OFFICES	10	34·9	35·2	33·8	34·3	34·9	34	35·7	36·6	35·9	36	36·4	36
	REQUIRED TOTAL	100	361	369·1	370·1	366·7	366·1	373·5	386·5	394·5	398·9	399·7	389·7	389·5
	ACTUAL PAYROLL		319	327										

Figure 2.11 Personnel planning–by-section report.

Individual section reports would clearly indicate a shortfall or overmanning of personnel by engineering classification. Adequate recruiting and training programs could be developed from this information.

Manpower requirements based on physical assessments can only be made for design groups where drawing-document takeoffs and man-hour assessments can be made. Historical relationships, the engineering department "charter" and/or responsibilities, control requirements, and company policy can determine allocations of service personnel to project work.

2.11 FLOWCHART OF OVERALL PROJECT CONTROL PROGRAM

The flowchart in Figure 2.12 shows the major elements of a project control program:

1. Project control specifications
2. Monthly progress report
3. Cost report
4. Trend report
5. Contingency rundown curve
6. Project master schedule
7. Historical engineering, procurement, and construction (EPC)
8. Monthly executive progress report

A contractor's project control program is developed from cost control and planning-scheduling specifications. Status and cost evaluations are carried out by the contractor for engineering, procurement, and construction, and this information is summarized in a monthly progress report. For further details, see Section 2.12 and Chapters 5 and 6.

2.12 MONTHLY PROGRESS REPORT

The monthly progress report should include narratives of cost and schedule status, progress curves, productivity curves, and manpower histograms for engineering, procurement, and construction.

The composition of the monthly progress report should be agreed upon with contractor soon after contract award.

Narratives for the reporting period should include status, trends, criticality, and significant deviations which are affecting the cost and schedule. Actions should be proposed for remedial action. Where recovery is not possible, a cost and schedule impact evaluation should be made.

A minimum package for the monthly report would include the following:

1. Project cost report
2. Project status report

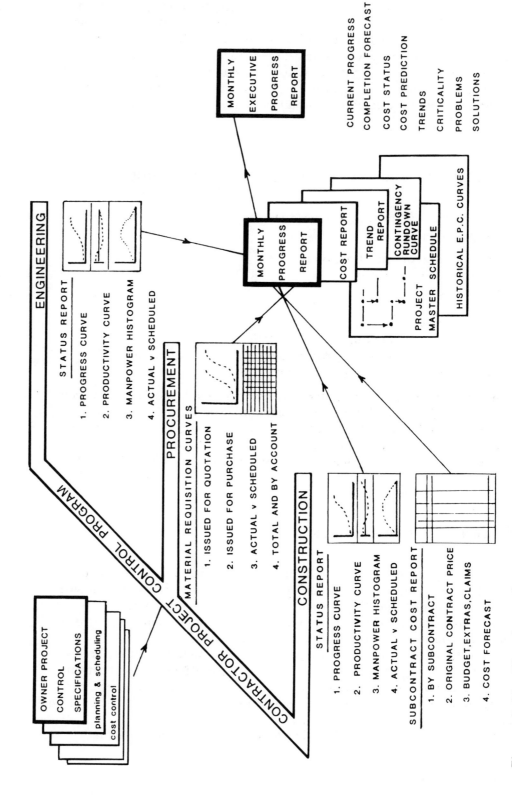

Figure 2.12   Flowchart of overall project control.

MONTHLY EXECUTIVE PROGRESS REPORT

PROJECT

LOCATION | JOB NO. | DATE

SCOPE (Brief Description)

FINANCIAL

AFE ESTIMATE – _____ DATE _____

REVISED AFE – _____ DATE _____

REVISED AFE – _____ DATE _____

SCHEDULE

ORIGINAL AFE SCHEDULE _____ REVISED TO _____ DATE _____

. REVISED TO _____ DATE _____ REVISED TO _____ DATE _____

CONTRACTOR

CONTRACT BASIS

PROJECT STATUS–COMMENTS

ENGINEERING	CONSTRUCTION

%

100
90
80
70
60
50
40
30
20
10

	CURRENT STATUS/FORECAST	ORIGINAL PLAN
MECHANICAL COMPLETION DATE		
OPERATIONAL COMPLETION DATE		
ENGINEERING % COMPLETE		
PROCUREMENT % COMPLETE		
CONSTRUCTION % COMPLETE		

PROJECT COST	AFE	COMMITED TO DATE	FORECAST LAST PERIOD	FORECAST THIS PERIOD

OWNER PROJECT MANAGER	CONTRACTOR PROJECT MANAGER

Figure 2.13   Monthly executive progress report.

Engineering progress
Material commitment progress
Construction progress
Engineering productivity and manpower curves
Construction productivity and manpower curves
3. Project master schedule
4. Subcontracts report (if project has major subcontract element)
5. Trend report
6. Contingency rundown curve

A brief narrative should outline the progress for the period, the cost status, deviations, and trends; highlight critical activities; and provide a forecast of cost and probable schedule completion.

Maximizing of graphical content will enable management to more quickly absorb the status, trends, and forecast.

2.13 MONTHLY EXECUTIVE PROGRESS REPORT

In addition to a weekly activity report and the detailed monthly progress report, a monthly summary report should be produced for executive management. Figure 2.13 illustrates a typical report format (one page).

This report will be prepared for each project by the project manager on a predetermined cycle which is convenient for reporting that project's affairs. Approved authorizations for expenditure (AFEs) each require a separate report. The report will be written in a terse style and will include the following: a concise, but complete, financial statement; a brief report on project progress versus predicted schedule and on anticipated delays with reasons why; and, finally, a statement on project affairs covering such items as personnel, contractor relations, labor conditions, and other general information which should be known to management. Each monthly report should be a complete statement of project status and should not rely on previous reports for a complete picture of the financial and schedule status. Actual versus planned progress curves for engineering and construction should be known.

3

OWNER PLANNING AND SCHEDULING:
PROCESS PLANTS

3.1 INTRODUCTION

Since 1973, many owners have experienced a deteriorating performance by contractors in the planning and scheduling of projects as
related to owners' needs. This is due, they believe, to uncertain
worldwide conditions, massive increases in size, and complexity of
projects and also—in some cases—to outmoded, in appropriate contractors' policies and corporate structures. Furthermore, since 1973, most
major process contractors have doubled their engineering staffs.
Owners claim that this has led to a dilution of expertise, talent, and
experience, especially in the area of project controls and services.
This has caused many owners to establish their own planning and
scheduling operation.

   The following is a list of major contractor scheduling problems as
experienced by owners:

Too many activities
Activity networks--poor quality
Early control lacking
   Front end schedule—engineering only
   No critical path
   No critical purchase plan
   No construction plan
Poor evaluation of logistic problems
No or poor subcontract plan
Manpower usage considered as engineering progress
Late, overcomplex, or nonexistent weekly construction programs
Slighting of subcontract controls

   Some of the specific problems owners experience are networks with
too much detail, networks with poor logic, lack of early identification
of criticality, hazy construction planning, and a minimal sense of
urgency in purchasing critical material. In too many instances, engineering progress is measured by man-hours expended instead of by
useful work performed; construction work progress is not quantified,
and subcontract progress is uncontrolled.

As to network size, the writer believes 10,000-20,000 activity networks are costly, unmanageable, and inefficient, even on large projects. Better control is achieved when the number of activities is reduced to a maximum of not more than 5000. This requires improvement in the quality of networks and improvement of reporting frequency and timeliness.

Early contractor control is essential. Owner-contractor cooperation is required in this very early stage to convey to contractor personnel the available details of project scope, the estimated cost of its components, and precontract planning and scheduling for its execution.

3.2 ENGINEERING MANPOWER

Figure 3.1 is an actual representation of a contractor's engineering manpower histogram. This situation can cause serious schedule slippage. Poor manpower planning is not always the contractor's fault. Scope changes by the owner can be a major factor.

This example demonstrates a poor man-hour estimate, resulting in frequent changes to the manpower plan. As shown, the original man-

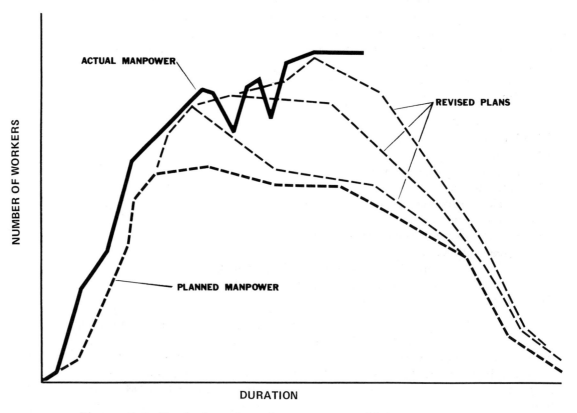

Figure 3.1 Typical engineering manpower histogram.

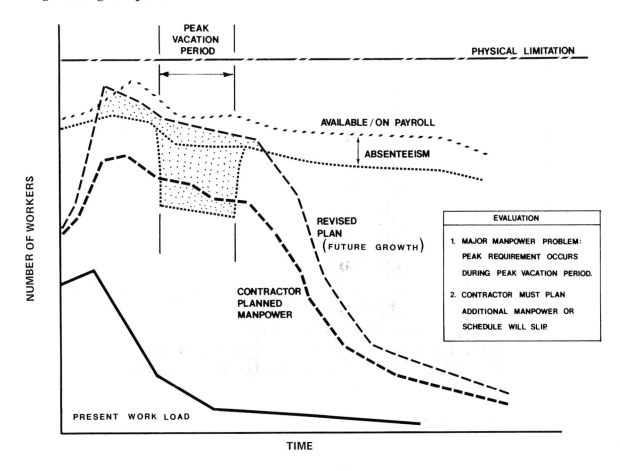

Figure 3.2 Overall manpower evaluation—comprehensive analysis.

power projection was overrun by 30%, and new manning levels were
developed as actual manpower overran planned levels.

This situation is not uncommon, and the following outlines a procedure to overcome the problem.

Figure 3.2 illustrates a method to ensure that the contractor has sufficient manpower available and planned to meet current and future requirements. The evaluation should cover the contractor's total work
load, past experience with scope growth, available manpower, possible
means of effectively augmenting manpower, allowances for lost time,
holidays, and vacations, and so forth.

A major element of this technique is a sensitivity evaluation or
allowance for future growth. On most large projects, the early engineering man-hour estimate will substantially increase. This can be
due to poor estimating, failure to recognize the complexity of the
project, additional owner requirements, or poor historical experience
of large projects. This illustration uses 30% for the increase in man-
hours and concludes there will be a significant manpower problem due
to the manpower peak coinciding with the peak vacation period.

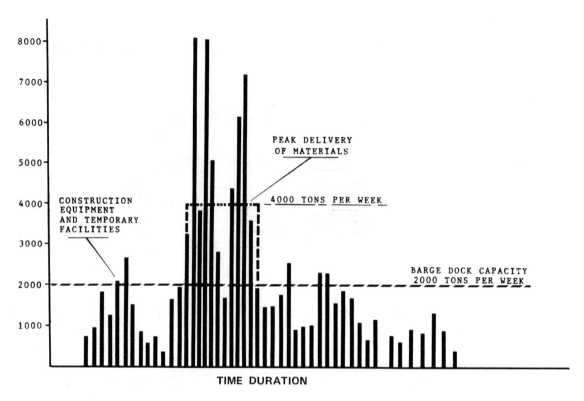

Figure 3.3 Material tonnage histogram—job site delivery.

3.3 MATERIAL LOGISTICS

On very large projects in remote locations, material logistics are a
major consideration. It is essential that material tonnage histograms
be prepared and evaluated against the capacity of proposed transport and unloading facilities. It is more than embarrassing to find that
the daily tonnage capacity of a shipping harbor will not handle peak
shipments of material to the job site. As per Figure 3.3, a tonnage
histogram should be developed by taking the estimated weights of
material and equipment against the scheduled job site delivery. As
shown, the early delivery of construction equipment and indirect material for temporary facilities is followed by delivery of the permanent,
direct material. Figure 3.3 is a *material tonnage histogram* illustrating
that the barge dock capacity will handle only half the peak delivery of
materials to the job site. This would be a very serious problem in a
real-life situation.

3.4 COMMUNICATION: A VITAL AND NEGLECTED FACTOR

Too often, schedules, especially logic networks, appear to be a mass
of arrows, lines, and circles. At first sight, engineering and construc-

tion managers throw up their hands in horror and resort to bar charts which they have maintained for just such a situation. When this happens, both owners and contractors lose--sometimes for the specific project and always in the long run. Schedule engineers need to be reminded, regularly and forcibly, that "their" schedule is not the end product. The successful completion of the project is the end product.

The best schedulers keep the following in mind:

Their fundamental purpose is to communicate.
Technical excellence will not compensate for noncommunicative
   schedules.
They cannot work in a vacuum but must make themselves part of
   the daily give-and-take of the project.
They must labor to avoid poor layouts and poor formats.
The activities they establish must be quantifiable.
Simplicity is essential.
Their schedule formats must be organized for updating and
   showing progress.

Last, they will find that when the preceding are observed, their schedules will have credibility and will receive the serious consideration and usage they deserve.

3.5 THE CONTRACTOR SCHEDULE ENGINEER

The following are major requirements for a contractor senior schedule engineer:

Education: Bachelor degree or equivalent
Eight years or more in related industry work
Knowledge of estimating and cost control
Three years of construction (job site) experience
Five years of scheduling experience
Self-starter, with capacity for teamwork
Good communicator—orally and in writing
Flexible and imaginative approach
Be prepared to travel

In a recent national 3-day seminar on planning and scheduling, a survey of attending contractors showed that approximately 10% of their schedule personnel fulfilled the requirements listed. Large, complex projects require capable and experienced schedule engineers. Too often, detailed and sophisticated scheduling systems have proven ineffective due to a lack of experience of the schedule engineers. Owners state that many contractor's career structures do not place sufficient weight on the position of schedule engineer. They have observed young, capable schedule engineers moving into more interesting supervisory responsibility within the engineering, project, and construction departments. Owners need to see such people moving into respected and responsible positions in scheduling.

3.6 OWNER SCHEDULING SERVICE

An owner's scheduling effort has two basic objectives:

Provide front-end planning and scheduling for capital projects.
Aid owner project teams in ensuring that the contractor's performance is effectively meeting company and project planning and
  scheduling objectives

Figure 3.4 is a flowchart depicting the work of an owner in developing schedule standards, historical data, front end schedules, and contractor monitoring systems. It is essential that early schedules be
simple but accurately reflect all basic relationships and constraints, so
higher management can quickly focus on activities of significant
schedule criticality. In later project stages, the owner's contractor
monitoring system must be sufficiently detailed to ensure that performance is measured with appropriate accuracy, and criticality promptly communicated throughout the owner-contractor project team, over
the entire project duration.

It cannot be emphasized too strongly that collection and analysis of
historical schedule and cost data are essential for effective project
control of both schedules and costs. Integration of scheduling with cost
control functions throughout project performance is vital for efficient
operation.

Data collection and analysis should be part of the overall development work, budgeted and authorized on an annual basis. Development
activity programs should be detailed, resourced, budgeted, and then
presented semiannually for review and approval.

The major scheduling effort is in support of projects. This would be
carried out by a small, experienced home office staff covering projects
on a suitcase basis and supervising personnel assigned to task forces.

A coordination procedure should be developed for this work, ensuring that objectives, functions, reporting lines, and responsibilities
are clearly outlined.

The schedule and cost groups could be combined with estimating
and function as a cost engineering department. Alternatively, the
schedule and cost group could be part of the project group.

The writer believes the better arrangement is a section, called the
project support or project control section, functioning within the project groups and supervised by a manager of equal status to the project
group managers. Project control is now receiving recognition at the
project level but not fully at the management level. This arrangement
would eliminate the audit image which cost and schedule groups often
have when separated from the project divisions. An additional benefit
from integration would be the easier rotation of project managers
through the project control group for training in cost and scheduling.
Acceptance by project managers would be higher, and manpower utilization could be significantly improved.

Figure 3.4 Flowchart of owner scheduling service engineering department.

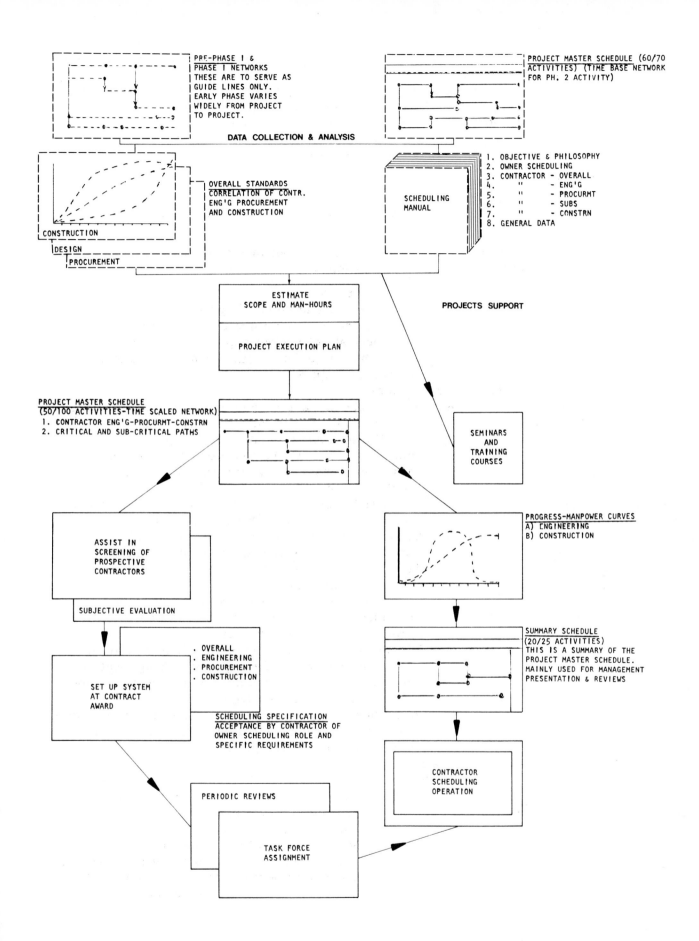

PRE-PHASE I &
PHASE I NETWORKS
THESE ARE TO SERVE AS
GUIDE LINES ONLY.
EARLY PHASE VARIES
WIDELY FROM PROJECT
TO PROJECT.

PROJECT MASTER SCHEDULE (60/70
ACTIVITIES) (TIME BASE NETWORK
FOR PH. 2 ACTIVITY)

DATA COLLECTION & ANALYSIS

OVERALL STANDARDS
CORRELATION OF CONTR.
ENG'G PROCUREMENT
AND CONSTRUCTION

CONSTRUCTION
DESIGN
PROCUREMENT

SCHEDULING
MANUAL

1. OBJECTIVE & PHILOSOPHY
2. OWNER SCHEDULING
3. CONTRACTOR - OVERALL
4.   "   - ENG'G
5.   "   - PROCURMT
6.   "   - SUBS
7.   "   - CONSTRN
8. GENERAL DATA

ESTIMATE
SCOPE AND MAN-HOURS

PROJECT EXECUTION PLAN

PROJECTS SUPPORT

PROJECT MASTER SCHEDULE
(50/100 ACTIVITIES-TIME SCALED NETWORK)
1. CONTRACTOR ENG'G-PROCURMT-CONSTRN
2. CRITICAL AND SUB-CRITICAL PATHS

SEMINARS
AND
TRAINING
COURSES

ASSIST IN
SCREENING OF
PROSPECTIVE
CONTRACTORS

SUBJECTIVE EVALUATION

PROGRESS-MANPOWER CURVES
A) ENGINEERING
B) CONSTRUCTION

. OVERALL
. ENGINEERING
. PROCUREMENT
. CONSTRUCTION

SET UP SYSTEM
AT CONTRACT
AWARD

SCHEDULING SPECIFICATION
ACCEPTANCE BY CONTRACTOR OF
OWNER SCHEDULING ROLE AND
SPECIFIC REQUIREMENTS

SUMMARY SCHEDULE
(20/25 ACTIVITIES)
THIS IS A SUMMARY OF THE
PROJECT MASTER SCHEDULE.
MAINLY USED FOR MANAGEMENT
PRESENTATION & REVIEWS

CONTRACTOR
SCHEDULING
OPERATION

PERIODIC REVIEWS

TASK FORCE
ASSIGNMENT

Training should be an essential feature of an owner's project control program. It is recommended that *training modules* be developed for hourly seminars or weekly courses. Course material should be structured for orientation-type seminars and detailed workshops for technical experts and experienced professionals.

3.7 SCHEDULE ENGINEER: DUTIES AND OBJECTIVES

The duties and objectives of a project task force lead schedule engineer can be summarized as follows:

   I. The engineer reports to
     A. The project task force (PTF) project manager-business manager as a line responsibility
     B. The supervisor of project support, at the home office, for technical guidance, functional responsibility, and career development
  II. General responsibilities
     A. Provide schedule engineering support to the PTF within the guidelines established by the project manager and the schedule manual
     B. Monitor and evaluate the contractor's scheduling methods to ensure they meet with the project requirements
     C. Review and evaluate contractor schedule personnel and their technical capability and experience
     D. Maintain constant communication with all PTF members to develop and disseminate schedule requirements
     E. Liaise with similar owner projects to obtain historical experience pertinent to their project
     F. Liaise with the home office (project support) on technical matters and additional assistance, with project manager concurrence
     G. Maintain continuous evaluation of schedule criticality and project status. Advise project management of criticality and status together with conclusions and recommendations to resolve problems.
     H. Accumulate, analyze, and furnish historical return data per the scheduling manual procedures along with unique features of the project
 III. Engineering
     A. Schedules
        1. Evaluate, approve, and monitor the contractor schedule implementation plan
        2. Monitor and analyze contractor project master schedules, front end schedules, and detailed engineering task force schedules and advise the PTF project manager of deviations and problems and recommend solutions.

      B. Progress and performance
          1. Contractor manpower utilization
          2. Evaluate, monitor, and analyze engineering
              progress and performance

IV. Procurement
      A. Evaluate contractor procurement plan and maintain
          requisition curves
      B. Review bid tabs for material delivery schedules
      C. Follow up scheduling of material purchase, manufacture,
          and delivery to job site. Make visits to major manufac-
          turers to evaluate production schedules versus project
          plans
      D. Review all subcontract packages for schedule compati-
          bility to project objectives

V. Construction: Based on the agreed construction plan, provide
  PTF management with weekly, biweekly, and monthly reports on
      A. Construction progress, overall and by area
      B. Manpower and productivity analysis, plans, actuals, and
          forecasts
      C. Schedule criticality
      D. Material delivery and receiving status identifying critical
          equipment
      E. Evaluations of subcontractor performance and schedule
          impacts and deviations
      F. Whether the weekly work plans are definitive and suf-
          ficient to meet the overall project progress and schedule
          objectives

VI. Meetings and coordination
      A. Attend and participate in owner-contractor weekly
          (periodic) progress meetings. Maintain a log, and issue
          action items with project manager concurrence
      B. Provide "schedule liaison" with engineering management
          (contractor office) and field construction PTF manage-
          ment
      C. Assist in establishing drawing completion dates and ma-
          terial delivery requirements
      D. Attend major subcontract progress meetings
      E. Attend and participate in job site weekly work planning
          meetings

VII. Owner schedules and reports (with concurrence of project
  manager)
      A. Prepare, maintain, and issue the required owner
          schedules
      B. Assist, prepare, and compile owner overall progress
          reports
      C. Assist and prepare special schedule studies as required
          for project analysis
      D. Prepare historical return data per instructions in the
          scheduling manual and any other unique project
          conditions not covered in the manual

These duties and objectives will form the basis of an annual performance appraisal. The appraisal is developed by the project manager,
reviewed and endorsed by the functional manager, and approved by
corporate management. Salary action should be tied to the performance
appraisal system. Performance interviews and counseling sessions
should be held with all personnel.

3.8 FEEDBACK DATA

Continuous evaluation of current experience and practices is essential
for a dynamic scheduling operation. Conditions change, methods improve, and technology advances, and it is vital that a scheduling data
base reflect present-day conditions.

The feedback of data, during the project and on completion, is a
responsibility of task force and suitcase schedule engineers. It is an
important function and should be an appraisal objective of the schedule
engineer's performance.

The majority of feedback data will be for a contractor, phase II operation. Data feedback is used to update standard schedules and also
to provide comparative data points and units to measure the performance of projects on a multiple basis. A typical data point is engineering man-hours per piece of equipment.

Following are some typical samples of feedback requirements. However, it must be emphasized that the type of feedback data will depend
on the data base of the particular scheduling system.

Figure 3.5 shows the actual progress experience of process, civil,
structural, piping-modeling, and overall design with their respective
manpower curves. In addition, manpower curves are plotted for
designers-draftspersons, specialist engineers, purchasers-expediters-
inspectors, and total home office personnel. This format should also be
used for major categories of construction work.

Figure 3.6 shows overall home office man-hours compiled by discipline and section and entered on a summary sheet. All drawings,
models, and related documents from engineering, together with the
number of pieces of equipment, provide man-hours per drawing, model
board, and piece of equipment.

The relationships of engineering man-hours per piece of equipment
and man-hours per drawing (on a total basis) are major data points in
evaluating engineering performance.

Large refining projects are currently showing 150 man-hours per
drawing and 1200 man-hours per piece of equipment.

Figure 3.7 shows the historical experience of the material requisitioning effort. This information will assist in evaluating procurement
performance and establishing data for determining a reasonable time
for the purchasing effort. The shape of the curve is also important as
it can show when peak effort occurs and how long the peak can be
sustained.

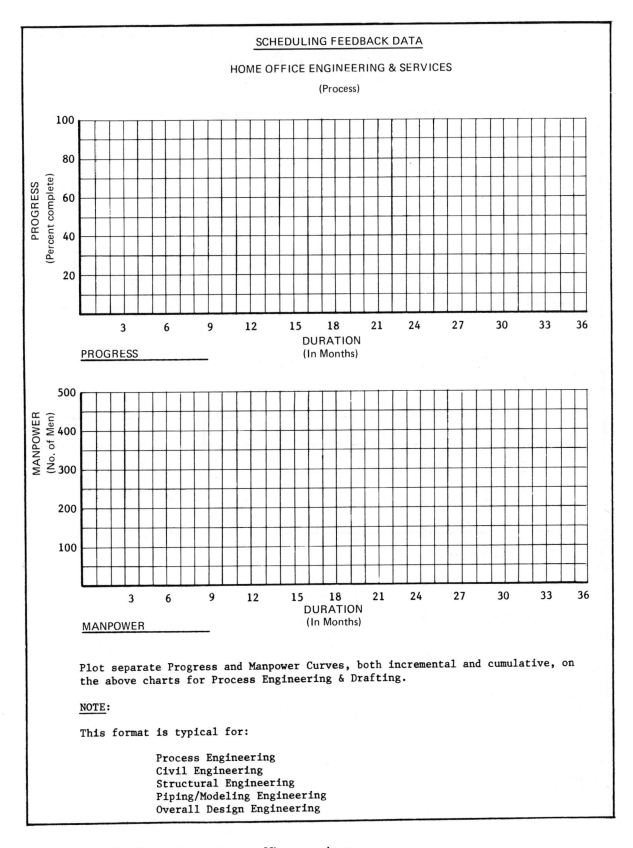

Figure 3.5 Feedback data--home office services.

SCHEDULING FEEDBACK DATA
HOME OFFICE ENGINEERING & SERVICES
(Summary)

	ACCOUNT	BUDGET MANHOURS	ACTUAL MANHOURS	WT % OF ACTUAL TOTAL MANHOURS	DRAWINGS		MODEL BOARDS
					MANUAL	COMPUTER	
E	Process						
N	Civil						
G	Structural						
I	Mechanical						
N	Piping/Model						
E	Electrical						
E	Instrumentation						
R	Project Engineering						
I	Technical Clerical						
N	TOTAL			100%			
G	M. H. Per Dwg.						
	M.H.Per Model Board						
	M.H.Per Piece of Eqpt.						
S	Purch,Exped,Inspect.						
E	Estimating						
R	Cost Control						
V	Planning/Scheduling						
I	Construction						
C	All Other Home Office						
E/S	TOTAL						
Total Project							
% Over (Under) Orig Eng. Budget							
% Over (Under) Orig Total Proj Budget							

Abbreviations

Wt.   Weighted
M.H.   Manhours
Dwg.   Drawing
Bd.   Board

TOTAL PIECES OF EQUIPMENT _____ __

Figure 3.6 Feedback data—engineering.

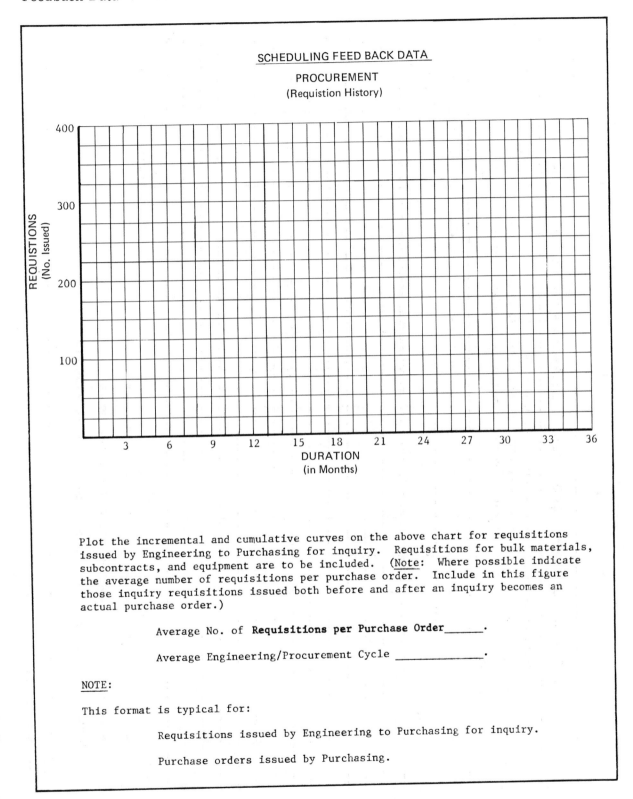

Figure 3.7 Feedback data—procurement.

DATA FEEDBACK – DELIVERY LEAD TIMES (EQUIPMENT & MATERIAL)

S – SOURCE (COUNTRY OF ORIGIN)
Q – QUOTED DELIVERY TIME
A – ACTUAL DELIVERY TIME

1. ALL DURATIONS ARE IN MONTHS .
2. FINAL EVALUATION OF VENDOR QUOTED DELIVERY VERSUS ACTUAL RECEIPT AT JOBSITE . ENTER IN CREEP % COLUMN .

CREEP %

PROJECT
JOB NO.
DATE
SHEET NO.

ITEM	P.O. 1			P.O. 2			P.O. 3			P.O. 4			PROJECT AVE.			CREEP %
	S	Q	A	S	Q	A	S	Q	A	S	Q	A	S	Q	A	%

OVERALL %

NOTES :
1. DELIVERY TIME IS MEASURED FROM P.O. PLACEMENT TO OUTSIDE DELIVERY .
2. ENTER MAJOR PURCHASES ONLY AND ABBREVIATE MATERIAL SOURCE .
3. AVERAGE DURATIONS OF SEVERAL PURCHASE ORDERS FOR SIMILAR MATERIAL .

Figure 3.8 Feedback data—delivery times.

SCHEDULING FEED BACK DATA

CONSTRUCTION
(MAN-HOURS/QUANTITIES/PROGRESS)

PROJECT: _____
LOCATION _____

WORK FUNCTION	START/FINISH (Dates)	DURATION (Months)	QUANTITIES	MANHOURS PER UNIT	DIRECT MANHOURS	AVERAGE MONTHLY PROGRESS	AVERAGE M.H. PER PIECE OF EQUIPMENT	WEIGHTED % OF TOTAL DIRECT M.H.
Site Prep **Excavation**			— C.Y.	C.Y.				
All Other								
Concrete			— C.Y.	C.Y.				
Civil & U.G. **All Other**								
Structural Steel			Tons	Ton				
Buildings			No.	Each				
			S.F.	S.F.				
			No.	Each				
Equipment			Tons	Ton				
			L.F.	L.F.				
			Tons	Ton				
A.G. Piping **U.G.**			L.F.	L.F.				
Electrical **A.G.**			L.F.	L.F.				
All Other								
Instrumentation			No.	Each				
Painting **Pipe**			S.F.	S.F.				
Equipment			S.F.	S.F.				
All Other								
Insulation **Pipe**			L.F.	S.F.				
Equipment			S.F.	S.F.				

Total Project Direct Man-hours _____

Total Project Direct Craft Proratable Man-hours _____

Total Project Indirect Man-hours _____

100%

Construction Density - Critical Unit	Total Pieces of Major Equipment
Battery Limit Area _____ **S.F.**	_____ Pieces
Peak Manpower _____ Men	
Density _____ **S.F./Man**	

Abbreviations

M.H. Man-hours   S.F. Square Feet
U.G. Underground   L.F. Linear Feet
A.G. Above Ground   No. Number
C.Y. Cubic Yards

<u>Note:</u>
All Data Shown Are For Completed Project Scope.

Figure 3.9 Feedback data—construction.

Figure 3.8 shows the experience of equipment deliveries. Actual experience versus original quoted vendor delivery is measured. This information is important in assessing current equipment delivery trends and will also provide a basis for determining the *creep factor*. *Creep* is the time difference from actual receipt at the job site compared with the original vendor-quoted delivery time. In practice, this will generally range from 5 to 30%, always additive.

Figure 3.9 provides man-hour, quantity, and progress data and, very importantly, labor density experience. This information will provide man-hours per quantity unit (man-hours per cubic yard-foot-ton, etc.). Also provided are the man-hours for the direct prime accounts, the direct proratable, and the indirect account. Man-hours per piece of equipment are collated and are used, similarly to the engineering statistic, to measure performance of comparative projects.

The labor density data are collated to check on the standard *density curves*. Monthly progress experience is used to check on the standard construction progress curve.

In addition to the return data samples shown, a very important historical element is the overall, milestone schedule and associated progress curves for material commitment, engineering, and construction.

It is important to analyze the relationship and duration of major activities which make up the standard project master schedule.

3.9 OWNER PLANNING AND SCHEDULING SPECIFICATION (FOR LARGE PROJECTS, PHASE II)

The following approach is based on a reimbursable contractual basis with an owner task force monitoring the contractor's operations. Generally, company requirements are as shown in a flowchart (Figure 3.10) entitled "Typical Contractor Planning and Scheduling System." The company will require that the contractor modify or add planning and scheduling techniques and methods which the company deems necessary. It is company practice, at contract award, to carry out a detailed review and evaluation of contractor systems and procedures. At this review, company scheduling personnel will present company requirements for discussion and mutual acceptance. The contractor will provide the company with an implementation plan and detailed schedule for completion of the planning and scheduling effort.

This flowchart shows current contractor practices and, where not adequate, modifications by the company. The following explanations are keyed to the item number of the flowchart.

Overall

Level I Schedule (No. 22)

1. The contractor shall provide a project master schedule within 1 month after contract award. This schedule will be a *time-scaled network* of the total project and will highlight critical and subcritical paths

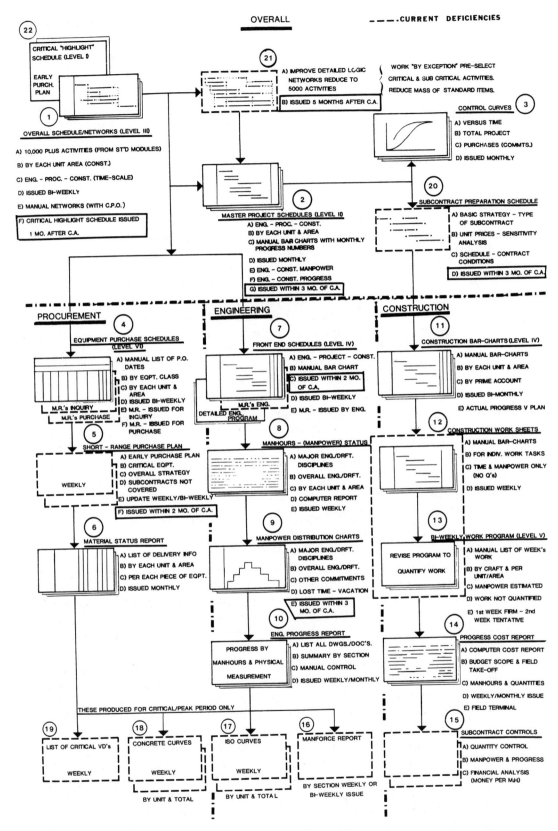

22

CRITICAL "HIGHLIGHT" SCHEDULE (LEVEL 0)

EARLY PURCH. PLAN

1

OVERALL SCHEDULE/NETWORKS (LEVEL III)

A) 10,000 PLUS ACTIVITIES (FROM ST'D MODULES)

B) BY EACH UNIT AREA (CONST.)

C) ENG. - PROC. - CONST. (TIME-SCALE)

D) ISSUED BI-WEEKLY

E) MANUAL NETWORKS (WITH C.P.O.)

F) CRITICAL HIGHLIGHT SCHEDULE ISSUED 1 MO. AFTER C.A.

21

A) IMPROVE DETAILED LOGIC NETWORKS REDUCE TO 5000 ACTIVITIES

WORK "BY EXCEPTION" PRE-SELECT CRITICAL & SUB CRITICAL ACTIVITIES. REDUCE MASS OF STANDARD ITEMS.

B) ISSUED 5 MONTHS AFTER C.A.

3

CONTROL CURVES

A) VERSUS TIME

B) TOTAL PROJECT

C) PURCHASES (COMMTS.)

D) ISSUED MONTHLY

2

MASTER PROJECT SCHEDULES (LEVEL II)

A) ENG. - PROC. - CONST.

B) BY EACH UNIT & AREA

C) MANUAL BAR CHARTS WITH MONTHLY PROGRESS NUMBERS

D) ISSUED MONTHLY

E) ENG. - CONST. MANPOWER

F) ENG. - CONST. PROGRESS

G) ISSUED WITHIN 3 MO. OF C.A.

20

SUBCONTRACT PREPARATION SCHEDULE

A) BASIC STRATEGY - TYPE OF SUBCONTRACT

B) UNIT PRICES - SENSITIVITY ANALYSIS

C) SCHEDULE - CONTRACT CONDITIONS

D) ISSUED WITHIN 3 MO. OF C.A.

PROCUREMENT　　**ENGINEERING**　　**CONSTRUCTION**

4

EQUIPMENT PURCHASE SCHEDULES (LEVEL VI)

A) MANUAL LIST OF P.O. DATES

B) BY EQPT. CLASS

C) BY EACH UNIT & AREA

D) ISSUED BI-WEEKLY

E) M.R. - ISSUED FOR INQUIRY

F) M.R. - ISSUED FOR PURCHASE

M.R.'s INQUIRY

M.R.'s PURCHASE

7

FRONT END SCHEDULES (LEVEL IV)

A) ENG. - PROJECT - CONST.

B) MANUAL BAR CHART

C) ISSUED WITHIN 2 MO. OF C.A.

D) ISSUED BI-WEEKLY

E) M.R. - ISSUED BY ENG.

M.R.'s ENG.

DETAILED ENG. PROGRAM

11

CONSTRUCTION BAR-CHARTS (LEVEL IV)

A) MANUAL BAR-CHARTS

B) BY EACH UNIT & AREA

C) BY PRIME ACCOUNT

D) ISSUED BI-MONTHLY

E) ACTUAL PROGRESS V PLAN

5

SHORT - RANGE PURCHASE PLAN

A) EARLY PURCHASE PLAN

B) CRITICAL EQPT.

C) OVERALL STRATEGY

D) SUBCONTRACTS NOT COVERED

E) UPDATE WEEKLY/BI-WEEKLY

F) ISSUED WITHIN 2 MO. OF C.A.

WEEKLY

8

MANHOURS - (MANPOWER) STATUS

A) MAJOR ENG./DRFT. DISCIPLINES

B) OVERALL ENG./DRFT.

C) BY EACH UNIT & AREA

D) COMPUTER REPORT

E) ISSUED WEEKLY

12

CONSTRUCTION WORK SHEETS

A) MANUAL BAR-CHARTS

B) FOR INDIV. WORK TASKS

C) TIME & MANPOWER ONLY (NO Q's)

D) ISSUED WEEKLY

6

MATERIAL STATUS REPORT

A) LIST OF DELIVERY INFO

B) BY EACH UNIT & AREA

C) PER EACH PIECE OF EQPT.

D) ISSUED MONTHLY

9

MANPOWER DISTRIBUTION CHARTS

A) MAJOR ENG./DRFT. DISCIPLINES

B) OVERALL ENG./DRFT.

C) OTHER COMMITMENTS

D) LOST TIME - VACATION

E) ISSUED WITHIN 3 MO. OF C.A.

13

BI-WEEKLY WORK PROGRAM (LEVEL V)

REVISE PROGRAM TO QUANTIFY WORK

A) MANUAL LIST OF WEEK's WORK

B) BY CRAFT & PER UNIT/AREA

C) MANPOWER ESTIMATED

D) WORK NOT QUANTIFIED

E) 1st WEEK FIRM - 2nd WEEK TENTATIVE

10

ENG. PROGRESS REPORT

PROGRESS BY MANHOURS & PHYSICAL MEASUREMENT

A) LIST ALL DWGS./DOC'S.

B) SUMMARY BY SECTION

C) MANUAL CONTROL

D) ISSUED WEEKLY/MONTHLY

14

PROGRESS COST REPORT

A) COMPUTER COST REPORT

B) BUDGET SCOPE & FIELD TAKE-OFF

C) MANHOURS & QUANTITIES

D) WEEKLY/MONTHLY ISSUE

E) FIELD TERMINAL

THESE PRODUCED FOR CRITICAL/PEAK PERIOD ONLY

19

LIST OF CRITICAL VD's

WEEKLY

18

CONCRETE CURVES

WEEKLY

BY UNIT & TOTAL

17

ISO CURVES

WEEKLY

BY UNIT & TOTAL

16

MANFORCE REPORT

BY SECTION WEEKLY OR BI-WEEKLY ISSUE

15

SUBCONTRACT CONTROLS

A) QUANTITY CONTROL

B) MANPOWER & PROGRESS

C) FINANCIAL ANALYSIS (MONEY PER M.H.)

Figure 3.10 Flowchart of scheduling specification.

for engineering, procurement, and construction. This schedule will be updated with actual progress and issued biweekly.

2. The contractor shall provide a plan for early purchasing within 2 months of contract award. This plan will identify critical or long lead equipment and material, outline a purchasing strategy, and schedule the required activities to efficiently place the purchase orders.

Level II Schedules (No. 2)

1. These project master schedules are an interim step in developing the detailed computer networks (level III) from the overall, level I schedule. They will be manual, time-scaled networks or bar charts for areas or units covering engineering, procurement, and construction. Issue is required within 3 months after contract award.

2. The contractor shall provide manpower histograms and progress curves for the engineering and procurement effort within 2 months of contract award. These histograms and progress curves will be updated with actual progress and issued weekly or monthly to suit the criticality of the project. Appropriate allowances should be shown on these histograms for contractor overall manning level, current work load, absenteeism, and vacation.

3. The contractor shall provide construction manpower histograms and progress curves within 6 months of contract award. The manpower histograms are to include appropriate allowances for absenteeism, holidays, and anticipated lost time due to normal labor practices and inclement weather. Curves and histograms will be updated on completion of the level III networks. It is expected that the contractor will complete, and thereafter maintain, an evaluation of the labor availability. Manpower curves are total only with a key discipline or craft shown separately, if appropriate.

Level III Schedules (Nos. 1 and 22). On large, complex projects, planning and scheduling are effectively accomplished with detailed critical path networks, together with an effective critical path method (CPM) computer system for reporting status.

The contractor shall complete the networks and have the computer system operational within 5 months after contract award. The networks will cover engineering, procurement, and construction and be tied together as a complete system.

Experience with network-computer systems has clearly demonstrated that a more effective operation is achieved with minimizing the number of activities and maximizing reporting frequency. Total activities should be in the range 3000-5000. Larger activity networks are not recommended.

This requires that the contractor work by exception and predetermine critical and subcritical activities to reduce the mass of standard and noncritical items. This is a task for experienced and quality schedule engineers as it will result in areas and units having varying degrees of detail and also will require that control areas for the project be determined at this time.

An effective method of accomplishing this objective is to first draw
up a matrix by function and major area-unit and then predetermine the
number of activities as a working target. It is recommended that this
approach be used as illustrated:

Area	Engineering	Purchasing	Contracts	Construction	Total
1					
2					
3					
4					
5					
6					
Total					3000

Manpower Histograms (No. 9). It is recommended that the overall manpower resource allocation of engineering and construction be carried
out on a manual basis. Computer resourcing of area schedules with a
minimum of activities is not too meaningful. The estimated man-hours
cannot be easily allocated, and the casting of the schedule in greater
detail so as to resource by computer is inefficient and unnecessary. The
level II manpower histograms should form the basis for further breakdown, by individual discipline and craft labor, to match the level III
schedules.

Subcontract Preparation Schedule (No. 20). The contractor shall provide a *subcontract preparation schedule* for field subcontracts within 3
months after contract award. This schedule will outline a subcontract
strategy and detail the required activities to efficiently let the subcontracts. The level of detail will depend on subcontract scope, business
strategy, and criticality. This schedule will be issued monthly or bi-
weekly.

Control Curves (No. 3). The following control cures, and others as
deemed necessary, will be required: curves to show a plot of money
against time, planned and actual:

Material commitments and expenditure
Cash flow

In addition the following curves will be required for:

Engineering development and scope change orders against time
Contingency reduction against time

The curves will be issued monthly or biweekly.

Procurement

Equipment Purchase Schedule (No. 4). A manual or computer program
showing planned and actual dates for engineering-purchasing activities
will be issued monthly or biweekly.

Material Requisition Curves (No. 4). A plot of the number of material requisitions for inquiry and purchase against time, planned or actual, will be issued monthly or biweekly.

Short-Range Purchase Plan (No. 5). This is an abstract of the overall purchasing plan and will generally be a one-page document showing the purchase planned for the week and will be issued weekly or biweekly.

Material Status Report (MSR) (No. 6). A manual or computer program showing the status of equipment and material in the vendor shop will be issued monthly.

Critical Vendor Drawings (No. 19). A one-page general abstract of the main control showing vendor drawings which are seriously delaying the progress of engineering will be issued weekly.

Engineering

Front End Schedules (No. 7). These are required within 2 months of contract award and are manual schedules showing the planned activities of engineering, procurement, and construction for the next 3-4 months. They provide a detailed interim control. They will be issued biweekly and will be discontinued when the level III program and the detailed engineering program are available.

Man-hour Status (No. 8). A manual or computer program showing man-hours, by engineering discipline and section, on an incremental and cumulative basis, will be issued weekly or biweekly.

Engineering Progress (No. 10). Physical progress, by quantity take-off and measurement, is required. A progress report will include planned and actual curves by section to match the breakdown of the level III manpower histograms.

Home Office Workforce Report (No. 16). This is a weekly head count of all personnel and is required at critical periods, as determined by the company.

Isometric Curves (No. 17). These are plots of planned and/or actual completion (construction issue) of total isometric drawings. They are cumulative curves against time, by critical units and in total. The period of issue is dependent on criticality.

Concrete Curves (No. 18). These curves use the same technique as the isometric curves but are for civil foundation drawings. The placement of concrete in the field can also be included on these curves.

Construction

Construction Bar Charts (No. 11). These are manual schedules by area showing greater detail or a 2- to 3-month period of the level III schedule and will be issued bimonthly.

Short-term Construction Program (Nos. 12 and 13). This program shall be based on quantities, man-hour units, productivity adjustments, and reconciliation to the overall program. (See the additional details of this program in Section 5.31)

Progress Report (No. 14). Progress should be evaluated by an analysis of physical quantities installed against the total required. Man-hours can be used only if the forecasted man-hours reflect total quantities and productivity experience.

Subcontract Control (No. 15). Controls shall be based on physical measurement of progress, and all schedules shall be properly interfaced with the overall project schedule. (See the detailed information contained in Chapter 7.)

Summation

The contractor shall respond, in writing, to this specification, showing a flowchart of proposed techniques and methods for the specified items.

It should be noted that scheduling techniques and methods are constantly being improved so that "blind compliance" to this specification should not be substituted for an intelligent approach. Small projects will not require this comprehensive program, and adjustments will be made as agreed upon by the company.

3.10 PROJECT MASTER SCHEDULE: LARGE PROJECTS, STANDARD

Figure 3.11 is a basic standard network for a phase II operation. It should be updated as economic conditions change. The notes require full consideration. The network can be used for most phase II process plant projects, but corrections must be applied for subcontract construction, overseas work, and remote job sites. The logic will generally apply for small projects, but with reduced activity durations and the minimum of site preparation. (See Figure 3.14 for further detail.) A major element of this standard is the sequencing of equipment delivery and installation based on historical data to provide sufficient nozzles for an efficient field piping program.

The data base for this standard network is outlined in Section 3.11.

Application

For feasibility studies this 70-activity network should be summarized to 30 activities.

For approved projects, the full network detail should be used, together with engineering and construction manpower curves. If battery limits are known, the construction duration should be evaluated using the labor density-productivity method (see Section 3.13). Midpoints of material and construction can be determined for estimating purposes.

Most schedules should be drawn up as time-scaled networks.

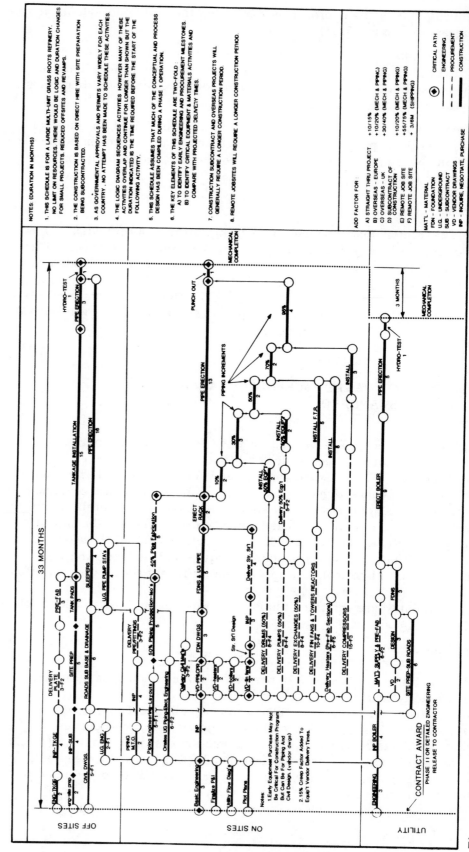

Figure 3.11 Standard project master schedule—large projects.

A creep factor is applied to equipment lead times: usually +5% for Japan, +10% for the United States, and +20-30% for Europe. This factor recognizes that the original vendor-quoted delivery is rarely achieved.

The purchasing-engineering cycle [inquire, negotiate, and purchase (INP)], usually 4-5 months for the United States and Europe, is determined with reference to Figure 3.18 and the proposed execution plan.

Add factors: Detailed consideration should be given to this section, shown at the bottom of the schedule. This network is based on a U.S., phase II, direct-hire operation, and the add factors are to compensate for an overseas location, subcontract operation, or additional engineering time if the project is on a straight-through basis (no phase I).

Environmental aspects and governmental regulations are rarely standard and must be treated on an individual basis.

3.11 OVERALL BREAKDOWN: LARGE PROJECTS

Typical contractor estimating phases are superimposed across the entire range of milestone activities as a guide for probable estimating accuracy in relation to engineering definition and material commitments. This standard bar chart and progress chart (Figure 3.12) shows the historical relationship of major activities (milestones) with related progress curves for engineering, material commitment, and construction on a percentage-of-time basis. The activity bars only show the amount of work critical to the project schedule. The data base is seven large projects constructed during the period 1968-1978. A large project is defined as one requiring approximately 500,000 home office man-hours and 5 million field man-hours. Engineering and construction curves show planned physical progress with construction on a direct-hire basis. The material commitment curve is completion of commitment on a financial basis and includes material supply and erect subcontracts, such as tankage, heaters, and field fabricated vessels.

Application

Once the schedule duration has been established from the standard project master schedule (Figure 3.11), specific project schedules and progress curves can be drawn using these percentage relationships plus knowledge of the specific job and related information. A detailed contractor schedule which lies significantly outside the bar chart relationship or progress curves alerts personnel that it is an exception to the norm and must be evaluated in detail to determine the causes of the variation. If actual performance falls significantly below past engineering or material commitment experience, it is probable that the construction progress curve will not be achieved. This can indicate

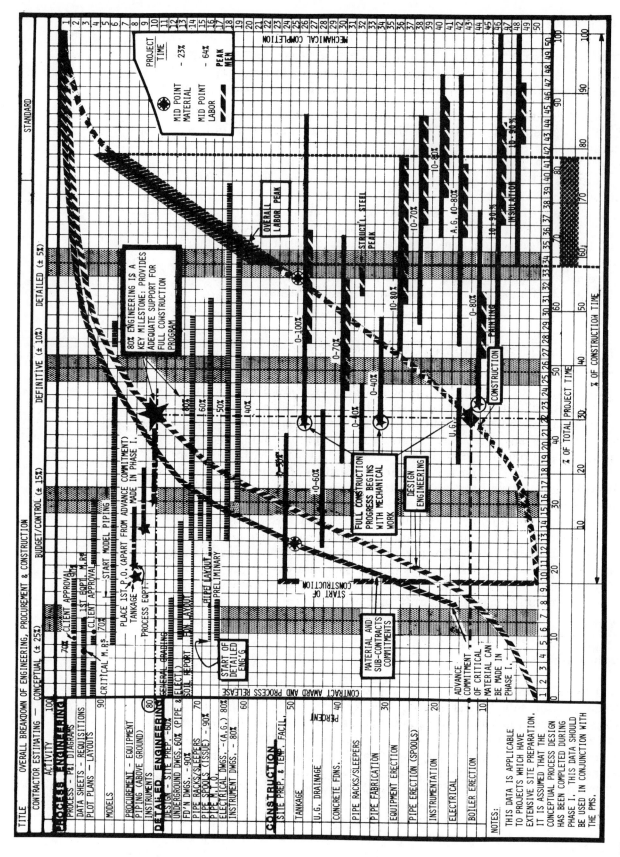

Figure 3.12 Standard breakdown EPC—large projects.

64

completion date slippage or the need for special efforts to prevent a potential schedule slippage. In most cases, the latter will increase costs. These three curves have a definite relationship to each other, particularly for engineering and construction, where the need for an adequate backlog of engineering drawings is vital to support an economic construction program. As shown, the milestone of 80% engineering is keyed to 15% construction, which is the start of mechanical work in the field. Purchasing slippage will impact on the engineering program due to lack of vendor data and may also delay field work.

Historical midpoints of material (23%) and construction (65%) quickly determine the escalation points for estimating. However, a manual evaluation of the project master schedule (PMS) should be carried out to ensure that a differing scope or purchasing plan is compatible with the standard data. The indicated percents, 23 and 64, are of the total project time from contract award to mechanical completion.

Example

1.   What would be the overall duration for contractor piping engineering? Refer to horizontal line No. 16—marked pipe spools (dwgs.)— 90%. It can be seen that pipe layouts (thin dotted line) start at 9% project time and that 90% pipe isometrics (heavy dotted line) finish at 61%. Assume 100% isometrics is at 70% project time; therefore, overall piping design is 70% less 9%, which equals 61% project duration. For a large U.S. project (Figure 3.11 shows 33 months), piping design will therefore be 20 months.

2.   What would be the probable start of detailed contractor engineering? The key elements with regard to the start of detailed design is owner approval of the process design [process piping and instrumentation diagrams (PIDs)] and equipment layout (plot plans) and completion of the soil survey and report. This approval would normally occur at about 70% of PIDs and plot plans. Refer to lines 2 and 4 (PIDs and plot plans, respectively) and client approval at 9% of project time. At the same time, foundation layouts (line 14) and piping layouts (line 16) commence. This is the start of detailed design.

The main drafting effort will start with foundation drawings, piping isometrics, and general arrangements.

3.12 CONSTRUCTION SCHEDULE: LARGE PROJECTS, STANDARD

Standard Schedule

The standard construction schedule for large projects (Figure 3.13) is used in conjunction with the overall breakdown (Figure 3.12) and the project master schedule (Figure 3.11). Together, they can provide a complete summary schedule, with progress curves for engineering, material commitments, and construction. As their underlying data base

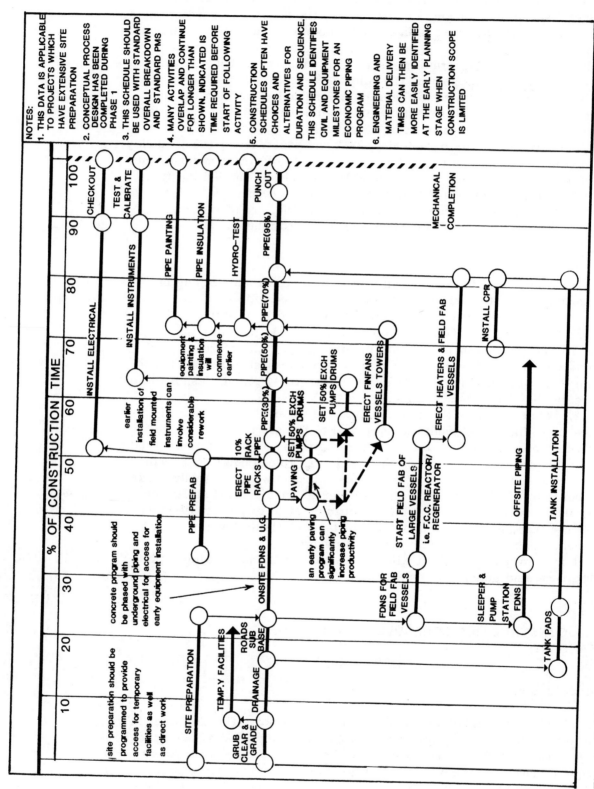

Figure 3.13   Standard construction schedule—large projects.

has been derived from completed process plant projects, planned or
actual project performance deviating from this pattern is an alarm signal
for detailed evaluation and corrective action. If the deviation is favorable, evaluation is just as important, since it can be a guide to improvement for future projects.

A key element of this standard is the sequencing of equipment
delivery and installation to provide an adequate flow of nozzles for an
efficient field piping program. Past experience has indicated equipment-
piping dependencies as follows:

Equipment	Release of Piping Work
Pipe rack	-10%
First 50% of pumps, exchangers, drums	-20%
Second 50% of pumps, exchangers, drums	-20%
Reactors, fin fans, towers	-20%
Field-erected vessels, heaters, compressor	-25%
Final punch-out	-5%
	100%

This listing also shows the general sequence of delivery and installation.
As can be seen, the pipe rack, pumps, exchangers, and drums will enable 50% of the piping to be completed and are therefore critical for a
maximum piping effort.

Application

This standard is mainly used to provide guidance in reviewing a contractor's construction program. A detailed analysis will include a
nozzle study where the number of available nozzles per piece of equipment is plotted in a cumulative curve against time. Man-hour units can
then be applied to the nozzles to adequately plot the available piping
erection work. Piping is generally the major portion of a construction
program.

3.13 CONSTRUCTION SCHEDULE DURATION: TRAPEZOIDAL TECHNIQUE

To improve construction schedule evaluation by substituting quantity
analysis for personnel judgment, the following technique uses battery
limit area, man-hours, and labor density data to calculate the overall
construction duration.

The construction duration is calculated using a trapezoidal approxi-
mation for manpower buildup, peak, and rundown over the construction

period, based on estimated construction man-hours and craft labor density evaluation, if the critical path is through a process area.

3.13.1 Definitions

Scope (man-hours): Construction man-hours for all work within defined battery limits at the level of productivity anticipated at the site; includes direct work, a proportion of indirect labor, and application of estimating allowance.

Build-up (months): Period of increasing manpower from the start of construction to the start of the peak.

Peak (months): Period of maximum manpower.

Rundown (months): Period of decreasing manpower from the end of the peak to construction completion.

Effective man-hours per month (workweek discounted by 10-15% × $4\frac{1}{3}$): man-hours expended each month in accomplishing the work. Effective man-hours do not include hours lost due to absenteeism, sickness, vacation, and similar nonproductive time not included in the scope.

Peak density level (square feet per man): Assessment of manpower density, within defined process battery limits, beyond which there could be a resulting reduction in productivity.

3.13.2 Trapezoidal Technique

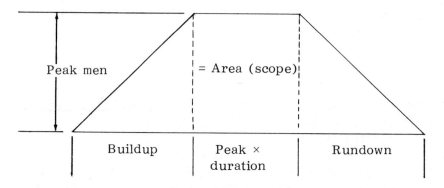

Calculation

Based on the standard PMS, the critical path is usually through engineering to construction of foundations, equipment installation, pipe erection, and final testing.

Use your judgment for foundation, equipment, and piping buildup to establish the total build-up duration.

1. Labor availability: If manpower is short, bias peak manpower.
2. Peak density level (will vary with location and labor) = _____ ft/man (basis, i.e., direct hire, subcontract—see curve).
3. Peak manpower = $\frac{\text{battery limits area}}{\text{peak density level}}$ = _____ men.

4. Effective man-hours per man-month = site weekly work hours ×
    $88\% \times 4\frac{1}{3}$ = _____ h.
5. Buildup = foundations + equipment + piping buildup (see standard
    schedule) = _____ months.
    Solve for peak duration, X:

$$\frac{\text{Scope in man-hours}}{\text{Effective monthly man-hours}} = \left(\frac{\text{Buildup}}{2} \times \text{Peak men}\right) +$$

$$\left(X \times \text{Peak men}\right) + \left(\frac{\text{Rundown}}{2} \times \text{Peak men}\right) \quad X \doteq \underline{\quad\quad} \text{ months}$$

Total construction duration = buildup + X + Rundown = _____ months

Note

1. Application of additional experience factors for engineering and
construction durations should be considered for large, complex projects
with a new and/or novel design, hostile environments, remote locations,
environmental-governmental hazards, and multiple engineering offices.
    2. *Scope:* When using labor density, the scope should reflect the
total direct work plus indirect labor working in the area (i.e., scaffolding, material handling, cleanup, etc.) and an allowance of the overall
contingency to reflect the final forecast of man-hours.
    3. *Peak density level:* See standard curves for labor density
versus productivity.
    4. *Buildup and rundown:* Historical expience or judgment.

The following are worked examples of the trapezoidal technique.

Example

Refinery FCC unit:

Plot area = 320 ft × 200 ft =   64,000 ft^2
Scope (direct hire)   = 445,000 man-hours
Allowance for indirect
  labor in area + 10%   =   44,500 man-hours
Estimating allowance + 15% =   66,700
                              ――――――――――
                              556,200 total scope for evaluation

Consider two cases: Case 1, direct-hire labor, and case 2,
subcontract labor.

Case 1: Direct-Hire Labor

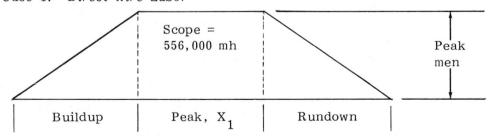

1. Labor availability: no restraint, no adjustment to manpower level.
2. Peak density level: U.S. large project, direct hire (from curves) = $\underline{200}$ ft^2/man.
3. Peak manpower = $\dfrac{64,000 \text{ ft}^2}{200 \text{ ft}^2/\text{man}}$ = $\underline{320}$ men.
4. Effective man-hours per man-month = $40 \times 88\% \times 4\frac{1}{3}$ = 153 h.
5. Buildup (by judgment) = 3 + 2 + 5 (piping buildup) = 10 months.
6. Rundown (by judgment) = 6 months.

Solve for peak, X_1:

$$\frac{556,200}{153} = \left(\frac{10}{2} \times 320 \right) + \left(X_1 \times 320 \right) + \left(\frac{6}{2} \times 320 \right)$$

$$X_1 = 3\tfrac{1}{2} \text{ months}$$

Therefore

Total construction duration (direct labor) = $10 + 3\frac{1}{2} + 6 = 19\frac{1}{2}$ months

Case 2: Subcontract Labor. The project strategy, based on experience, is that local subcontractors are more productive than prime contractors (direct hire).

Scope = 556,200 man-hours for direct hire
       less 10% productivity adjustment for local subcontractor labor

  - 55,600

  = 500,600 man-hours

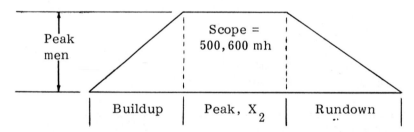

1. Labor availability: No restraint, no adjustment to manpower level.
2. Peak density level: U.S. large project, subcontract labor (from curves) = 250 ft^2/man.
3. Peak manpower = $\dfrac{64,000 \text{ ft}^2}{250 \text{ ft}^2/\text{man}}$ = 256 men.
4. Effective man-hours per man-month = $40 \times 88\% \times 4\frac{1}{4}$ = 153 h.
5. Buildup (by judgment) = 3 + 2 + 5 = 10 months.
6. Rundown (by judgment) = 6 months.

Solve for peak, X_2:

$$\frac{500,600}{153} = \left(\frac{10}{2} \times 256 \right) + \left(X_2 \times 256 \right) + \left(\frac{6}{2} \times 256 \right)$$

$X_2 = 4.8$ (say 5 months)

Therefore

Total construction duration (subcontract labor) = 10 + 5 + 6 = 21 months

This confirms that a subcontract operation, even though more productive, will generally take longer than one on a direct-hire basis.

3.14 PROJECT MASTER SCHEDULE: SMALL PROJECTS, STANDARD

The basic standard network (Figure 3.14) for a phase II operation (PMS for small projects) should be updated as economic conditions change. The notes require full consideration, The network can be used for most phase II process plant projects, but corrections must be applied for subcontract construction, overseas work, and remote job sites. A major element of this standard is the sequencing of equipment delivery and installation based on historical data to provide sufficient nozzles for an efficient field piping program. The data base for this standard network is outlined in Figures 3.12 and 3.13.

Application

For feasibility studies this 39-activity network should be summarized to 25 activities.

For approved projects the full network detail should be used, together with engineering and construction manpower curves. If battery limits are known, the construction duration should be evaluated using the labor density-productivity method (see Section 3.13). Midpoints of material and construction can be determined for estimating purposes. Most schedules should be drawn up as time-scaled networks.

A creep factor is applied to equipment lead times: usually +5% for Japan, +10-20% for the United States, and +20-30% for Europe. This factor recognizes that the original vendor-quoted delivery is rarely achieved.

The purchasing-engineering cycle (INP), usually 4-5 months for the United States and Europe, is determined with reference to Figure 3.18 and the proposed project purchasing plan.

Add factors: Detailed consideration should be given to this section shown at the bottom of the schedule. The network is based on a U.S., phase II, direct-hire operation, and the add factors are to compensate for an overseas or subcontract operation or additional engineering time if the project is on a straight-through basis (no phase I).

Environmental aspects and governmental regulations are not standard and must be treated on a case-by-case basis.

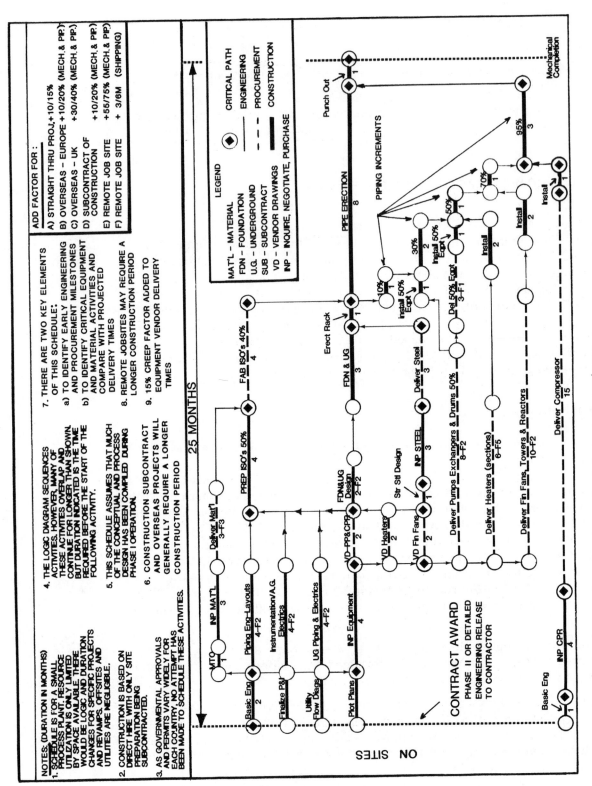

Figure 3.14 Standard project master schedule—small projects.

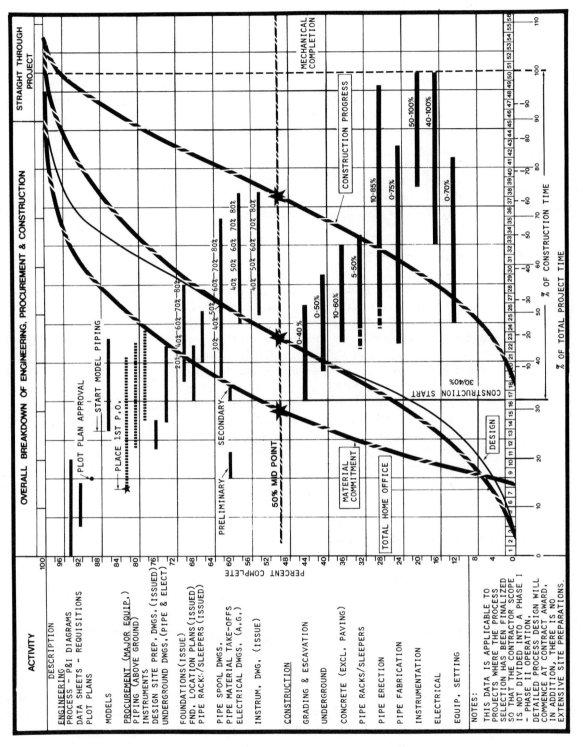

Figure 3.15 Standard breakdown EPC—small projects.

3.15 OVERALL BREAKDOWN: SMALL PROJECTS, STRAIGHT THROUGH

The standard network and progress chart in Figure 3.15 (overall breakdown, small projects) is similar to Figure 3.12. It depicts the historical relationships of major activities. The progress curves for procurement, design, and construction are developed from the individual activities. Data for this chart is based on 50 projects completed by various owners using various contractors. These projects were implemented during 1955-1970; their costs ranged from $0.5 to $100 million. Most of them were less than $20 million. Projects were executed as straight through. This project mode results in later midpoints of material (29% project duration) and midpoint of labor (70%). The start of construction is also later, commencing at 32% of project duration.

Application

Once schedule durations have been established, project progress curves can be drawn using the data from this chart plus any specific project related data. Contractor schedules which differ significantly from the bar chart and progress curves should be considered exceptions to the norm and must be evaluated in detail to determine their acceptability. When actual progress falls behind the leading curve, it is probable that succeeding curves will not be achieved. This could lead to a potential delay in mechanical completion. This often requires special efforts to maintain mechanical completion and generally results in increased cost.

The chart shows a very aggressive construction program. The monthly peak rates of progress would generally be too high for large projects unless the size affect is already reflected in the project duration.

3.16 ENGINEERING SCHEDULE: LARGE PROJECTS, STANDARD

Figure 3.16 indicates typical relationships and durations for phase II engineering of a large grass roots refinery. The schedule data base is the same as that for the project master schedule, large projects (Figure 3.11), that is, large projects requiring approximately 500,000 home office man-hours. The same logic will apply to small projects, but the activity duration will change significantly.

The durations shown indicate only the amount of work critical to the project schedule. Activities will extend beyond the periods indicated. Engineering activity will continue through completion of construction.

Critical activities generally experienced during the engineering phase of a large project are as follows:

Site preparation, roads, drainage
Receipt of vendor drawings

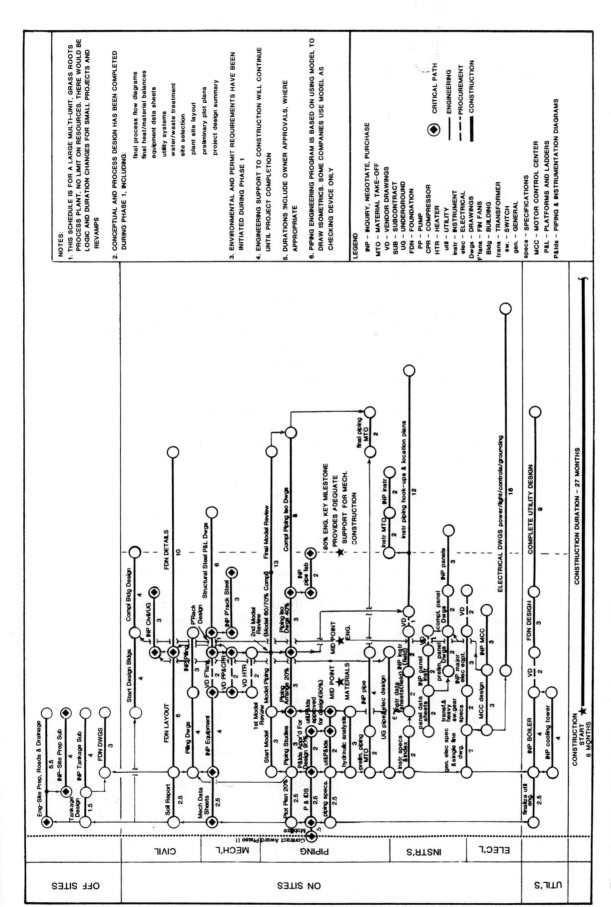

Figure 3.16 Standard engineering schedule—large projects.

Civil and underground pipe design
Piperack design and procurement
Piping isometric drawing production

Application

This schedule may be used in conjunction with Figure 3.12 to monitor contractors' engineering schedules and schedule performance. In making this evaluation, the following factors should be considered:

1. The schedule represents a phase II project with conceptual and process design having been accomplished beforehand during phase I. A straight-through approach would extend the overall duration by 3-4 months.
2. A large multiunit process plant may be engineered in more than one contractor's office. Owners may be multipartner conglomerates. In these instances, approval cycles and communications may be extended and have major impact on engineering durations.
3. Environmental Protection Agency (EPA) permit procedures may be the controlling factor in executing large grass roots projects (see Figure 3.20). Normally, appropriate applications and studies for governmental approvals will have been initiated during phase I. However, schedule engineers should review the impact of these regulations on phase II engineering activities.

3.17 CONSTRUCTION LABOR DENSITY

3.17.1 Introduction

The basis of a labor density technique is that labor increases bring a corresponding reduction in productivity. Labor can be increased so that the density level is at saturation. The application of additional men will not then be productive. However, there is a practical correlation of productivity to labor density.

The *established norm* for these curves is the estimate base, which does not normally consider *acceleration actions* to improve the schedule.

Figure 3.17 shows construction density-productivity curves. The heavy curve, based on completed U.S. projects on a direct-hire basis, provides the historical experience for labor density versus productivity. This shows that 200 ft^2/man is the recommended density limit for medium to large projects. Increasing manpower, to a theoretical saturation of 100 ft^2/man, will reduce productivity as indicated (30%). Subcontract experience has shown that competitively negotiated subcontracts (lump sum or unit price) will not allow density at the same level of a direct-hire, reimbursable project. This curve has 250 ft^2/man as the break-even point, and this can be applied to U.S. and European subcontract operations. The top curve is a "device" to calculate construc-

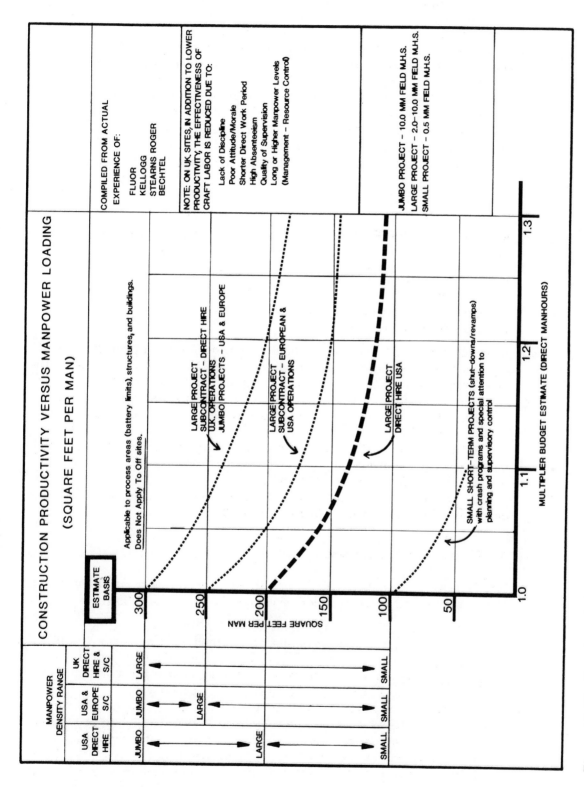

Figure 3.17 Construction density curves.

tion durations for the United Kingdom where steadily reducing labor productivity has raised man-hours to very high levels. This, coupled with a poor industrial environment, has led to a further reduction in the effectiveness of labor and has produced a very difficult man-management situation. Use 300 ft^2/man as the break-even point.

The bottom curve, with a recommended saturation limit at 100 ft^2/ man, is for small short-term projects such as shutdowns and turn-arounds. These projects are highly labor intensive and are almost always carried out on an *accelerated basis* with detailed hourly planning and additional supervision. This will allow a higher degree of man-power density without reducing productivity from the estimated level.

3.17.2 Application

Refer to Section 3.13. Schedules produced on an economic basis for large projects will generally use the following break-even rates:

U.S. direct hire: 200
U.S. subcontract: 250
European direct hire and subcontract: 250
U.K. direct hire and subcontract: 300

However, specific evaluations should be made for each project as plot layouts are rarely standard. Project size and complexity of construction are further factors in determining an appropriate density level.

The highest density achieved on a critical process area for one of the largest refinery projects was 250 with four critical units averaging at 300.

Small-medium projects could operate at higher density levels without suffering a productivity loss (i.e., 150-200 ft^2/man), whereas jumbo projects would fall into the 250-300 range.

When the specific project density level has been selected, use the calculation method outlined in Section 3.13.

3.17.3 Labor Effectiveness

(See Figure 3.17.) On U.K. sites, in addition to lower productivity, the effectiveness of craft labor is reduced due to the following:

1. Lack of discipline: petty disputes, walkouts, etc.
2. Poor attitude-morale: "Pushing" by supervision is more difficult, vastly improved messing and personnel facilities have not led to greater efficiency, but there is a greater desire for more facilities without an accompanying increase in productivity.
3. Shorter direct work period (tea breaks, walking, washing time, wet time, etc.): This is generally reflected in the labor productivity factors; however, most U.K. field indirects greatly overrun, further reducing the direct work labor resource.
4. High absenteeism: Compensation can be made by increasing hiring and payroll levels. However, the disruptive effects of one worker to others is very real (but difficult to measure).

5. Quality of supervision.
6. Longer-higher manpower: Reduced productivity requires higher manpower peaks for longer periods to reduce construction duration. This adds to the problems of man-management, resource control, and communication and results in a further reduction of efficiency.

Refer to the study by the National Economic Development Office (U.K.) entitled "Engineering Construction Performance" (published December 1976), pages 3-23, for additional information for U.K. conditions. Allowances for the preceding in schedule evaluations are made by adjusting the density of manpower loading versus the reduction in productivity.

3.18 ENGINEERING-PROCUREMENT CYCLE, STANDARD

Figure 3.18 provides major milestones and logic for the engineering-procurement cycle for equipment and bulks. Durations are based on historical experience.

Large, complex projects with worldwide purchasing, multiple engineering offices, and joint venture partners having consultation and approval requirements can increase the 12-18 week procurement cycle. Generally, projects with a minimum of worldwide purchasing would have a purchasing cycle of 12-14 weeks.

Application

Assess project size, complexity, joint venture requirements, and proposed purchasing strategy and determine the duration for the specific project. Check against current project experience that the evaluation is realistic.

Only the total duration of the engineering-procurement cycle is used for overall schedules (see the standard PMS) and is normally the activity designated INP.

Evaluation of the individual activities will be required when analyzing and monitoring contractors' detailed schedules.

3.19 PHASE I SCHEDULE, TYPICAL

Figure 3.19 shows the general functions, logical relationships, and average durations of a contractor phase I operation.

Application

This phase I schedule is used to provide guidance regarding typical functions carried out by a contractor on a phase I operation. Specific activities will depend on the individual project.

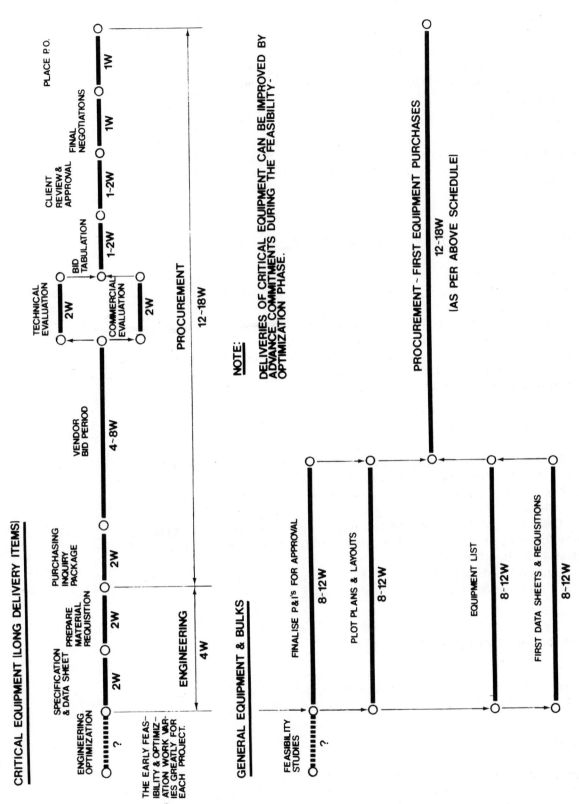

Figure 3.18 Standard engineering-purchasing cycle.

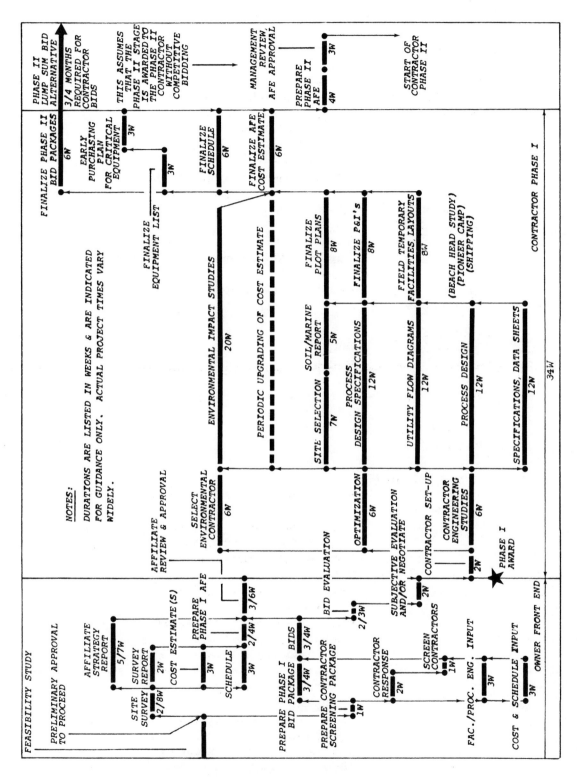

Figure 3.19 Typical phase I schedule.

Table 3.1 Phase I Projects and Their Degree of
Documentation Completion

Description	Definition	O = by Owner, C = by Contractor
General		
Bid package for phase II	Suitable for reimbursable or lump sum bids comprising 1. Proposal request 2. Proposed articles of agreement 3. Project instructions 4. Scope of technical work	O & C
Environmental impact study	Completed and under review by EPA	O & C
Surveys	All soil, topographical, & hydrological surveys completed	C
Major equipment quotations	Received & evaluated	C
Engineering		
Basis of design	Defined	O
Process description	Defined	C
Process design	All material & heat balances complete	C
Process control system	Defined	C
Process data sheets for equip.	Completed for major equipment	C
Process flow diagrams	Completed (incl. control mode)	C
Process PIDs	50% complete; line & control valve sizing, control loops, and instrumentation indicated	C
Utility & Off-site requirements	Defined	C
	Steam & condensate balance complete	C
	Steam generation & distribution complete	C
	Water resource & treatment 50% complete	C
	Cooling water system 50% complete	C
	Plant & instrument air 50% complete	C
	Effluent control 50% complete	C
	Storage & terminal facs. 50% complete	C

Table 3.1 (Continued)

Description	Definition	O = by Owner C = by Contractor
Engineering (continued)		
Utilities & offsite PIDs	40% complete	C
Location & site plan	Complete	O
Plot plans & elevations	Complete (overall only)	C
Grading, paving, and drainage plans	Preliminary	C
Structural & foundation design	Design sketches, estimated quantities, no factors	C
Building requirements	Preliminary	C
Equipment list	Major equip. completed, estimated sizes for remainder	C
Mechanical data sheets	Completed for major equipment	C
Engineering specifications	Completed for major equipment. Job specs for piping, civil, electrical, and instrumentation 50% complete	O & C
Engineering guides	Appropriate sections included	O
Piping material takeoff	Estimated from PIDs & layouts	C
Line & valve sizing	50% complete	C
Instrument schedule including control valves	Control valves sized (preliminary)	C
One line elec. diagram	Preliminary	C
Electrical equipment list	Preliminary	C
Electrical material takeoff	Based on one line diagram	C
Painting & insulation	Quantities factored	C
Fire protection	50% complete	C

Table 3.1 (Continued)

Engineering (continued)		
Tie-ins	Existing facilities surveyed & measured to verify scope of tie-ins & valving	C
Scheduling	Overall PMS (phase I)	O & C
	Project master schedule for phase II	O & C
	Early purchasing plan for critical equipment	C
	Manpower and progress curves for phase II engineering	C
	Manpower and progress curves for phase II construction	C
	Subcontracting plan	O & C
	Evaluation of labor availability	C
Cost engineering	Detailed estimate, about 15% accuracy; based on quotations for major equipment; bulk materials quantity takeoffs from plot plans & PIDs; construction man-hour unit rates; local labor wages and conditions	C

Note: Major equipment includes items such as the furnace system, fractionator, compressor and driver, and boiler feedwater pumps.

Table 3.1 lists documentation developed during phase I engineering and the degree of completion for a maximum effort. The completion indicated for documents will vary with the size and complexity of the project and the time available. The documents shown completed should be finalized regardless of project size or lack of time.

The phase I contractor would be expected to prepare an overall PMS for the entire project and further develop a more detailed phase II schedule, incorporating quoted delivery times for major equipment and other information developed as project definition is improved.

Specifications relating to planning and scheduling requirements for phase II would be included in the project instructions of the phase II bid package.

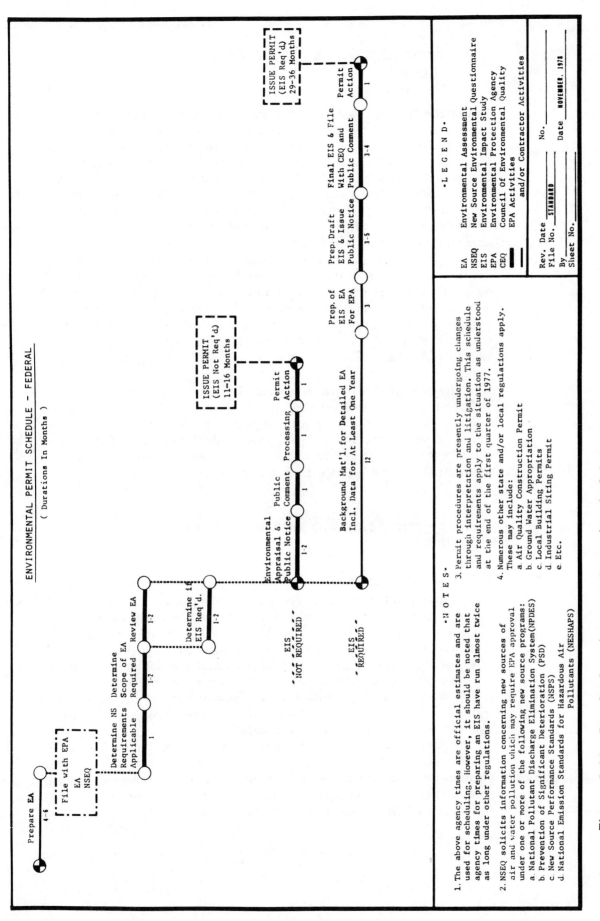

Figure 3.20   Standard environmental permit schedule.

3.20 ENVIRONMENTAL PERMIT SCHEDULE, FEDERAL

Traditionally, applications for granting permits on projects were taken as a matter of course and did not have a major impact on the overall schedule. However, with the passing of the National Environmental Policy Act of 1969, permit procedures are frequently the controlling factor in the execution of industrial projects.

An indeterminate and major factor in scheduling permit procedures is the decision regarding whether an Environmental Impact Statement (EIS) is required. This decision is made by the EPA after receipt of the new source environmental questionnaire.

Figure 3.20 (federal environmental permit schedule) indicates the overall duration and steps necessary for granting EPA permits. The action required is shown for (1) projects which do not require an EIS and (2) projects which do require an EIS. Indicated durations are estimates, but it is probable that the decision to prepare an EIS can extend the period for granting permits from 16 to 36 months. In addition to federal permits, numerous state and local regulations will apply.

The local political and economic climate, as well as the industrial environment, has considerable influence on the timing and issue or permits. Generally, the venture group is responsible for executing permit procedures. Schedule engineers should obtain information on requirements and current local conditions from venture or affiliate groups through the owner's project engineering section.

3.21 CONSTRUCTION PARAMETERS: JUMBO PROJECTS

The current breed of energy projects, particularly synthetic fuel plants, will probably fall into the jumbo class. Experience and historical data on which to base schedules and estimates are almost nonexistent.

Figure 3.21 provides a base for broad feasibility schedules. Experience has shown that the project duration is greatly affected (more so than the engineering phase) by job size and the construction schedule.

Once the construction duration has been determined, it is relatively simple to add the interfacing engineering and procurement activities. Environmental activities must be determined on an individual basis as state requirements vary widely.

This chart (Figure 3.21) covers only U.S. projects. Chart durations for overseas projects may have to be increased according to the overseas location and the remoteness of the job site. As explained at the right-hand side of the chart, the base for establishing the construction duration is the estimated field man-hours for the project.

NOTES:

THESE CURVES ASSUME NO CONSTRAINT OF ENGINEERING DRAWINGS, EQUIPMENT AND LABOR AVAILABILITY.

EVALUATION METHOD

Working from a base of construction manhours (bottom horizontal scale) at 40 hours per week.

1. From curve 1 read off Peak Progress rate (left vertical scale).

2. From curve 2 read off Duration (top horizontal scale).

3. From curve 3 read off Peak Manpower (right vertical scale) for 40 hour work week.

4. Mechanical adjustments must be made in the case of a work week greater than 40 hours, as noted below.

a) Constr. Manhours (Overtime Basis) = Constr. Manhours (40 Hr. Basis) Labor Efficiency*

b) Constr. Duration (Overtime Basis) = Constr. Duration (40 Hr. Basis) x 40 Work Week x Labor Efficiency*

c) Peak Manpower(Overtime Basis) = Constr. Mhrs. (O.T. Basis) x Peak Progress (O.T. Basis)* Work Week x Labor Efficiency*

Example: 30,000,000 Manhours (40 Hr./week basis)
Peak Progress...............3.7%
Duration....................45 months
Manpower (40 Hrs.)..........6400
*See curve , Labor Efficiency vs. Overtime

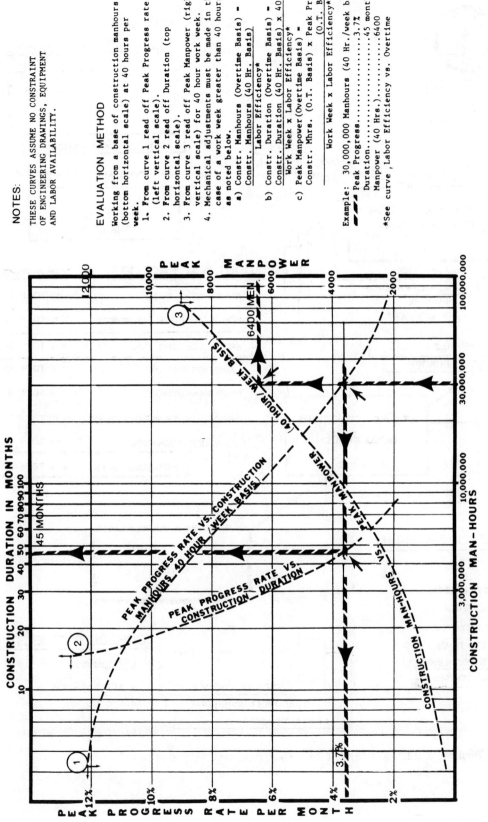

Figure 3.21   Standard construction duration and peak progress vs. man-hour curves.

87

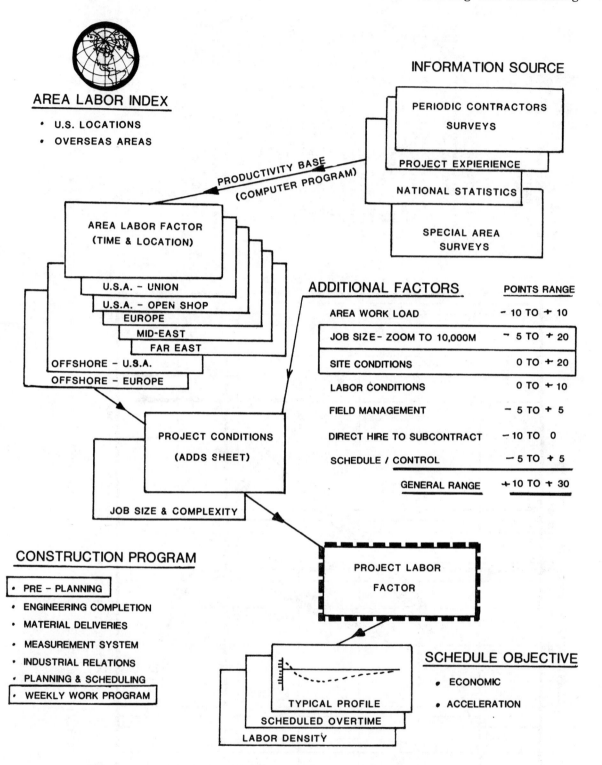

Figure 3.22   Flowchart of labor productivity system.

3.22 LABOR PRODUCTIVITY ANALYSIS AND CONTROL

The flowchart for labor productivity analysis and control (Figure 3.22) shows a typical system for compiling a data base of construction labor productivity indexes on a worldwide basis and then evaluating "additional factors" required for the specific project.

The final product of this system is a *project labor factor*. This is used to estimate the direct construction man-hours for the time and location of the project. Thereafter, field operations can further impact on the estimated productivity.

Figure 3.22 shows a data base of U.S. and overseas area productivities (area labor factors) being maintained by productivity information from periodic surveys, actual project experience, national statistics, and special area surveys. Some companies carry out surveys of contractor companies to add to their own information of current productivity levels.

As shown, the major factors affecting the productivity of a specific project are the following:

Project size (this factor goes only to 10 million h)
Site conditions (access, weather, revamp, hazards)
Construction preplanning
Quality of weekly work program
Acceleration

The general effect of these factors would be to add 10-30 points to the area labor index for the project. If the index were 1, then the effect would be a reduction in productivity of 10-30% or an increase in estimated man-hours of 10-30%.

A reliable data base, intelligent evaluation of project factors, and effective monitoring techniques are essential for evaluating labor productivities for a worldwide capital projects program.

3.23 PRODUCTIVITY GUIDELINES

Figure 3.23 provides general guidelines for establishing a direct-labor productivity profile for the construction phase. These guidelines cover incremental and cumulative profiles. As bad weather can have a significant impact on productivity, separate guidelines are provided.

This profile should be developed as soon as the physical site conditions are known and a detailed construction schedule is available. The horizontal axis should be translated from percent complete to a calendar time frame.

As construction labor can be 20% of total project costs, it is important that labor productivity be tracked as early as possible. Productivity can only be properly measured if construction progress is evaluated with physical quantities and associated work measurement units.

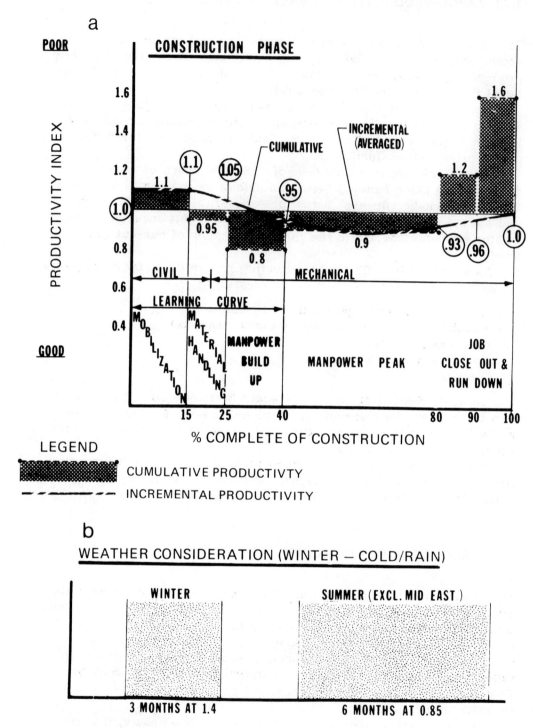

Figure 3.23   Construction productivity guidelines.

Application

These guidelines show incremental productivity periods for the major phases of construction.

The mobilization phase (first 15%) is shown with a reduced productivity of 10% from the construction estimate. It then improves with phases of 5 and 20% for the material handling and manpower buildup phases. At manpower peak (40% of construction), the incremental productivity is shown to be still good at 0.9. Thereafter, for the last 20% of construction, it is shown as rapidly deteriorating.

The cumulative curve is calculated and is shown as tracking from poor to good and ending at 1.0. Additional factors for weather would be superimposed on the top profile. If the winter occurred at 40% of construction, the 0.9 could be multiplied by 1.4, resulting in a projection of 1.3 for the period. If the other periods were as shown on the chart, then the overall productivity of 1.0 would not be achieved.

This evaluation can be made early in the project, and these guidelines and this method can greatly assist in monitoring and forecasting productivity levels.

4

OWNER COST CONTROL

4.1 INTRODUCTION

This chapter is based on an owner-contractor relationship where the owner has a directing and monitoring role and the contractor has day-to-day control responsibility.

On reimbursable projects, it is the owner's responsibility to provide cost-financial objectives and requirements for control and reporting and to develop an organization which can work with contractors on an equal-partner basis.

The contractor is responsible for day-to-day control and should be responsive to the owner's needs and requirements, provided they are intrinsic to the contractual agreement.

This chapter, then, covers the owner's cost control methods for a contractor monitoring role and also specifies procedures to control owner costs and covers responsibilities which should not be delegated to the contractor.

4.2 COST CONTROL PHILOSOPHY

4.2.1 Cost Control Defined

Cost control is early identification and communication of actual and potential cost deviations from an established scope. Effective cost control should focus management's attention on areas of concern, with meaningful proposals to minimize the effects of potential cost overruns. This section is essentially a guide for project task force personnel, detailing techniques for monitoring the project's cost performance throughout the project life cycle.

A good cost control system provides the following benefits:

An early warning system
Analyzes problems
Quickly evaluates the magnitude of cost and schedule deviations
Recommends alternative solutions

Monitors effectiveness of remedial actions
Accurately forecasts, timely reports
Is concise and attention getting.

4.2.2 Contracting Strategy

A significant element affecting project cost is the quality of precontract strategy, negotiation, and the final type of contract. A poor contract provides a poor foundation for cost control. It is important that the cost engineer review, in depth, the approved contractual documents for areas of cost exposure and future risk. It can be beneficial to have an experienced cost engineer as part of the negotiating team to provide cost evaluations of proposed variations during the negotiating process.

4.2.3 Lump Sum Contracts

The control of time and money becomes the primary concern of the contractor, as performance directly affects profits. Here, the owner concerns himself or herself primarily with checking the contractor's compliance with project design, evaluating cost extras, and monitoring the project schedule.

4.2.4 Cost-Plus Contracts

The contractor has limited incentive for controlling time and money beyond professional responsibility. The owner's personnel should closely monitor the contractor's preparation of the definitive cost estimate and project control systems. It is imperative that cost estimates and schedules are prepared for facilities that meet the owner's needs.

The phases of cost control can be divided into the following major phases:

During conceptual engineering (process design)
Through detailed engineering and purchasing
Through construction, commissioning, and start-up

4.2.5 Conceptual Engineering Phase

Design decisions made during the conceptual engineering phase set the minimum project cost. Cost options open during the conceptual phase are generally greater than at any other time. Hence, this phase offers the greatest opportunity for cost savings. Once the design basis has been established, the minimum project investment has been established. At this stage, prior to completion of the control estimate, a trending system should be set up so that engineering changes can be quantified and reflected in the forecast. The next major step is preparation of a control estimate. This should reflect all design changes to date. A quality estimate requires the maximum use of quantities rather than factors and statistical relationships. Engineering and construction staff requirements should be detailed in organization charts and schedules; field temporary facilities should be sketched out and quantity takeoffs made; construction equipment should be itemized and scheduled.

After completion and approval of the control estimate, an engineering change log system should be maintained to track variations from the estimate scope. Random sampling of engineered equipment and bulk material should evaluate deviations of quantities, specifications, and unit pricing levels.

4.2.6 Cost Control Through Detailed Engineering

Cost control continues in the contractor's design office and the duties of the owner's cost control engineers fall into the following:

To ensure that the contractor's personnel are cost-sampling the developing design and performing value engineering; to continuously update the engineering change log and subsequent cost trends (vital at this stage); to review with owner engineering specialists project trends that are resulting from day-to-day decisions

To advise management on cost trends, forecasts, cash flow, and owner's costs and prepare monthly project reports

4.2.7 Cost Control Through Construction

The ability to effectively control and forecast construction costs is dependent on the quality of the field budget. Too often, insufficient care and insufficient attention to the construction scope are given when the project control estimate is developed in the engineering phase. This lack of attention is particularly evident in field indirects. Factors are applied to direct labor costs instead of developing quantity takeoffs. This requires drafting layouts for temporary facilities, developing a detailed organization for the field staff, and preparing detailed construction equipment lists, together with time frame schedules.

When drawings are approved for construction, they should be verified against the quantity take-offs in the control estimate. Effective field measurement is essential to evaluating the productivity of direct-hire labor and the performance of subcontractors.

4.2.8 Summary

In conclusion, an effective cost control program provides the following:

A quality control estimate based on good scope definition
Quickly identifies and evaluates potential cost deviations
Communicates simply and effectively to project management
Provides tools to measure status and make meaningful forecasts

4.3 OWNER COST CONTROL SYSTEM

Figure 4.1 is a flowchart depicting the work of an owner in developing cost correlations and standards, training programs, and a project-contractor monitoring system. Development of cost correlations and standards is dependent on feedback data from ongoing and completed projects.

Specific objectives and development programs should be instituted on an annual basis. These programs should be budgeted and scheduled and biannual reviews held with management.

The end product of a development program should be a cost control manual.

It cannot be emphasized too strongly that collection and analysis of historical cost data are essential to maintaining effective control tools and techniques.

The estimate is the control base. However, its composition, which is generally on a system basis, is not entirely suitable for control. The transition of the conceptual estimate from systems to cost centers and/ or areas is essential for control.

Similarly, the transition from the owner's estimate to the contractor's estimate is necessary for effective control. Some owners use their estimate as the control base and impose it on the contractor at contract award. This arrangement can reduce the contractor's commitment to the estimate and can also restrict the study of alternatives, optimization, and initiative by contractors. Some owners believe "imposing their estimate" is justified due to their experience of ineffective contractor control.

Throughout the project, the project task force (PTF) monitoring system must be sufficiently detailed to ensure that the contractor's cost operations are effectively monitored. Cost deviations must be promptly communicated to project management and to the contractor. The project estimate is the key to establishing control.

A significant feature of a successful cost control operation is the relationship between the contractor and company personnel. As seen from the flowchart, an early item of a capital project is screening and qualifying contractors prior to contract award. During this activity, the company's cost control requirements should be clearly explained and performance commitments obtained from the contractor. After contract award, these commitments will be tested during detailed discussions for the purpose of establishing a mutually acceptable system. These discussions should be conducted in a spirit of equal partnership.

The owner cost control specification will be the basis of discussions on organization, procedures, systems, and controls. The early discussions are meant to prevent reorganizations, reassignments, and system changes at a later date. The discussions should be promptly followed by meetings with the contractor's engineering, procurement, construction, and project services groups to verify that the common approach to cost control is understood and accepted.

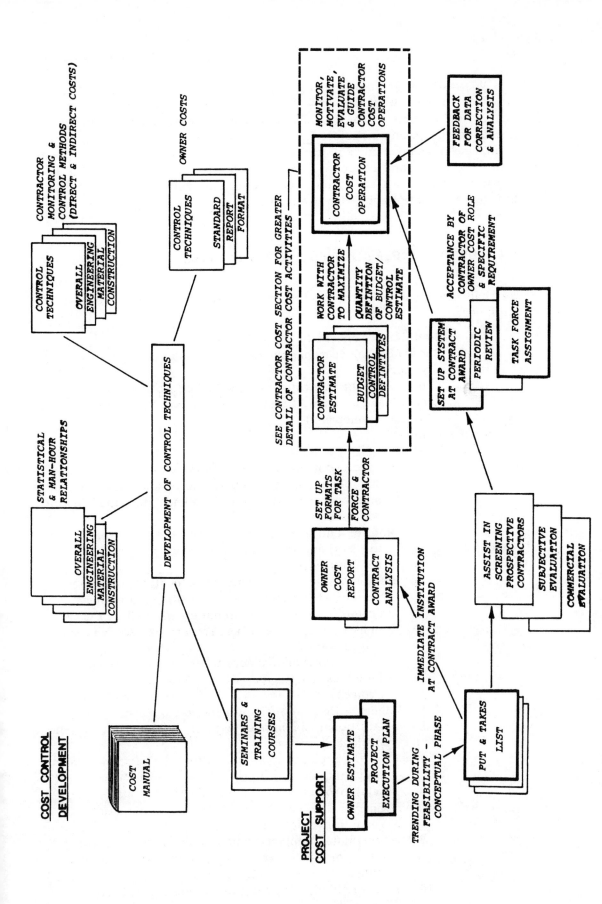

Figure 4.1 Flowchart of owner cost control service.

97

Most owners are now placing major emphasis on project control. Most cost control work is carried out by a small, experienced home office staff covering projects on a suitcase basis and also supervising personnel assigned to project task forces. A coordination procedure should be developed for this work, ensuring that objectives, functions, reporting lines, and responsibilities are clearly outlined. It is vital that the home office staff and project personnel understand their responsibilities and relationship with each other.

4.4 COST ENGINEER: DUTIES AND OBJECTIVES

We shall now summarize the duties and objectives of a PTF lead cost engineer.

I. The cost engineer reports to the following:
   A. The PTF project manager-business manager as a line responsibility
   B. The supervisor of project support, home office, for technical guidance, functional responsibility, and career development

II. Responsibilities
   A. Overall
      1. Provide cost engineering support to the PTF within guidelines established by the project manager and standard procedures and policies contained in the cost control manual
      2. Monitor and evaluate the contractor's cost engineering methods to ensure they meet project requirements
      3. Review and evaluate contractor cost engineering personnel for technical capability and experience
      4. Maintain constant communication with all PTF members to develop and disseminate project cost requirements
      5. Liaise with other projects to obtain appropriate historical cost information pertinent to their project
      6. Liaise with home office on technical matters and additional assistance, with the concurrence of the project manager
      7. Maintain a continuous evaluation of the total project cost status
      8. Advise project management of cost deviations together with conclusions and recommendations to resolve problem areas
      9. Accumulate, analyze, and furnish historical cost data per the return data guidelines, along with unique features of the project
      10. Ensure the contingency allowance is adequate

B. Engineering-procurement

1. Assist in the development and evaluation of the contractor's project control estimate
2. Review and approve the contractor's project cost code of accounts
3. Evaluate the contractor's project cost procedures, reporting programs, and cost systems and recommend improvements, if required, to the cost programs
4. Review and approve all estimates for changes to the project control estimate; ensure the engineering change log is adequate
5. Participate in the evaluation of subcontractor bids
6. Participate in the evaluation of major material and equipment purchases
7. Ensure the validity of backcharge documentation and assess potential recovery of backcharges
8. Monitor man-hour expenditures by major discipline and in total
9. Monitor contractor expenses, overheads, and man-hour costs
10. Monitor total expenditures and commitment curves for home office labor and materials; evaluate design allowance forecasts

C. Construction

1. Ensure smooth transfer of cost controls from the home office to the field
2. Monitor the following on a periodic basis:
   a. Direct labor costs, weekly
   b. Local procurement
   c. Labor productivities
   d. Craft mixes and labor wage rates
   e. Subcontractor costs, unit rates of expenditures, etc.
   f. Construction equipment costs
   g. Miscellaneous indirect costs such as temporary facilities, field staff, field office expenses, small tools, and consumables
3. Monitor actual construction costs versus the project control estimate
4. Evaluate and advise the project manager on all cost deviations, trends, scope change estimates, and cost forecasts

D. Meetings and coordination

1. Attend and participate in all project estimate review meetings
2. Attend project progress meetings
3. Coordinate the owner cost engineering effort with the contractor
4. Attend major subcontractor progress meetings
5. Participate in construction weekly progress meetings

E. Owner cost control and reports
    1. Review, analyze, and forecast owner costs; provide
        curves and analysis of task force costs
    2. Provide a weekly *puts and takes* list, independent of
        the contractor cost trending system
    3. Assist in the development and review of owner
        appropriation requests
    4. Develop monthly cost reports for all project costs,
        including contractors, subcontractors, owner costs,
        etc.
    5. Prepare historical cost return data per the instruc-
        tions in the cost control manual

These duties and objectives will form the basis of an annual performance appraisal. The appraisal is developed by the project manager,
reviewed and endorsed by the home office functional manager, and
approved by corporate management. Salary action should be tied to the
performance appraisal system. Performance interviews and counseling
sessions should be held with all personnel.

4.5 FEEDBACK DATA

The continuous evaluation of current experience and practices is essential for a dynamic cost operation. Conditions change, methods improve,
and technology advances, and it is vital that a cost data base reflect
present-day conditions and future trends.

Feedback data, during the project and on completion, are a responsibility of task force and suitcase cost engineers. It is an important
function and should be an appraisal objective of the cost engineer's
performance.

Data feedback is used to update cost correlations and also to provide comparative data points and units to measure performance of
projects on a multiple basis.

The following are typical cost correlations:

Material escalation rates
Labor escalation rates
Material unit prices
Labor rates, benefits, and burdens
Engineering costs (wage rates and allowances)
Engineering productivity
    Man-hours per drawing
    Man-hours per piece of equipment
Construction productivity
    Man-hours per work operation
    Man-hours per piece of equipment
Construction staff costs (wage rates and allowances)
Temporary buildings—dollars per square foot
Field office expenses—dollars per direct man-hour
Small tools and consumables—dollars per direct man-hour

Construction equipment—dollars per direct man-hour
Percent breakdowns
    Engineering man-hours
    Equipment-material accounts
    Construction man-hours
Subcontract labor costs (all in)—dollars per hour

See Chapter 10 for information on typical data points for process plants. This information can be used to spot-check estimate levels and ongoing project performance. The viability of the data should be maintained by the continuous feedback of project experience.

4.6 OWNER COST CONTROL SPECIFICATION (FOR LARGE PROJECTS, PHASE II)

The following approach is based on a reimbursable/cost-plus contract with an owner task force monitoring the contractor's operations. Generally, company requirements are as shown in the flowchart (Figure 4.2) entitled "Project Cost Control—Typical Contractor System." The company will require that contractor modify or add techniques and methods which the company deems are necessary. It is company practice, at contract award, to carry out a detailed review and evaluation of contractor systems and procedures. At this review, company cost personnel will present company requirements for discussion and mutual acceptance. The contractor will provide the company with an implementation plan and detailed schedule for completion of the cost control program.

    This flowchart shows current contractor practices. The following explanations are keyed to the item of the flowchart.

4.6.1 Overall

Project Control Estimate (No. 2). The contractor shall provide a control estimate within 2-3 months after contract award. This estimate shall generally follow the owner format, with quantities maximized and statistical-factor relationships kept to a minimum. Engineering and construction indirects shall be detailed to the maximum extent possible.

Site Survey Report. As required, the contractor shall conduct a detailed site survey to investigate local conditions and overall cost conditions:

Climate
Geology
Transportation
Sociological factors (church, schools, medical, etc.)
Governmental regulations
Job site regulations and requirements
Material supply, dock, and customs
Construction equipment resources
Communications
Labor

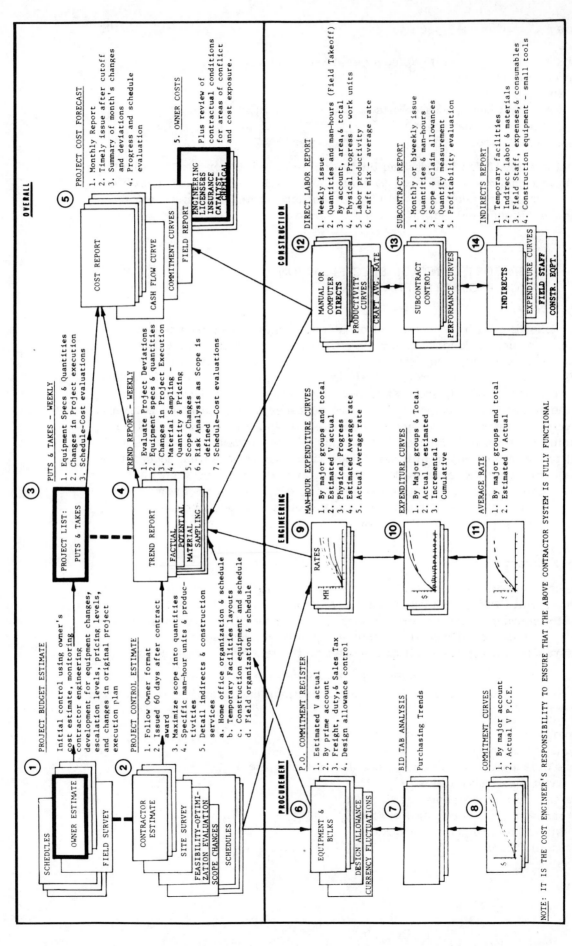

Figure 4.2 Flowchart of contractor cost control specification.

Scope Change Procedure. The contractor shall provide a procedure which accurately reflects changes in scope. All such changes shall be adequately documented, evaluated for cost-schedule impact, and presented to the company for approval and authorization.

Schedules. A project master schedule shall provide the time frame for the estimate and specify midpoints of material, engineering, and construction for timing and cost of escalation.

Trend Report (No. 4). A weekly trend report shall be issued, outlining actual and potential trends. All trends should be identified to source and evaluations made of cost and schedule impact.

Material Sampling. The contractor shall specify a procedure for quantity sampling of engineering design. Major elements, such as earthwork, concrete, and piping, should be randomly sampled for quantity deviation as engineering design progresses.

Monthly Project Cost Report (No. 5). The contractor shall issue to the company a monthly cost forecast 2 weeks after the cutoff point. The report shall list deviations from the previous month, together with appropriate cost and schedule evaluations.

Cash Flow. The contractor shall provide a 3-monthly forecast of cash flow requirements. This forecast shall be supported by adequate documentation and detailed analysis of cash requirements. Cash requirements for owner costs, as covered by the contract agreement, shall be included.

4.6.2 Procurement

Purchase Order Commitment (No. 6). The contractor shall produce a monthly commitment register of all purchases. Actual commitments versus budget value shall be shown. The register shall be summarized by prime account to include evaluations of design allowance, currency fluctuations, freight, duty, and sales taxes.

Commitment Curves (No. 8). Planned commitment curves shall be developed for equipment, bulk materials, and subcontracts. These curves shall be updated monthly with actual commitments. Separate curves may be required for major accounts.

Backcharge Register. The contractor shall issue a monthly report of potential backcharges, identifying source, cause, and estimated cost recovery.

4.6.3 Engineering

Expenditure Curves (Nos. 9 and 10). Planned curves for major engineering disciplines and in total shall be developed and issued monthly. Curves shall show actual versus planned expenditures. Separate curves shall be produced for man-hours and for money.

Average Rate Control. An all-in, average rate shall be developed in curve form from the start to finish of engineering. This profile shall be issued monthly with actual plotted against estimated. Separate profiles may be required for major disciplines.

Engineering Change Log. A record showing engineering changes shall be maintained as design is developed. These changes shall be items which were not part of the scope on which the control estimate was based. In most cases, these changes will be covered by contingency, and additional budget will be allowed only where changes can be clearly identified as additional requirements (scope changes) of the owner.

4.6.4 Construction

Labor Man-hour Report (No. 12). A weekly man-hour-progress report shall be issued at the job site. This report shall show actual man-hours expended versus budget hours earned. Physical progress in quantities and work units and associated productivity shall be shown. Direct work shall be reported by area.

The report shall, separately, identify direct and indirect man-hours.

Labor Rate Control. An all-in, average rate shall be developed, in curve form, from the start to finish of construction. This profile shall be issued weekly with actual plotted against estimated. Separate profiles may be required for major crafts.

Subcontract Cost Control (No. 13). See Chapter 7 for details.

Control of Indirects (No. 14). Expenditure curves shall be developed for major indirect accounts, such as temporary facilities, field office expenses, field staff, construction equipment, camp costs, training, etc. As appropriate, these curves shall show money and man-hours. These curves shall be issued monthly, showing actual versus planned expenditure. An overall indirects report shall be part of the monthly field cost report.

Field Cost Report (No. 5). The field cost report shall be issued monthly, showing actual and forecasted costs for direct work and indirect activities. Summaries of this report shall be included in the monthly project cost report.

Project Rundown Control. On large projects, the contractor shall develop a control system to ensure an efficient rundown to resources at the end of the project. It is recommended that when construction is 80% complete, the remaining work be separated from the overall project and individually controlled on a periodic and cumulative basis.

4.6.5 Summary

The contractor shall respond, in writing, to this specification, showing a flowchart of proposed techniques and methods for the specified item.

It should be noted that cost control methods are constantly being improved so that "blind compliance" to this specification should not be substituted for an intelligent approach.

Small projects will not require this comprehensive program, and adjustments will be made as agreed upon by company.

4.7 COMMERCIAL BID REVIEW: REIMBURSABLE PROJECT

The following is a method to review commercial terms of a contractor proposal on a fixed fee, reimbursable project.

An owner bid package should ask for the following summary:

	Man-hours	Costs
Home office		
Home office expenses (personnel)		
Field staff		
Field expenses (personnel)		
Fixed fee		
Total	_____	_____

This summary, while giving a comparison of multiple bids, does not give a true comparison of the contractor proposals. The bids should be "conditioned" so that estimated man-hours and the mix of engineering and construction personnel are the same.

The owner cost engineer should develop typical staff breakdowns plus associated man-hours for home office personnel, engineering disciplines, and field categories as per the following.

The objective of this exercise is to develop personnel rates for home office personnel and field staff on a common mix and man-hour basis but using salary levels quoted by each contractor.

1. Home Office

	Man-hours	Rate	Cost
Project management			
Section managers			
Section leaders			
Design engineers			
Engineers			
Draftsmen			
Cost Engineers			
Schedulers			
Clerks			

	Man-hours	Rate	Cost
Secretaries			
Typists			
Total	_____	_____	_____

2. Field Staff

	Man-hours	Rate	Cost
Construction manager			
Field superintendent			
Area superintendent			
Craft supervisor			
Chief engineer			
Construction engineer			
Field engineer			
Cost and schedule engineers			
Local staff	_____	_____	_____
Total			

The difficulty with this approach is to exactly match individual contractor personnel categories, as they can operate quite differently, particularly in engineering. Judgment will be required in this conditioning process to arrange a common grouping of individual contractor personnel categories. Cost engineers should then apply their man-hours to the personnel groupings but at each contractor's quoted salary (plus burdens) level.

Further judgment will be required to determine a suitable salary level, as salary ranges are often quoted. It is recommended that salary levels be selected in the 50-80% part of the range.

The resulting all-in rates for the home office and the field are now comparable, and a true assessment of reimbursable rates, plus fee, can now be made.

Contractors will often put part of their overhead costs and profit in the reimbursable rates. Thus, they are assured of additional return if their estimate of scope is low, which is often the case, or if owner adds to the scope.

Other costs, such as travel and living expenses, reproduction, computer, relocation allowances, etc., can be directly compared.

A further check is to compare the contractor's proposals against the owner budget estimate. Fees can be compared, from historical experience, as a percentage of total cost. This check will show whether all proposals are high as compared to the owner budget estimate and will provide a basis for further price negotiations.

4.8 COMMERCIAL BID REVIEW: LUMP SUM

A lump sum bid is only as good as the quality of scope included in the bid package.
  The following are considered essential for a quality lump sum bid:

Feed stock characteristics
Product requirements
Licenser requirements
Flow sheets
Heat and material balances
Piping and instrumentation diagrams (process and utility)
Plot plans
General specifications
Equipment specifications and data sheets
Site development and grading drawings
Underground piping and electrical layouts
Concrete foundation layouts
Above-ground piping layouts
One-line electrical drawings
Milestone schedule
Detailed project execution plan
Project-owner conditions and requirements
Environmental and governmental requirements
Equipment quotations

  The preceding can be supplied by the owner, developed by the contractor, or established by both parties. As lump sum bidding is expensive, a process design package, developed by the owner or contractor, is usually supplied to the contractor. There can be variations to this arrangement, and a quite common approach would be a straight-through project on a reimbursable basis where the contractor would provide a lump sum bid on completion of process design work. On a large project, this would require about 6-9 months.
  Lump sum bid proposals require a detailed technical and commercial review. Specifications should be thoroughly scrutinized, proposed equipment reviewed for technical acceptance, instrument-control system evaluated, contractor execution plan and project schedule fully understood and accepted, and organization plans and project control systems agreed upon.
  After agreement, technical or project changes requested by the owner will generally result in a scope change request from the contractor. This will increase the lump sum price.
  The essence of lump sum bids is that the owner must thoroughly review the proposal for technical acceptance and, thereafter, make no change requests unless the detailed design is not meeting operating requirements, safety standards, project general specifications, or the equipment specifications.
  Technical specialists need to understand that changes resulting in lower-priced equipment can still add costs, as the contractor may have

to change or raise purchasing documentation, check calculations, change drawings, and revise specifications.

4.9 ASPECTS OF A CONTRACT AGREEMENT

In conjunction with the schedule engineer, the owner cost engineer should carry out a detailed review of the contract agreement. This review should look for contract anomalies and questions of interpretation which could provide cost and schedule hazards. All conditions which are specifically tied to payment should be thoroughly evaluated.

4.9.1 Fee

A usual contract condition is a fee payment schedule. An important condition should be that fee payments are dependent on the progress of the project. Many owners have paid fees long before the project is completed because the fee payment schedule is related to time and not progress.

A reasonable method for measuring progress is to *weight* together the expenditures for engineering, material, and construction. As there can be considerable disagreement on the value of these weightings, a procedure should form part of the contract agreement. Most contractors will claim that their fee is tied to their technology and engineering capability. Therefore, they will want a heavy weighting for engineering. This will also enable them to obtain the majority of the fee at the early part of the project.

The actual cost breakdown of a project is generally as follows:

Engineering   15%
Material   65%
Construction   20%

However, contractors will often claim the following weighting for progress measurement of fee:

Engineering   60%
Material   30%
Construction   10%

Contractors claim that their expertise is mainly in technology and engineering and hence the very heavy weighting for engineering.

An owner's project team should resist this approach and attempt to have the heavier weighting in construction.

A significant aspect of fee is on a bonus-penalty contract where the measuring base is a target cost. Contractors may attempt to inflate the target cost by providing high estimates of extras and changes. Target cost provisions can also prevent an owner from rejecting low bids or having preferences for higher-priced equipment. Procedures for such items should be specified in the contract agreement.

4.9.2 Home Office Services

Individual fees for engineering and procurement based on a percentage of cost can be counterproductive. A poor performance, resulting in added costs, earns a greater fee.

Contractor personnel policies should be thoroughly reviewed in relation to the conditions outlined in the contract agreement. Is training and recruiting reimbursable or part of the fee? Are contractor-quoted salary ranges fixed for the duration of the project, or are salary increases automatically passed on the the owner? Are traveling expenses and proposed trips subject to owner approval before or after the fact? Are transfer and assignment of overseas personnel subject to approval by the owner?

A common contention is payment for engineers temporarily transferred to the job site. The overhead on field personnel is generally half that of home office personnel. Which rate should apply?

Is there adequate identification of personnel and services considered part of the fee and those which are reimbursable?

Purchasing policies, vendor servicemen, insurances, duties, inspection, and expediting services are costly items. Are adequate procedures contained in the contract agreement?

Payment for reproduction and computer services should be thoroughly reviewed.

Payment of costs for resident owner personnel should be clearly outlined. These costs would cover offices, equipment, services, and secretarial and typing assistance.

4.9.3 Construction Services

As personnel policies for the construction staff are quite different from those for home office personnel, they need to be clearly stated in the contract agreement. Job site allowances, home leave, completion bonus, family and bachelor status, relocation, replacement, etc., should be clearly outlined, particularly on overseas projects.

Payment conditions for construction equipment, maintenance, small tools, and consumables should be clear and not open for interpretation. There is always contention on these items. What is the relationship between construction equipment rental rates and transportation costs? When does rental start—on dispatch from the storage yard or at the date received on the job site? Are there adequate buy-out clauses? Are the terms for major and minor maintenance clearly stated?

Payment for construction services is often fixed at a unit cost per field man-hour. Again, what field man-hour? Direct and indirect; direct hire, subcontract, and field staff? The costs on differing man-hour bases can be considerable.

The contract agreement should be specific. If it is not, cost engineers should estimate potential costs against each item.

4.10 ESTIMATE TYPES AND DEFINITIONS

Owner and contractor estimates are prepared at various stages of project development. They have two major purposes:

To establish cost levels for economic evaluation
To provide a base for cost control as the project develops

The following briefly summarizes a typical series of estimates:

4.10.1 Appropriation Estimate (25% Accuracy)

The owner appropriation estimate should be produced after completion of conceptual design and process selection and would be an update of the conceptual estimate prepared during feasibility studies. The following would be the basis:

Overall flow diagrams
Heat and material balances
On-site and off-site facilities and layouts
Preliminary plot plans
Equipment list—by size and category
Preliminary execution plan
Completed cost survey

This would be an equipment and bulk ratio estimate for direct labor and material costs. Indirect costs would be factored from direct costs.

4.10.2 Control Estimate (25% Accuracy)

The control estimate, prepared by owner, is on the same basis as the appropriation estimate but broken down into further detail so as to provide a checking basis of the contractor's first estimate.
   The following would be the further breakdown:

Itemized equipment list: material cost and labor man-hours
Bulk materials: material costs and labor man-hours by category
Off-site systems: material costs and labor man-hours
Home office costs and engineering man-hours
Field indirects: material costs, labor and staff man-hours
Owner costs: capital and expenses
Estimating allowance: risk analysis

4.10.3 Contractor's Conceptual Estimate (25-30% Accuracy)

Even though a contractor's first early estimate is generally of a lesser quality than the owner's estimate, it is recommended that the contractor provide an estimate 2-3 months after contract award. This very quickly establishes a base for contractor cost control and should provide the contractor with a sense of commitment and responsibility for his or her estimate.

Due to the lack of time, it is probable that this early estimate would be a capacity-cost or curve-type estimate for direct costs with indirects on a percentage basis.

Even though lacking time, the contractor should be encouraged to put as much quality (definition) into the estimate as possible as this estimate will become the control base for the project.

4.10.4 Contractor's Detailed Estimate (10-15% Accuracy)

This estimate can be developed only when the process design has essentially been completed. It will also require underground and above-ground engineering layout drawings so that bulk material takeoffs can be further refined.

The following would be the basis:

Approved process descriptions—feedstock and product slate
Licenser engineering (schedule A package)
Approved flow sheets
Heat and material balances
Approved process piping and instrumentation diagrams (PIDs)
  (process and utilities)
Approved plot plans
General specifications
Equipment specifications and data sheets
Completed site-soil survey and report
Site development and grading drawings
Underground piping and electrical layouts
Concrete foundation layouts
Above-ground piping layouts
One-line electrical drawings
Milestone schedule
Detailed project execution plan
Project-owner conditions and requirements
Environmental and governmental requirements
Equipment quotations-transportation costs
Bulk material takeoffs
Labor cost-productivity data
Layouts for construction temporary facilities
Organization charts (project, engineering, and construction)
Personnel schedules and manpower histograms
Construction equipment schedules

A detailed estimate would be quantity based with separate unit costs for material, labor, and man-hours. Construction would be based on an area breakdown rather than on the "system" basis of a conceptual estimate. This estimate could be an updated, trended version of the first conceptual estimate and subsequent updates or a completely separate exercise. In most cases, it would be a separate exercise, as the format and work breakdown structure would be different and more detailed than that of a conceptual estimate. In particular, the construction estimate would be on an area basis with takeoffs by work units and man-hour unit rates.

Apart from trend updates, this estimate breakdown could be sufficient to control costs to completion of the project. This estimate could be developed 8-12 months after contract award.

A more detailed or definitive estimate (5-10% accuracy) is sometimes developed. This requires engineering and material purchase to be 60-80% complete and, on large projects, would occur about 2 years after contract award.

The most significant element of a quality estimate is the maximizing of quantities and minimizing of factors and statistical relationships.

4.11 REVIEWING CONTRACTOR'S ESTIMATES

4.11.1 Scope Review

To ensure that the contractor's scope definition agrees with the owner's scope, the cost engineer should make a detailed review of all basic design documents, their revision numbers, and dates of issue:

Check that all major equipment is included and is listed by equipment number.
Review all items shown on plot plans, flow sheets, PIDs, and equipment lists to ensure their inclusion in the contractor's estimate.
Equipment and system capacities, flow rates, temperatures, and pressures should be checked for deviation.
Check that owner costs are included.
Evaluate deviations in the scope, design, or estimating basis from those assumed in the appropriation estimate and include these on a puts and takes list.
Owner specialist engineers assigned to the project should review and verify the total scope.

4.11.2 Overall Project Conditions

Prior to examining the line-by-line details of the estimate, an overall evaluation should consider the following:

Project location considerations, i.e., site characteristics (high winds, weather, soil conditions) and local affiliate-governmental practices or regulations
Schedule, i.e., start of engineering, start of construction, mechanical completion, and milestone dates
Labor basis, e.g., subcontract or direct hire
Economic outlook
Contracting mode and execution plan
Estimate for compatibility with contract conditions

4.11.3 Significant Overall Relationships

Compare the following:

Engineering man-hours per piece of equipment
Construction man-hours per piece of equipment
Ratio of direct field man-hours to engineering man-hours
Contractor's home office and engineering cost as a percent of total cost
Contractor's fee as a percent of total cost
Indirect construction costs as a percent of direct labor cost
Percent breakdown of engineering man-hours by prime account
Percent breakdown of construction man-hours by prime account
All-in engineering man-hour rate
All-in field man-hour rate
Escalation allowances for material and labor
Productivity factors for engineering and construction

4.11.4 Major Equipment and Material

The cost of major equipment can be established by actual quotations or from historical data. The method depends on the type of equipment involved and its relative cost. For example, quotations should be obtained for large compressors, but small mixers may be estimated from catalogues or estimating manuals.

   I. *Developmental (or growth) allowances.* Estimates based on vendor quotes, catalogue prices, or initial inquiries should include an allowance for future increases in scope. Costs can rise as much as 10% from an original purchase price as a result of design changes. Verify that the contractor has included an appropriate design allowance (typically 4-8%) for future changes. Based on the general specifications and detailed equipment specifications and data sheets, evaluate as follows:

  II. *Vessels (towers, reactors, drums).* Check unit costs; adjust for size, material, shop versus field fabrication, operating temperature-pressure, metallurgy, number of manholes and platforms, internals required, and the need for insulation-stiffening rings and lifting lugs.

 III. *Heat exchangers.* Check the cost per square foot of useful transfer surface.

  IV. *Heaters and furnaces.* Check the cost per British thermal unit of heat absorbed. Evaluate the degree of prefabrication prior to field erection.

   V. *Boilers and superheaters.* Check the cost per pound of steam generated.

  VI. *Pumps.* Check the cost per horsepower. Pumps of similar capacity can very greatly in price depending on type and materials of construction. It is important to know all special service requirements and design characteristics.

VII. *Storage tanks.* Check the cost per barrel capacity and the cost per pound of fabricated weight. Ensure that tank foundations are adequate for duty and soil conditions.

VIII. *Evaluate project-schedule conditions* which could influence prices, e.g.:
   A. Market conditions
   B. Purchasing preference or bias of domestic affiliate
   C. Schedule acceleration (premium costs)
   D. Escalation rates
   E. Freight, duties, taxes
   F. Size of order

Use a *cheapest source* program for guidance on the source for a worldwide purchasing program.

4.11.5 Bulk Materials: Quantities and Costs Evaluation

I. *Concrete*
   A. Spot-check design quantities for large equipment foundations.
   B. Average cost per cubic yard installed (with rebar, formwork, excavation, and backfill).
   C. Quantity of rebar, formwork, excavation, and backfill per cubic yard of concrete.

II. *Roads and paving.* Cost per square foot installed--overall areas from plant layout.

III. *Underground piping and sewers*
   A. Total linear feet from drawing layout
   B. Location and number of manholes
   C. Cost per linear foot of installed piping, including excavation, backfill, manholes, and sumps

On large projects, underground quantities are often underestimated.

IV. *Miscellaneous concrete work.* Ensure sufficient requirements for cooling tower basins, API separators, pipe sleepers, culverts, and particularly road and electrical crossings.

V. *Fireproofing*
   A. Check the cost per area of surface fireproofed.
   B. Ensure adequate allowance for cutouts and rework.

VI. *Buildings, structures.* Review individual costs for the substructure, heating, ventilation, air conditioning, plumbing, and lighting as a function of the floor area and total cost. Look at all-in square-foot costs of building.

VII. *Site preparation*
   A. Review grading and site preparation; check costs per cubic yard.
   B. Check soil conditions, i.e., type, frost depth, dewatering, sheet piling, and draining requirements.
   C. Consider possible underground obstructions.

On large grass roots projects, earth-moving quantities are often underestimated.

VIII. *Piling*
   A. Check the all-in cost per linear foot (including mobilization and demobilization) and the type of piles (e.g., precast, in situ, or timber) and the cutting of pile caps.
   B. Check who does the layout work (the prime contractor or a subcontractor?).

IX. *Fencing and railroads*
   A. Total linear feet
   B. All-in subcontract installed costs

X. *Piping estimating methods.* Following are four methods of preparing a piping estimate. The specific method would depend on detail and accuracy of the estimate.
   A. *Estimating by length method.* This method is based on historical data and assumes an average number of fittings and flanges for a "standard" piping configuration. Costs would be on a unit length basis by pipe size and schedule. Fabrication would be separated from field installation. It is necessary to add only the cost of valves, pipe supports, testing, etc., to arrive at a total direct cost for the piping system. Care should be taken to check allowances for unusual complexity of piping arrangements (especially on-site units or revamps).
   B. *Estimating by weight method.* In this method, piping materials are assumed to have a value approximately proportional to their weight. Pipe is assigned a cost per pound for material and a number of man-hours per ton for fabrication and erection. Adjustments should be made for unusual materials and labor productivity for the plant location.
   C. *Estimating by ratio method.* This method calculates piping as a percentage of the major equipment cost. Ratio methods can be used only with an appropriate data base. This is not a very accurate method and is usually applied to conceptual estimates.
   D. *Estimating by unit cost method.* This method is more accurate but is costly and time-consuming as detailed takeoffs must be made of all labor and material units in the system. This method requires that engineering be well advanced before accurate takeoffs can be produced. It also requires detailed historical data.
   E. *Piping estimate review.* Examine the method and extent of takeoff by sampling line takeoffs, and compare actual quantities and costs with estimate. Review the basis of fabrication, impact of special materials, etc. Also check the following:
      1. Total linear feet and total weight as a function of plant capacity and plant area.
      2. Overall cost of pipe, fittings, valves, and flanges to total cost of piping material.

3. Separately, compute the cost per ton for material, prefabrication, and erection of both small- and large-bore piping.

4. Cost per foot of pipe tracing (steam or electrical).

XI. *Electrical.* In estimating electrical work, a schedule of the number and size of motor drives is a basic requirement. Motor control center and power distribution items usually constitute a major part of the electrical work. Since their prices can vary considerably, budget prices should be obtained from potential suppliers. The cost of power cable should be estimated in reasonable detail. A plot plan-layout is useful in assessing quantities, while material unit prices may be estimated from historical data. Minor, miscellaneous services, such as emergency lighting, fire alarms, intercoms, power outlets, and telephone systems, can be assessed approximatley or represented as an allowance. Plant lighting may be estimated on an area or unit length basis. A gross estimate of electrical work based on horsepower can be inaccurate. The estimate should take into consideration local electrical codes and area classification. Climatic conditions may require a different type of cable and hardware and therefore could affect cost.

A. *Electrical estimate review.* Review the motor list against the equipment list and the single-line diagram. Also check the following:

1. Overall cost of the power supply related to the total horsepower or thousands of kilowatts

2. Cost of the power supply per motor related to the size of the motor

3. Lighting cost per square foot, per linear foot, etc.

4. Cost of grounding related to the area covered

XII. *Instrumentation estimating methods.* The following are those generally used:

A. *Factor estimating.* With an adequate data base, instrumentation can be factored relative to the installed major equipment cost. Additional points for consideration are the following:

1. Local electrical and environmental codes.

2. Degree of computer control.

3. Does the plant need clean, dry air? If so, an instrument air compression system may be required.

4. Electronic or pneumatic system.

B. *Estimating by instrument loops.* Instrument costs are estimated at a cost per loop. This can be done by using previous return data to establish costs for typical loops based on instrument type and materials of construction and multiplying these by the number of estimated loops in the system. Loop configurations should be developed by the instrument engineer.

C. *Total installed cost per unit.* In this method, instruments are priced from a preliminary list by means of quotes, catalogue prices, or past data. Auxiliary material and installation costs (e.g., tubing, wiring, racks, supports, testing, etc.) are assessed for each instrument based on past experience and judgment.

D. *Detailed estimating.* This is the most accurate approach and requires a detailed instrument list. This can be priced from past data or quotes. Labor man-hours for each instrument are added. Instrument tubing and wiring should be established by detailed takeoff. Auxiliary material and labor cost can be taken as a percentage of the total instrument cost.

E. *Instrument estimate review.* Examine process and instrumentation diagrams for numbers-complexity of instrumentation. Check for conflicts between owner and contractor specifications. Also review the following:

   1. Interface between the contractor's and the owner's scope of work for additions to existing plants
   2. Electronic-pneumatic requirements
   3. Total number of instruments related to the number of pieces of major equipment
   4. Ratio of the cost of instrument piping and instrument wiring to the basic instrument cost
   5. Average cost of piping and wiring per instrument

XIII. *Insulation.* Review requirements for heat conservation, winterizing, cold insulation, and personnel protection for equipment and piping. Analyze the cost of pipe insulation as a factor of the total installed piping value.

XIV. *Painting.* Not normally large enough to justify a detailed estimate. Review any prorated method and values allowed.

4.11.6 Direct Construction Labor

I. *Equipment installation (man-hours).* A check of man-hours required for equipment installation may be made as follows:
   A. Man-hours per material cost
   B. Man-hours per weight and type of equipment
   C. Man-hours per piece and type of equipment

II. *Bulk materials installation (man-hours).* The following would be major items to check:
   A. Man-hours per cubic yard for excavation (machine, hand, or weighted average).
   B. Man-hours per cubic yard for foundation concrete (including forming, pouring, reinforcing steel, and embedments). Review dewatering, sheet piling, and shoring requirements for a civil program.
   C. Man-hours per ton of structural steel (for field fabrication and erection).

   D. Man-hours per ton or per foot of piping by size and
        pipe schedule.
   E. Man-hours per valve and specialty item.
   F. Man-hours per instrument installed (including cable,
        termination, and testing).
III. *Productivity (man-hours).* Depending on the quality of the
      estimating base, the preceding man-hours would normally then
      have to be factored for time and the location of the project. A
      geographic productivity system is essential for a quality
      estimating program. General items (handling, scaffolding,
      testing, rework, etc.) would be on a man-hour percentage
      basis for a detailed estimate and included in man-hour rates
      for a conceptual estimate.
IV. *Labor costs.* Review current labor agreements and conditions,
      productivity factors, manpower availability, site conditions,
      and project conditions. Review total man-hours as well as the
      craft man-hour distribution:
   A. Subcontract versus direct hire: What is covered in the
        all-in subcontract wage rate, especially field indirects?
        What must be covered by the prime contractor?
   B. Average wage rate.
   C. Inclusion of appropriate fringe benefits, taxes, and
        insurances.
   D. Allowances for premium pay on overtime and shift work.

4.11.7 Construction Indirect Costs

Ensure that conceptual estimates have dimensional sketches showing
layouts of temporary facilities which can then be quantified for estimating.

   I. *Temporary facilities.* Review estimates for the following:
   A. Temporary utility lines and utilities consumed during
        construction
   B. Temporary roads and parking and laydown areas
   C. Fencing and security
   D. Temporary buildings, furnishings, and equipment
   E. Personnel transportation and equipment receiving facilities
   F. Erection-operation of construction camp if required
      Most of these items would be estimated on a cost per foot and
      square-foot basis.
   II. *Construction tools and equipment.* Discuss and check the
        methods adopted by contractors in establishing estimated
        costs. Check the following:
   A. List and scheduled duration of all major equipment
   B. Small tools (normally estimated as cost per labor
        man-hour or percent of direct-labor cost)
   C. Availability of equipment; start and termination of
        rental period
   D. Equipment maintenance, major and minor
   E. Equipment purchased; equipment rented and source

F.   Review of cranage and heavy lift requirements
G.   Construction equipment cost per direct-hire man-hour

III.   *Construction staff.* Examine the site organization chart and assignment durations of personnel; also review the following:
   A.   Relocation costs, travel and living allowances, fringe benefits and burdens, and overseas allowances
   B.   Total staff man-hours related to total labor man-hours
   C.   Supervision cost related to the construction labor cost
   D.   Average monthly rate for the technical staff

IV.   *Field office expenses.* Review the estimates of field office supplies, reproduction, telephone, telex, office equipment, and consumables. These items are usually estimated as cost per labor man-hour or as a percent of direct field costs.

4.11.8 Home Office Costs

I.   *Percentage of project costs.* This method requires considerable analysis of previous projects, but can provide a reasonable estimate of H.O. costs for a conceptual estimate. Normally, H.O. costs would be expressed as a percentage of the following bases:
   A.   Total "constructed cost" (i.e. material + labor + subcontracts + field indirects. A typical range would be 10-15%.
   B.   Direct material and labor (subcontractor or direct hire). A typical range would be 18-22%.

II.   *Engineering man-hours based on pieces of major equipment.* A typical range would be 1000-1500 man-hours/piece of equipment. Factors may be applied to reflect size, complexity, prototype, and revamp work. These man-hours will cover all engineering and design man-hours. Man-hours for services such as planning and scheduling, estimating, cost control, and procurement are derived as percentages of engineering hours.

III.   *Man-hours per drawing (or work item).* This method requires major completion of the process design so that a detailed drawing list can be developed. It is necessary that PIDs, plot plans, and equipment lists be available from which a total number of drawings can then be estimated.

IV.   *Reviewing home office estimate.* Review the basis of establishing man-hours with the contractor. Analyze the following:
   A.   Man-hours per major piece of equipment
   B.   Man-hours per drawing using the estimated total number of drawings
   C.   Percentage relationship of discipline man-hours for abnormalities
   D.   Average all-in rate for total home office technical personnel
   E.   Benefits, burdens, and overhead rates

      F. Fee basis on reimbursable and cost-plus contracts
      G. General specifications for conflict or "gold plating"
      H. Service group estimates by organization chart,
           manning schedule, and statistical relationship
      I. New technology contingency for prototype design

4.11.9 Contingency

The contingency or estimating allowance is a function of the following:

Design definition (process unit, off sites, revamps)
Estimating methods (data base and level of detail)
Time frame and schedule probability
New technology and prototype engineering
Remoteness of job site; infrastructure requirements
Engineering physical progress (percentage complete)
Material commitment
Construction physical progress (percentage complete)

    See Section 4.12 for further information in evaluating the appropriate contingency level on an ongoing basis.

4.11.10 Escalation

Escalation is usually included as a separate line item or is built into the estimate details. Either method is acceptable—assuming that escalation rates and cost centroids have been developed properly. Escalation rates for material and labor costs should be separately identified.

4.11.11 Currency Conversion

As currency conversion rates can fluctuate widely over the life of a project, it is recommended that one use the rate established at the time of appropriation and track deviations thereafter as a one-line item. Corporate and affiliate financial groups should be consulted when establishing currency conversion rates for the estimate.

4.12 CONTINGENCY EVALUATION

Most contractors have a contingency evaluation method or risk analysis system. However, it is recommended that owners carry out their own evaluation, particularly on reimbursable/cost-plus projects.
    The curve in Figure 4.3 represents a typical rundown of contingency over the life of the project on a percent of time basis. Figure 4.3 shows a rundown which is calculated on the basis of uncommitted and unspent costs and is computed as follows:

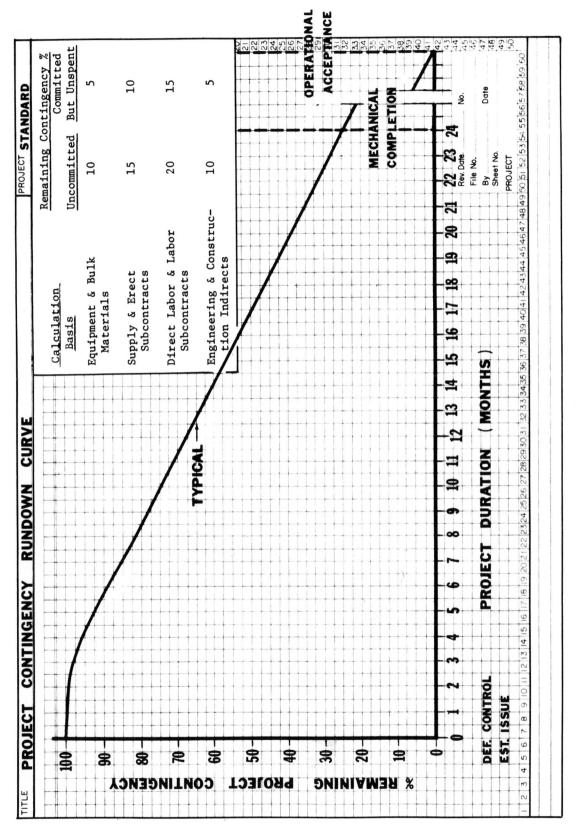

Figure 4.3 Typical contingency rundown curve.

TREND REPORT

Report No. _____

Report Date _____

Project _____

Job No. _____

Report No.	Report Date	Description (All Costs Shown in 1,000's)	Cost	(±) Period Forecast Change
		APPROVED AND POTENTIAL		

Page _____ of _____

Figure 4.4 Typical trend report.

	Cost Prediction Uncommitted (%)	Committed but Unspent (%)
Material and equipment	10	5
Labor	20	15
Labor subcontracts	20	15
Material and labor subcontracts	15	10
Home office, engineering, and fee	10	5
Field indirects and temporaries	10	5
All other costs	10	5
Owner costs	10	5

This simple, but practical, method covers risk on work yet to be committed and work committed but not completed. Construction labor and subcontracts are generally the most volatile items and therefore carry the greatest contingency percentage.

The curve in Figure 4.3 will generally result when this method is applied to the phase II of a process plant. This method applies only to contractor-detailed estimates which are based on completed plot plans, PIDs, equipment lists, equipment and material specifications, and bulk material takeoffs.

A contingency or estimating allowance for conceptual and factored estimates should be developed as part of the estimate evaluation. The maximum contingency that this method will develop is 13%. This would not be sufficient for a conceptual estimate.

This method provides that approximately 25% of the contingency is remaining at mechanical completion. This is to ensure that funds are available for late changes, commissioning accidents, start-up requirements, and final invoices-claims which were not anticipated.

Worked Example

The following is a typical cost breakdown of a jumbo process plant in millions of dollars:

	Prediction	Committed	Spent
Equipment & material	$1000	$ 500	$100
Labor	600	200	50
Labor and material-- subcontract	400	200	--
General contractor field indirects	500	150	50
Home office engineering- services & fee	300	250	200
Subtotal contractor cost	$2800	$1300	$400
Owner cost	200	100	50
Total cost	$3000	$1400	$450

Table 4.1

	Uncommitted	×	%	=	Contingency Requirement	Unspent	×	%	=	Contingency Requirement
Equipment & material	500		10		50	400		5		20
Labor	400		20		80	150		15		22.5
Labor & material—subcontract	200		15		30	200		10		20
General contractor indirects	350		10		35	100		5		5
Home office engineering & fee	50		10		5	50		5		2.5
Owner cost	100		10		10	50		5		2.5
Total	1600				210	950				72.5

Total contingency required; $210 + 72.5 = 282.5$ or 9.4%

Using the same approach, the contingency at project start would have been 380 or 12.6%

The contingency required at mechanical completion for late changes and start-up items would be 25% of the original contingency or $380 \times 0.25 = 95$ or 3.2%

Application of the contingency evaluation method would result in the computation shown in Table 4.1.

4.13 OWNER TRENDING SYSTEM

On reimbursable projects, it is vital that the owner maintain an independent trending program. Compared with a small owner project task force, a contractor's operations and organization tend to be cumbersome, inflexible, and slow to respond. In most cases, an owner trending program will be more current, accurate, and responsive to changing circumstances.

A difficult time for cost control is during the transition from the owner feasibility estimate to the contractor conceptual estimate. This is often called the *blackout period,* and the time interval can be longer than 6 months. During this period, many engineering decisions are made, without full recognition of the cost impact as the owner's estimate has been discontinued and the contractor's estimate is working from an engineering cutoff point.

It is recommended that owners maintain a full estimating program well beyond the period of the contractor's 90-day conceptual estimate. This will ensure that the owner's estimate is being updated with ongoing engineering-project trends while the contractor is developing an estimate from an engineering scope which is no longer current.

On most reimbursable projects, most major engineering decisions are initiated by owner engineers or approved by them. This generally occurs during the process design phase, and cost engineers should ensure that communication channels with all engineers provide an accurate assessment of the developing design.

General specifications and equipment specifications should be monitored for conflict and gold plating. Where quantity takeoffs exist, they should be monitored for change.

Figure 4.4 illustrates a typical trend report. All project changes, engineering specifications, the scope, procurement, subcontract, etc., should be recorded as they occur or are considered.

Changes to the project execution plan should be included. These changes could be contractual, environmental, regulatory, or schedule oriented. Potential and approved changes should be reported, and appropriate cost estimates should be included.

Approved changes are those which have been formally authorized by the owner project manager. Potential changes would cover items verbally approved and items which the cost engineer, through discussions with task force personnel, believes are likely to occur.

Potential changes should be shown separately from approved trends.

4.14 OWNER COSTS

Apart from offices and miscellaneous services supplied by the contractor, the owner cost engineer should identify and control owner
costs independently of the contractor.

A major owner cost is personnel: the project task force and the
corporate and affiliate personnel assigned to design, build, and
operate the plant. Personnel schedules and man-hour-cost expenditure
profiles should be developed and updated on a regular basis.

Aside from personnel costs, other costs might be as follows:

Catalysts and chemicals
Royalties and licensing fees
Construction permits
Special consultants and soil surveys
Land acquisition charges
Venture-affiliate charges, e.g., engineering and purchasing,
  training, start-up crews, etc.
Taxes on "other owner costs"
Certain insurance coverages on these costs
Warehouse spare parts (whether capitalized or expensed)

All owner costs chargeable to the project should be included in the
owner monthly cost report.

4.15 MONITORING CONTRACTOR COST OPERATION

The overall objective on reimbursable projects is to have the contractor
efficiently and effectively control his or her own work. Contractor
deficiencies and/or poor performance often result in owners taking
over part or all of the control responsibility. This is an undesirable
situation.

The cost control specification and cost engineer duties and objectives provide the basis for monitoring a contractor's cost operation.

As it is not possible to check every detail, the following highlights
significant items to monitor:

1. Overall
        Maximize the quantification of the control estimate.
        Check on the effectiveness of the trending system.
        Ensure that the fee payment reflects the progress of the project.
        Review cash flow requirements.
        Review the contingency evaluation.
        Check on the effectiveness of the organization and quality of
          personnel.
2. Engineering
        Check on the accuracy of the engineering change log.
        Review productivity profile(s).
        Review man-hour expenditure curve(s).

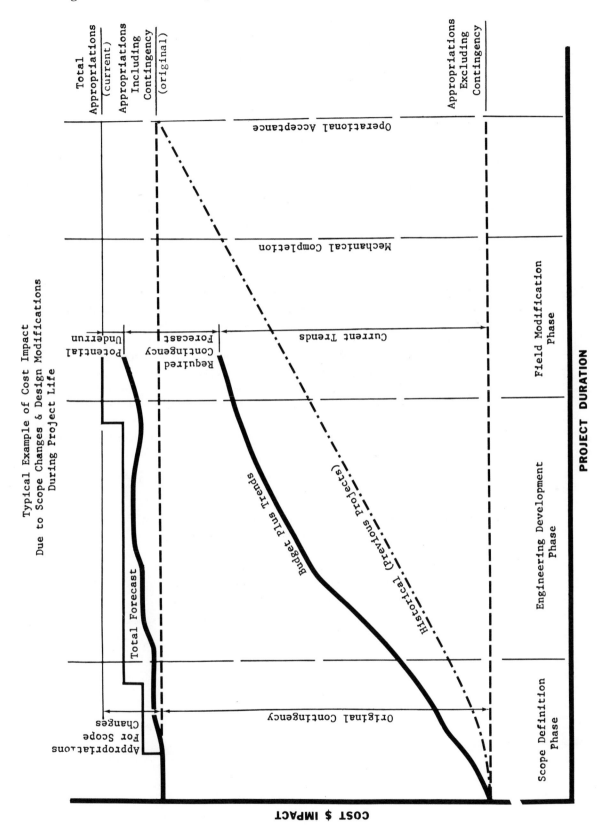

Figure 4.5 Typical tracking curve of overall cost forecast.

       Review the all-in rate profile.
       Check on the effectiveness of the quantity sampling program.
3.   Procurement
       Review commitments versus budget levels.
       Check on the quality of the bid tabulation analysis.
4.   Construction
       Review labor productivity profile(s).
       Review man-hour expenditure curve(s).
       Review the labor rate profile.
       Review expenditure curves for indirects (man-hours-money).
       Check subcontract cost predictions.
       Review subcontract performance evaluations.
5.   Overall cost forecast. The end product of the contractor cost control program is a project cost forecast. A quality forecast should track costs, scope changes, and usage of contingency.

The tracking curve in Figure 4.5 encompasses all these elements, and Figure 4.5 is thus a tracking curve for the overall cost forecast. The baseline is the approved appropriation, usually the conceptual estimate, without contingency. Ongoing trends are plotted against a historical rundown of contingency; approved scope changes resulting in additional appropriations are added as shown at the top of the chart, resulting in a total forecast. As shown, this particular example shows an underrun against the total appropriation. During actual execution, this set of curves should be plotted against calendar time. If there were no scope changes to account for an overrun against a planned curve based on past experience, it is probable that this example would result in a cost overrun.

This concludes the chapter on owner cost control. In summary, the essential elements are the following:

Motivate the contractor to produce a quality estimate.
Provide control during the design development stage.
Establish an effective trending system.
Develop an effective contractor cost operation.
Provide effective analysis and good return data.
Produce "no-surprise" cost predictions.

5

CONTRACTOR PLANNING AND SCHEDULING

5.1 INTRODUCTION

In this chapter we shall deal with a contractor's project scheduling operation, mainly of reimbursable, phase II projects. Owners would have a project task force working with a contractor on an equal partnership basis.

The operation of a contractor home office scheduling group would be similar to an owner's group, as outlined in Chapter 3. However, it is not likely that contractors would devote significant resources to an ongoing development operation. For competitive reasons, many contractors develop procedures and methods on existing contracts.

It is a wise owner who will allow some contractor methods development in the contractual agreement. It is a smart contractor who will accept some financial penalty to develop adequate control systems.

5.2 CONTRACTOR PLANNING AND SCHEDULING SYSTEM

Figure 5.1 is a flowchart showing the essentials of a typical contractor planning and scheduling system. This same chart is outlined in the owner planning and scheduling specification, and it is assumed that the specification and comments would be acceptable to contractors. As this chart has been developed from current contractor practices, the writer believes this to be a reasonable approach.

The contractor proposal, contractual agreement, project execution plan, and owner control specification will determine the planning and scheduling requirements and schedule objectives for the specific project.

At contract award, the proposal schedule should be updated to reflect current circumstances and, together with specific schedule objectives and recommendations, presented to the owner. It is anticipated the proposal schedule will become the project summary schedule, as requested by owner. During the proposal stage, "selling" to an

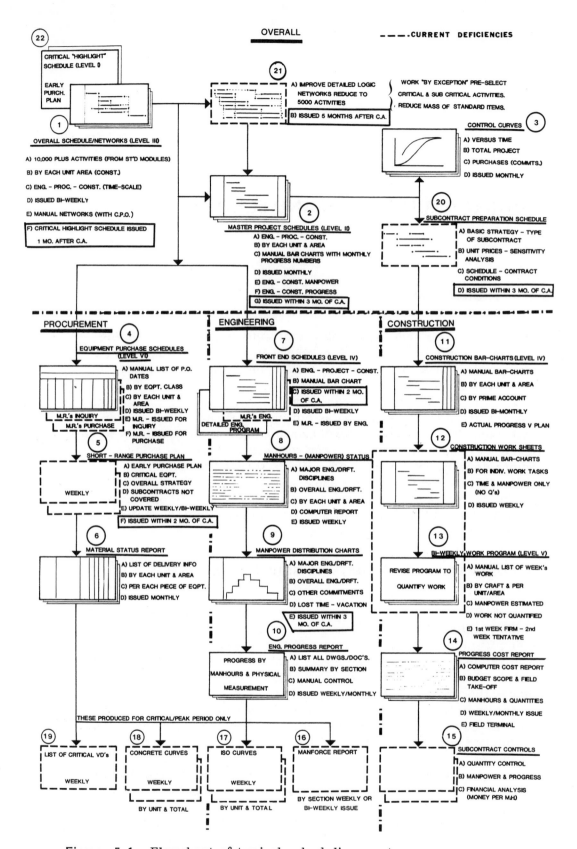

Figure 5.1   Flowchart of typical scheduling system.

130

owner will sometimes produce a very optimistic schedule. Although this is a natural tendency, it should be resisted. Updating after contract award should, therefore, be a matter of timing and not duration. The project can get off to a poor start if the contractor has to confess that the proposal schedule was very optimistic, or, alternatively, it is so discovered as the project advances through engineering.

An overall planning and scheduling program, as agreed upon with the owner, should be implemented with personnel assignments to develop detailed networks and additional personnel assigned to plan and schedule current work.

The owner's engineering bid package and the contractor's initial budget estimate should provide sufficient information to develop detailed networks. At this early stage, engineering will probably be in more detail than construction.

The following briefly covers the overall contractor scheduling program. Further detail is covered in the owner specification.

1. *Project summary schedule:* usually an update of the proposal schedule, covering the overall duration of the project and showing significant milestones and the critical path. The format should be a manual, time-scaled network comprising 20-30 activities. This schedule will be used by the owner at quarterly project review meetings and should be included in the monthly progress report.

2. *Project master schedule* (critical highlights): similar in format to the summary schedule and usually 50-60 activities, covering all areas and units, showing critical and subcritical paths. It should be produced within 1 month of contract award.

3. *Project control implementation schedule:* This schedule should cover all elements of the proposed control system and should be reviewed and updated biweekly until the control system is fully operational.

4. *Environmental schedule:* An environment permit schedule showing required procedures and estimated times for permits from local, state, and federal authorities.

5. *Level II schedules:* to cover all major start and finish dates for engineering, procurement, and construction. These should be produced within 3 months of contract award and should be manual bar charts on an area basis. The number of activities would be about 1500-2000 or 150-200 per control area.

6. *Subcontract preparation schedule:* to cover major activities from requisition to commitment for all major subcontracts. It should be produced within 3 months of contract award. See Section 7.4 for further detail.

7. *Detailed network program (level III):* a critical path method (CPM) type of program covering engineering, procurement, and construction. The program should consist of a maximum of 5000 activities and be based on level II schedules and the subcontract preparation schedule.

The following Early and Critical Activities should be discussed in detail with the contractor's groups.

<u>Project/Construction</u>

    Project Organization Chart
    Site Survey/Report
    Formal Response to "Owner's Planning
      and Scheduling
    Co-ord. Procedure
    Eng. Organization Chart
    Construction Org. Chart
    Budget Estimate
    Temporary Fac. Layouts (Access).

    Monthly Report Format
    Construction Labor Evaluation
    Cost Control Procedure
    Constr. Equipt. Requirements
    Site Prep. Evaluation

<u>Planning and Scheduling</u>

    Critical Highlight Schedule
    Detailed Front End Schedule
    Discipline/Section Manpower Curves
      (To Match Early Schedule)
    Overall Expenditure/Commitment
      Curves
    Site Prep. Schedule
    Subcontract Preparation Schedule
    Networks
    Computer Program/Output

    Project Control - Progress
      (Response to "Owner's Planning
      and Scheduling System)

<u>Procurement</u>

    Purchasing Plan-Critical Mat.
    Site Prep. Subcontract Pkge.
    Appointment Subcontract Admin.
    Purchasing Procedure
      (To avoid delays at satellite
      offices)
    Vendors Lists
      (Coordinate with Owner Purch.)
    Bid Tab Procedures (Quality)
    Vendor Tab Procedures (Quality)
    Inquiry and P.O. Control (Delays)
    Subcontract Conditions (Control & Site)
    Subcontract Strategy (Early Work)

<u>Engineering</u>

    Process Design
    Flow Sheets
    P&Is
    Plot Plans
    Equipment List
    Mat. Reqr. (M.R.) List
    Eng. for Site Prep.
    Specifications
      (Coordinate with Owner Spec.)
    Equipment Data Sheets
    Manpower Plans (Staff and Agency)
    Governmental Permits
    Environmental Impact Study

This Listing Is not All-Inclusive

Figure 5.2 List of early and critical activities.

5.3 EARLY AND CRITICAL ACTIVITIES

Figure 5.2 is a typical list of early and critical activities. This list will form the basis of the control implementation schedule, and items should be scheduled on a priority basis.

At this early stage, the major scheduling thrust is to efficiently build up the engineering effort as quickly as possible.

A short-term manual schedule should be developed for activities as outlined on the early and critical activity listing. This schedule should be available within 2 months of contract award.

Manpower resources should be applied to this schedule. Figure 5.3 shows a typical short-term (90-day) schedule, covering early engineering-procurement activities to purchase equipment. These should be manual bar charts covering activities for engineering, procurement, and construction preplanning work. These schedules should not be necessary when the detailed network program is available. Depending on criticality, these schedules should be updated for status biweekly or weekly.

As these schedules are the major control tool until the detailed computer network program is operational, the quality of work is vital. It is also important that all departments support and work to these schedules.

5.4 EARLY MANPOWER CONTROL

As rapid buildup of engineering and project personnel is essential for most projects, the following manpower control is recommended. Figure 5.4 is a weekly report of allocated manpower. This report should be produced immediately after contract award and could be discontinued when detailed schedules are operational or when there is no criticality. Monitoring of actual allocation against the plan can provide early warning of lack of manpower or lack of work. Both items can impact on the project schedule.

5.5 OVERALL BREAKDOWN OF ENGINEERING, PROCUREMENT, AND CONSTRUCTION

A significant element of overall schedule evaluation is the duration and relationship of progress curves for engineering, procurement, and construction. Historical experience can indicate the validity of planned curves and, therefore, the probability of the overall program.

These curves are also used for reporting monthly progress. Figure 5.5 shows historical progress curves for procurement, engineering, and construction. Progress will be measured on a physical basis (quantities) for engineering and construction. The material curve will be commitments on a financial basis and will include material supply and erect subcontracts, such as tankage, heaters, and field-fabricated vessels. Labor subcontracts will not be included. Specific project curves should be developed but against a calendar time frame. Actual performance should be compared with historical experience. Resulting deviations can indicate short-term or long-term trends, which would require further investigation. This report should be updated monthly.

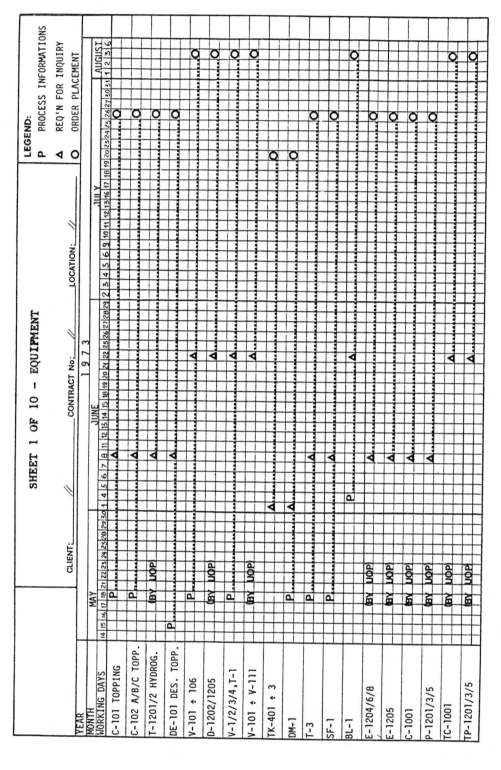

Figure 5.3   Typical 90-day schedule.

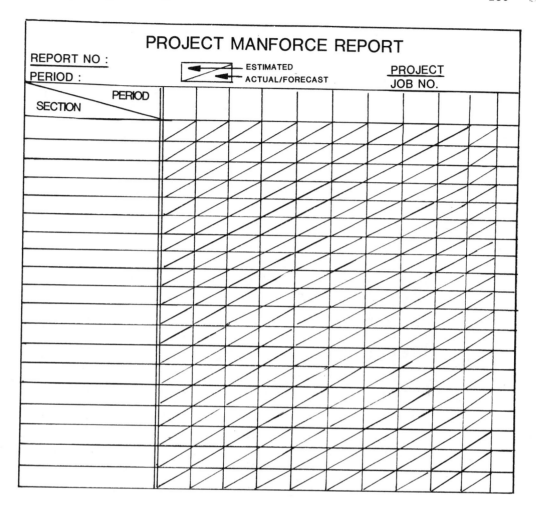

Figure 5.4 Project manpower report.

5.6 MONTHLY PROGRESS REPORT

The monthly progress report should include narratives, progress curves, productivity curves, and manpower histograms for engineering, procurement, and construction.

The composition of the monthly progress report should be agreed upon with the owner soon after contract award.

Narratives for the reporting period should include status, trends, criticality, and significant owner deficiencies which are affecting the schedule. Actions should be proposed for schedule slippage. Where recovery is not possible, a schedule impact evaluation should be made.

A minimum schedule package for the monthly report would include the following:

1. Project master schedule
2. Progress curves for
        Engineering

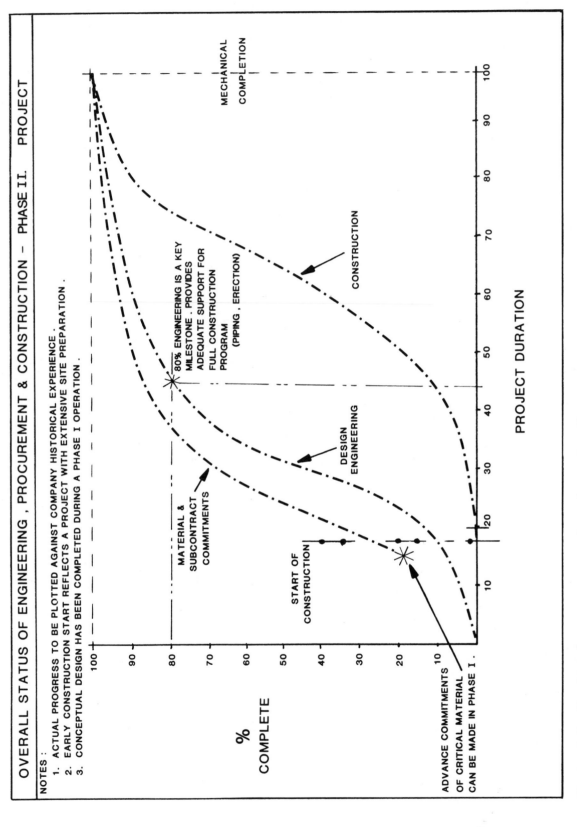

Figure 5.5   Engineering, procurement, and construction curves.

      Material commitments (equipment, bulks, subcontract)
      Construction
3. Manpower histograms for
      Engineering
      Total home office
      Direct labor
      Indirect labor
      Subcontract labor
4. Productivity curves for
      Engineering
      Construction

     The project master schedule, progress curves, and manpower histograms should be updated to the reporting period. A brief narrative should outline the progress for the period, highlight critical activities, and provide a forecast of schedule completion.

5.7 TYPICAL BREAKDOWN OF SCHEDULING OPERATION

		Individual Weighting (%)
1.	Set up the overall network: engineering, procurement, construction	3.7
2.	Issue a barline schedule for the first 2 months' work and monitor until a detailed engineering schedule is available	1.9
3.	Detail engineering and procurement networks, including subcontracts	6.3
4.	Computer schedule for engineering and procurement	6.0
5.	Input writing of the computer program	1.4
6.	Monitoring of projects schedules (1, 3, and 4)	5.5
7.	Complete schedule rationalization and set up control curves	5.1
8.	Set up and issue the master project schedule (MPS)	2.1
9.	Monitor the master project schedule and control curves (8 and 7)	6.0
10.	Contract change investigation and analysis	3.1
11.	Issue critical analysis reports	5.5
12.	Updating of engineering and procurement schedules (1, 3 and 4)	3.6
13.	Updating of the MPS and control curves (7 and 8)	2.4
14.	Carry out investigation requested by the project manager	5.3
15.	Liaison with field forces and meetings	1.4
16.	Statistics (lost time, industrial disputes, absenteeism, productivity, etc.)	3.8

		Individual Weighting (%)
17.	Set up detail construction networks for the job	6.5
18.	Time analysis of construction networks	5.0
19.	Input writing of construction networks	--
20.	Liaise with the construction department on the overall construction schedule for man-power loading, timings, phasing, etc.	2.8
21.	Rationalization of the construction schedule	1.5
22.	Issue monthly reports (7)	--
23.	Supervision and coordination	15.5
24.	Monitor and update construction schedules (17 and 18)	2.6
25.	Update the MPS with shipping and construction progress figures	3.0
	Total	100.0%

This list of activities breaks down the tasks performed by a scheduling department into typical categories and assigns them percentage weightings. From a scheduling standpoint, contractors historically handle projects in two distinct phases, projects (engineering and procurement) and construction. In addition, project and construction schedules are often prepared by different departments, so this typical breakdown can assist in evaluations of the work content of these phases if they are separate functions.

This breakdown can be used to assign the total estimated project planning and scheduling man-hours to these categories. When used to assess manning levels, they can indicate realistic timings for early planning documents.

Specific operations may vary from these general categories. However, planning and scheduling activities can usually be assigned to one or more categories. Conversely, several categories may be combined to cover one activity.

Where planning and scheduling is done by one group, supervision and coordination covers both project and construction groups.

Example

For a 100,000-home-office-man-hour, full-scope job, we would typically expect 2.0% or 2000 h for total scheduling. This exhibit assigns 3.7% for setting up the overall project master schedule and will equate to 74 man-hours. If one man is employed on this task, a schedule should be produced within 2 weeks.

5.8 ENGINEERING SCHEDULING, OVERALL

The major elements for effective control of engineering are a firm process design (approved by the owner), man-hour estimates based on

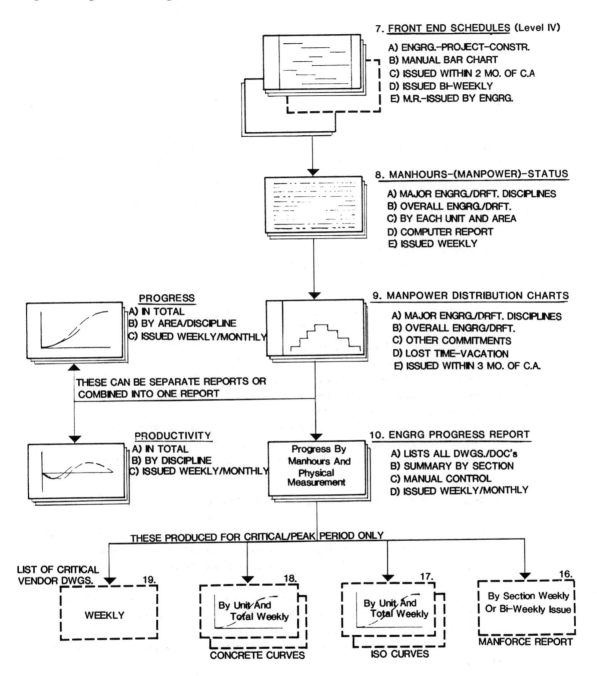

7. <u>FRONT END SCHEDULES</u> (Level IV)

A) ENGRG.-PROJECT-CONSTR.
B) MANUAL BAR CHART
C) ISSUED WITHIN 2 MO. OF C.A
D) ISSUED BI-WEEKLY
E) M.R.-ISSUED BY ENGRG.

8. MANHOURS-(MANPOWER)-STATUS

A) MAJOR ENGRG./DRFT. DISCIPLINES
B) OVERALL ENGRG./DRFT.
C) BY EACH UNIT AND AREA
D) COMPUTER REPORT
E) ISSUED WEEKLY

PROGRESS
A) IN TOTAL
B) BY AREA/DISCIPLINE
C) ISSUED WEEKLY/MONTHLY

9. MANPOWER DISTRIBUTION CHARTS

A) MAJOR ENGRG./DRFT. DISCIPLINES
B) OVERALL ENGRG./DRFT.
C) OTHER COMMITMENTS
D) LOST TIME-VACATION
E) ISSUED WITHIN 3 MO. OF C.A.

THESE CAN BE SEPARATE REPORTS OR
COMBINED INTO ONE REPORT

PRODUCTIVITY
A) IN TOTAL
B) BY DISCIPLINE
C) ISSUED WEEKLY/MONTHLY

Progress By
Manhours And
Physical
Measurement

10. ENGRG PROGRESS REPORT

A) LISTS ALL DWGS./DOC's
B) SUMMARY BY SECTION
C) MANUAL CONTROL
D) ISSUED WEEKLY/MONTHLY

THESE PRODUCED FOR CRITICAL/PEAK PERIOD ONLY

LIST OF CRITICAL
VENDOR DWGS.   19.

WEEKLY

18.

By Unit And
Total Weekly

CONCRETE CURVES

17.

By Unit And
Total Weekly

ISO CURVES

16.

By Section Weekly
Or Bi-Weekly Issue

MANFORCE REPORT

Figure 5.6 Flowchart of engineering scheduling.

numbers of drawings and requisitions, manpower histograms, a physical
measurement system, and tracking of productivity.

Figure 5.6 is a flowchart of a typical engineering scheduling system. This flowchart is an abstract from the flowchart for a typical
contractor planning and scheduling system. It displays many methods
by which effective control can be exercised.

The following are exhibits and explanations covering detailed control of engineering.

5.9 MEASUREMENT OF ENGINEERING PROGRESS-PRODUCTIVITY

Figure 5.7 shows a typical format of an engineering progress and productivity report. The following is a brief explanation of this report:

Column 4, physical completion (engineering only): evaluation of physical completion of drawings and documents, by engineering discipline and/or department, where work in progress is evaluated as per the following guide.

Column 5, weighted factor: based on budgeted hours for each discipline or department. This weighting will not change for minor revisions to the budget.

Column 6, weighted percent complete: physical completion multiplied by weighted factor (col. 4 × col. 5); addition to the bottom line total will give engineering progress.

Column 7, earned man-hours: allocation of budgeted hours based on physical completion (col. 3 × col. 4).

Column 8, man-hours expended: actual man-hours charged to the work.

Column 9, productivity: actual man-hours divided by earned or budgeted hours (col. 8 ÷ col. 7).

Columns 10, 11, and 12: can be used if drawing and document performance data are required. However, physical completion and productivity are adequately evaluated using columns 1 to 9.

Guide to Completion of Design and Drafting

The stages of completion given in Table 5.1 are a guide to determining the percentage of a specification or drawing completed. Each specification and drawing must be carefully examined before determining its percentage of completion.

This guide covers only drawings and specifications. There are other items (such as coordination and supervision) within the engineering scope which are not easily quantified. These items should be treated as "below-the-line" items and given the same measure of completion as the quantified work.

5.10 ENGINEERING-DRAWING STATUS REPORT

Figure 5.8 is a typical format for reporting the status of engineering drawings. This document provides source information for evaluating engineering progress. The individual drawing status will be evaluated by discipline squad leaders and spot-checked by the scheduling group. This report covers progress, the schedule, and man-hours.

PROJECT   PERIOD

ENGINEERING PROGRESS & PRODUCTIVITY REPORT

1	2	3	4		5	6		7		8		9		10	11	12	
			%		WTD. FACTOR	WEIGHTED %		EARNED HOURS		ACTUAL HOURS		PRODUCTIVITY		NO. OF DWGS.	BUDGET HOURS PER DWG.	ACTUAL HRS. PER DWG.	
A/C	SECTION	BUDG. HRS.	INC.	CUM.		INC.	CUM.	INC.	CUM.	INC.	CUM.	INC.	CUM.			INC.	CUM.

TOTAL

Figure 5.7 Engineering progress and productivity report.

Table 5.1 Stages of Completion

	Percent Complete
Specifications	
Complete draft	20
Write specification	70
Check specification	85
Issue for approval	85
Issue for construction	85
Issue revisions as required	95-100
Architectural drawings	
Complete sketches and general arrangements (GAs)	15
Issue sketches and GAs for approval as required	25
Complete drawing	75
Check drawing	85
Issue for approval	90
Issue for construction	95
Issue revisions as required	95-100
Civil drawings	
Complete preliminary site plan (building locations & site elevation)	10
Issue preliminary site plan for approval as required	25
Complete design calculations	30
Complete drawing	80
Issue for approval	85
Issue for construction	95
Issue revisions as required	95-100
Concrete and foundation drawings	
Complete design calculations	25
Complete drawing	60
Check drawing	85
Issue for approval	90
Issue for construction	95
Issue revisions as required	95-100
Steel and superstructure drawings	
Complete design calculations	25
Complete drawing	60
Check drawing	85
Issue for approval	90
Issue for construction	95
Issue revisions as required	95-100
Electrical drawings	
Complete design calculations	15
Complete drawing	75
Check drawing	85

Table 5.1 (Continued)

	Percent Complete
Issue for approval	90
Issue for construction	95
Issue revisions as required	95-100
Instrumentation drawings	
Complete design calculations	50
Complete drawing	70
Check drawing	85
Issue for approval	90
Issue for construction	95
Issue revisions as required	95-100
Mechanical general arrangement drawings	
Complete design calculations	15
Complete preliminary GA drawings	20
Issue preliminary GA drawings for approval	40
Complete drawing	65
Check drawing	75
Issue for approval	80
Issue for construction	95
Issue revisions as required	95-100
Mechanical and piping drawings	
Complete design calculations	10
Complete drawing	65
Check drawing	85
Issue for approval	90
Issue for construction	95
Issue revisions as required	95-100
Flow sheet drawings	
Complete design calculations	40
Complete drawing	60
Check drawing	70
Issue for approval	80
Issue for construction	95
Issue revisions as required	95-100

5.11 ENGINEERING PHYSICAL PROGRESS

The curves shown in Figure 5.9 monitor overall cumulative engineering progress. Actual progress and forecasted engineering progress are shown relative to the original or revised schedule curves. This technique is outlined as item 10 on the flowchart of the contractor scheduling system.

ENGINEERING DRAWING STATUS REPORT

ACCT.	ACT./ DRG. NO.	ACTIVITY		START DATE	COMPLETION DATES			% COMPLETION											BUDGET ACTUAL HOURS HOURS		REMARKS	FORECAST HOURS
					ORIG.	REV.	REV.	10	20	30	40	50	60	70	80	90	100					
			S																			
			A																			
			S																			
			A																			
			S																			
			A																			
			S																			
			A																			
			S																			
			A																			
			S																			
			A																			
			S																			
			A																			
			S																			
			A																			
			S																			
			A																			
			S																			
			A																			

COMPLETION DATE
SCHEDULE
ACTUAL

ISSUED FOR:		CONTRACT NO.	SECTION	REPORT NO.	STATUS AS OF		TOTAL THIS SHEET	
A — APPROVAL		CUSTOMER					GRAND TOTAL	
C — CONSTRUCTION			DRAWING NO.	SHT. NO.	DATE	DEPT.	compiled by	
D — DESIGN								
M — MICROFILM		PLANT						
P — PURCHASE								
Q — QUOTATION								

Figure 5.8 Engineering drawing status report.

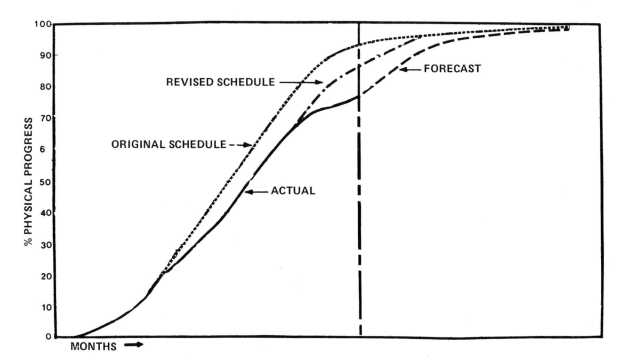

Figure 5.9 Engineering progress curves.

Overall engineering progress is compiled from individual curves developed for each engineering discipline. Progress should be physical measurement based on completion of drawings and engineering documents, as per the previous techniques.

Work unit tracking curves for production of concrete foundation drawings and piping isometrics provide a substantial part of the data required to assess overall engineering progress.

Man-hour expenditure can be a poor basis for reporting progress. However, until drawing and document quantities are known, this method must be used.

5.12 ENGINEERING PRODUCTIVITY

An estimated productivity profile should be developed as early as possible. This should be based on past history and specific project conditions. This profile can provide an early warning to potential overrun if actual productivity varies significantly from the anticipated curve.

5.12.1 Engineering Productivity Profile

Figure 5.10 shows a typical cumulative productivity profile. Productivity is assessed by comparing *earned value*, which is based on percent of

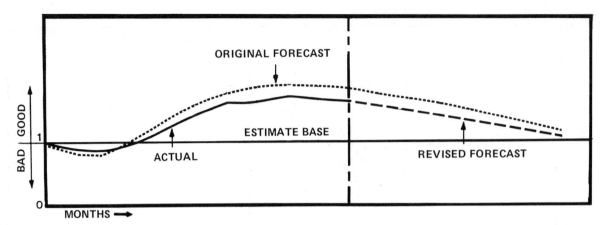

Figure 5.10 Engineering productivity profile.

budget man-hours complete, against the number of actual man-hours expended, i.e.,

$$\text{Productivity} = \frac{\text{Physical completion} \times \text{Budget man-hours}}{\text{Actual man-hours}}$$

Productivity during the initial stage of engineering is usually low due to unproductive man-hours expended at kickoff meetings, the setting up of project controls, the recycling of the process design, abortive layout work, etc. Productivity should normally improve and stabilize during production engineering. Productivity gradually decreases over the latter period when proportionally more man-hours are required for engineering rework and closeout.

For ease of reporting, progress and productivity curves could be combined on a single report.

5.12.2 Engineering Productivity Report

Figure 5.11 is another form of productivity report. This format covers performance data and forecasted man-hours in addition to the productivity curve.

This example shows a sharp deterioration at period 10. As a result, the cumulative curve drops below the historical curve, and an overrun (poor productivity) forecast is made.

5.13 MANPOWER ALLOCATION

This technique, as detailed in Section 3.2, should be used to evaluate overall manpower requirements. The planned histogram and progress curve will be drawn by weighting together curves for all disciplines and then by checking against the historical standard curve as per the overall breakdown.

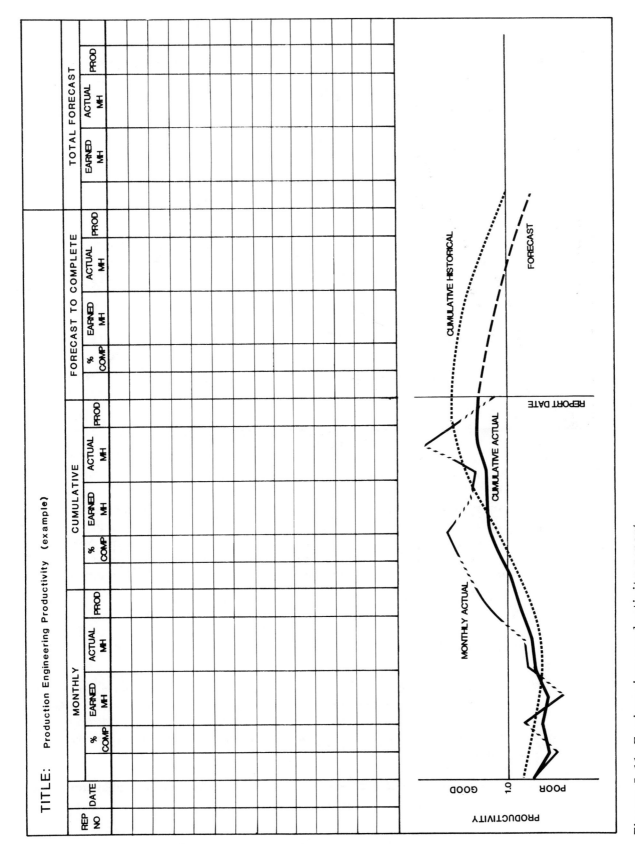

Figure 5.11 Engineering productivity report.

147

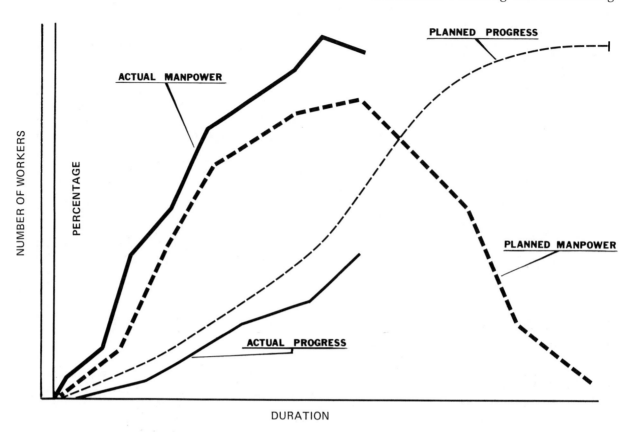

Figure 5.12 Engineering manpower histogram.

Individual manpower histograms based on the engineering budget and level II schedule should be developed for each engineering discipline. Figure 5.12 shows a typical manpower histogram. As early control is essential, these curves should be drawn up as early as possible. Concurrence and commitment of engineering supervision should be obtained.

5.14 ENGINEERING WORKFORCE REPORT

As stated earlier, manpower should be assigned as soon as productivity possible. In the early stages and at critical periods, the report shown in Figure 5.13 is recommended; it is a typical format showing engineers and draftsmen, by discipline, assigned for the week and also manpower planned for the following week. Lost days are also reported. Significant lost time can result in schedule slippage. Large differences between the weekly actual manpower and the amount planned for the following week can indicate lack of manpower or lack of work.

ENGINEERING MANFORCE REPORT

REPORT NO. _____   PROJECT _____

PERIOD _____   JOB NO. _____

SECTION	ACTUAL THIS PERIOD	PLANNED NEXT PERIOD	MAN DAYS LOST LAST PERIOD DUE TO			COMMENTS
			VACATION	SICK	OTHER	
SUPERVISION & COORDINATION						
PROJECT MANAGEMENT						
PROJECT CONTROL						
ENGINEERING DISCIPLINES						
TOTAL						
CUMULATIVE TOTAL						

Figure 5.13 Engineering workforce report.

5.15 ENGINEERING MATERIAL REQUISITION CURVE

Following process design, plot layouts, and engineering specifications, the requisitioning of equipment would normally be the critical path. Plotting the actual issue of requisitions against time can provide an excellent overview of the work.

Figure 5.14 shows a typical engineering material requisition control curve together with tabulated data. The table may be more detailed than shown, categorizing requisition by code of account or discipline. This example shows actual issues to be significantly behind the planned curve. If the planned curve has been drawn from the detailed engineering schedule, this situation could be serious, requiring further investigation at the detailed level.

The curves represent the planned and actual issues of material requisitions from the engineering department to the procurement department. The procurement department will require another 2-4 weeks to add the commercial sections and issue the completed inquiry package. A curve representing the later issue is shown in the procurement section.

The number of requisitions approved by engineering for purchase may also be tracked. This curve would normally be 3-4 months later than the inquiry curve.

As early as possible, the total number of requisitions should be estimated and then updated as engineering progresses.

These curves are key documents in evaluating the progress of the engineering-purchasing cycle.

Delay in issuing material requisitions can result in late ordering and corresponding late delivery of materials and equipment to the job site. Feedback of the vendor's information into engineering is also affected, which in turn can delay the engineering program. For these reasons, careful monitoring and control of the material requisition program is essential.

5.16 ENGINEERING TRACKING CURVES

Rates of production of concrete foundation drawings and piping isometrics usually require careful monitoring. Both sections utilize a high proportion of engineering man-hours and are usually critical to the project schedule. Figure 5.15 would be used to monitor concrete and piping drafting progress and productivity; a separate form is used for each.

Productivity curves (upper diagram) record monthly and cumulative values for the average number of man-hours spent per drawing. This information can be used to compare the performance of different projects. The histograms (center diagram) indicate the planned and actual

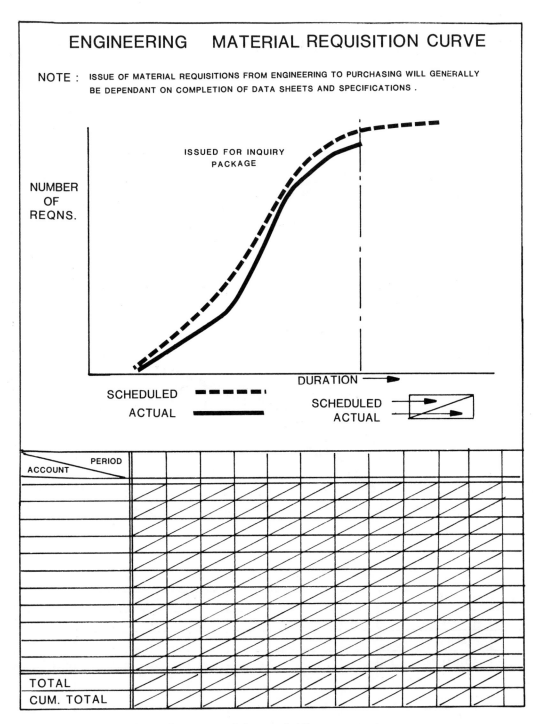

Figure 5.14 Engineering material requisition curve.

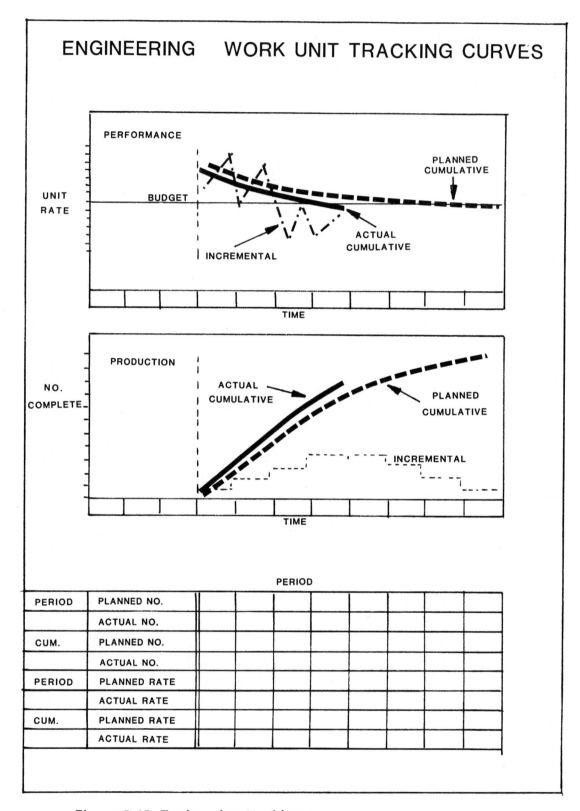

Figure 5.15 Engineering tracking curve.

numbers of drawings issued each month. Cumulative totals are also plotted. Statistical data are tabulated at the bottom of the form.

This technique can be used for any significant element of work. During critical periods, the frequency of monitoring would be increased from monthly to biweekly or weekly as necessary.

5.17 PIPING DESIGN ACTIVITIES AND PROGRESS CURVE

As piping design is often the critical path, detailed schedules and programs should be developed for piping work. Figure 5.16 is one such example. Manpower resources should be applied to the individual activities. Figure 5.16 shows a typical relationship of major piping design activities for a single unit and weights them together for overall progress.

It should be noted that there are two design philosophies for a plant model:

Model built first; then isometrics drawn from model
Isometrics drawn first; then model built to check isometrics

This schedule shows the model being used to draw piping isometrics.

As projects can vary considerably in their process design, plot layouts, and detailed engineering philosophies, this typical schedule should be adjusted for specific project circumstances.

Specific project schedules should be drawn against a calendar base. This typical schedule is based on return data and can therefore be used to develop a specific project schedule.

5.18 VENDOR DRAWING CONTROL

A significant element of the engineering schedule is the timing of vendor drawings. Foundation design and piping design depend on vendor drawings for details of foundation bolts, bearing loads, nozzle orientation, pressure, and capacity data.

An effective vendor drawing control system is essential for planning and scheduling engineering work. A bid tab evaluation should cover the issue of vendor drawings, and the successful vendor should be monitored thereafter to ensure compliance with promised or "need" dates. This is particularly necessary for critical vendor drawings.

A vendor material expediting program should also cover the supply and issue of vendor drawings. Schedule engineers should coordinate this effort with the expediting department.

Figure 5.17 shows a typical format for control of critical vendor drawings. The same format can be used for all vendor drawings; however, critical drawings should be identified separately. Vendor drawing control is sometimes the responsibility of the procurement department.

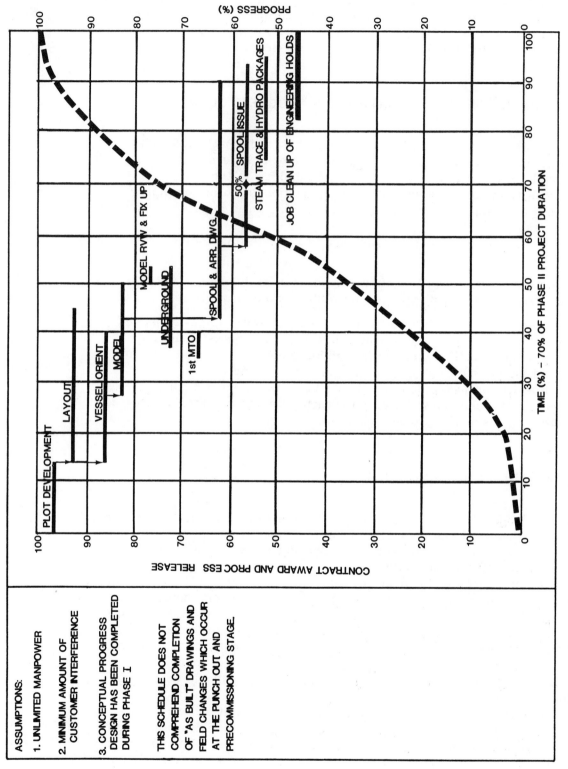

Figure 5.16 Standard piping design schedule.

DATE			CRITICAL VENDOR DRAWING LIST		PROJECT			
P.O. NO	EQUIPMENT	VENDOR	VENDOR DRAWING	FOR APPROVAL			FINAL	
				REQ'D	REC'D	RET'D	REQ'D	REC'D

Figure 5.17 Critical vendor drawing list.

5.19 PROCUREMENT SCHEDULING, OVERALL

Major elements for effective scheduling of purchasing work are an accurate material requisition list, a purchase order schedule, and a viable contracting strategy for commitment of all materials.

Figure 5.18 is a flowchart of a typical procurement scheduling system. This flowchart is an abstract from the flowchart of the typical contractor's planning and scheduling system. It shows methods by which effective control can be exercised.

It is important that the procurement operation be functional immediately after contract award, with personnel assigned to concentrate on the following:

Purchasing plan for critical material
General buying strategy and purchasing procedure
    (worldwide purchasing and use of overseas satellite offices)
Vendor lists and document control
Bid tab procedure—contractor and owner
Subcontract strategy and control procedures

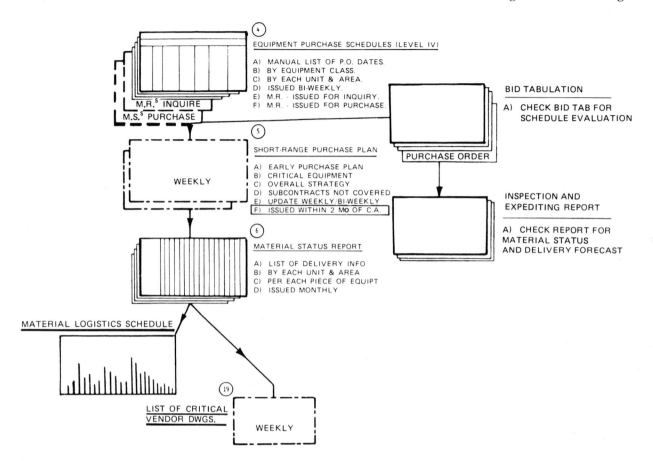

Figure 5.18 Flowchart of procurement scheduling.

Inquiry and purchase order control procedures
Lead times for material delivery durations
Engineering-procurement cycle

The schedule engineer, in conjunction with project purchasing manager, should establish an implementation plan for the preceding items and other items as deemed necessary. The plan should include manpower allocations and completion dates to accomplish the work.

Activities making up the engineering-procurement cycle should be agreed upon with the owner at a very early date so that overall scheduling may have a realistic time for this operation. Owner approval requirements should be carefully evaluated.

Reference to the flowchart shows the following procurement requirements:

1. Equipment purchase schedules (level IV)
2. Material requisition curves for inquiry and purchase
3. Short-range purchase plan

4. Material status report
5. List of critical vendor drawings
6. Material logistics schedule

Schedule commitments should be obtained from the purchasing group as the timing of material and equipment requirements becomes known. The commitment should cover the placement of purchase orders and associated lead times for delivery of material.

5.20 EQUIPMENT PURCHASE SCHEDULES

Equipment purchase schedules can be computer-based or manual schedules. Detailed activities from requisition to purchase order commitment and corresponding dates should be listed.

See the owner standard schedule, Figure 3.18, for details of typical activities and durations. The purchasing schedule tends to be a very large document, requiring considerable research to check out status and criticality.

It is vital that the purchasing schedule be current and up-to-date as the status of equipment purchasing is essential to the evaluation of criticality.

5.21 PURCHASING MATERIAL REQUISITION CURVES

On large projects, visibility of the overall purchasing effort is helpful for quickly determining status and performance effectiveness. This can be achieved with the use of requisition curves. The curves in Figure 5.19 represent the number of requisitions issued for quotation and purchase. The purchase curve should normally follow the quotation curve by 8-12 weeks.

Planned curves are developed from front end engineering schedules and the overall network program.

Several engineering requisitions may be combined into one purchasing inquiry and vice versa; one engineering requisition may be split into several purchase orders. The engineering requisition total may include requisitions used to generate *labor-only* packages. They would not appear in the purchasing requisition total and should be dealt with separately, as per the subcontract procedure.

Purchasing curves are sometimes plotted against monetary value instead of number of orders placed. The front portion of a monetary curve is steeper than a cruve based on numbers due to the high value of early equipment orders.

The tabulated data should cover only requisitions issued for purchase. The tracking of material requisitions through engineering

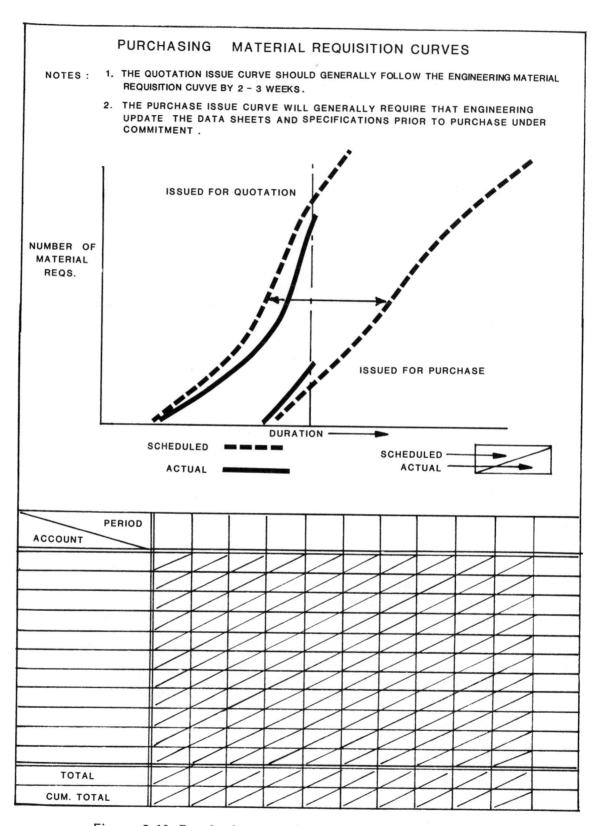

Figure 5.19 Purchasing material requisition curves.

and purchasing can provide a meaningful assessment of the status of the engineering-purchasing program.

As there can be many reasons for slippage, detailed analysis will be necessary to pinpoint specific cause.

5.22 SHORT-RANGE PURCHASE PLAN

The short-range purchase plan requires simple documentation, easily outlining short-term plans for critical and long-lead equipment. It is suggested that this program cover 2 weeks and show equipment items to be committed in this period.

At critical purchasing periods, weekly owner-contractor meetings should be held to determine the status and the need for additional action. Project managers should attend these meetings.

5.23 MATERIAL STATUS REPORT

Like the purchasing schedule, the material status report (MSR) is voluminous. Special abstracts and summary information are essential for effective control.

The important information of the MSR is the anticipated date of delivery of equipment to the job site.

5.24 BID TABULATION

Bid tabulations should include schedule evaluations. The schedule engineer should check all quotes and provide a comprehensive schedule evaluation.

On occasion, the schedule is more important than the cost, and the schedule evaluation should then reflect the sensitivity and probability of quoted delivery dates. Evaluation should also cover the issue of vendor drawings.

When equipment delivery is critical, the schedule engineer should participate in vendor review meetings to check out schedule detailes with vendors.

5.25 INSPECTION AND EXPEDITING REPORTS

Inspection and expediting reports should be passed through schedule engineers to check on the status of critical equipment and trends of general equipment deliveries.

As required, schedule engineers should visit vendor shops during manufacture to check on status, especially that of critical equipment.

5.26 MATERIAL LOGISTICS SCHEDULE

On very large projects in remote locations, material logistics are a major problem. It is essential that material tonnage histograms be prepared and evaluated against the capacity of proposed handling and unloading facilities. This technique is described in Section 3.3. Figure 5.20 is drawn by taking material and equipment weights from the estimate and placing them against the schedule on-site delivery dates. As a detailed estimate and schedule are not normally available until 30% of project time, early detailed evaluations will require special handling and may be based only on historical experience.

5.27 CONSTRUCTION SCHEDULING, OVERALL

Major elements of an effective construction scheduling operation are the following:

Quantity-based field budgets
Detailed weekly work program
Physical measurement system, based on quantities
Productivity measurement system
Good overall schedule (bar charts and network program)

At the start of a project the construction group is often slow in carrying out detailed construction investigations. Their precontract work for the estimate proposal is often limited to statistical man-hour-indirect relationships and a standard approach for the construction execution plan.

Figure 5.21 is a flowchart of a typical construction scheduling system. This flowchart is an abstract of the flowchart of the typical contractor planning and scheduling system. It shows methods by which effective control can be exercised.

5.28 CONSTRUCTION PREPLANNING

Preplanning for construction at the early stages of a project is most important. At this early stage, detailed planning is restricted by lack of scope definition. However, there are areas where preplanning can be effective: for example, work accessibility, traffic patterns, laydown areas, rigging studies, preassembly and modularization, material selection, temporary facilities, and many other interdependent activities which require early attention.

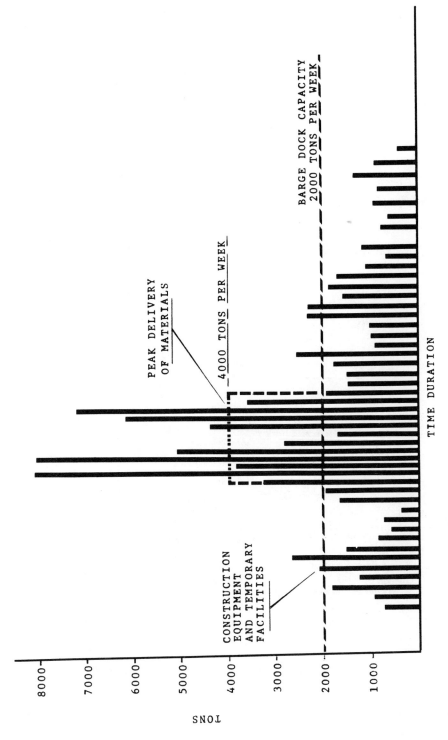

Figure 5.20   Material logistics and tonnage histogram.

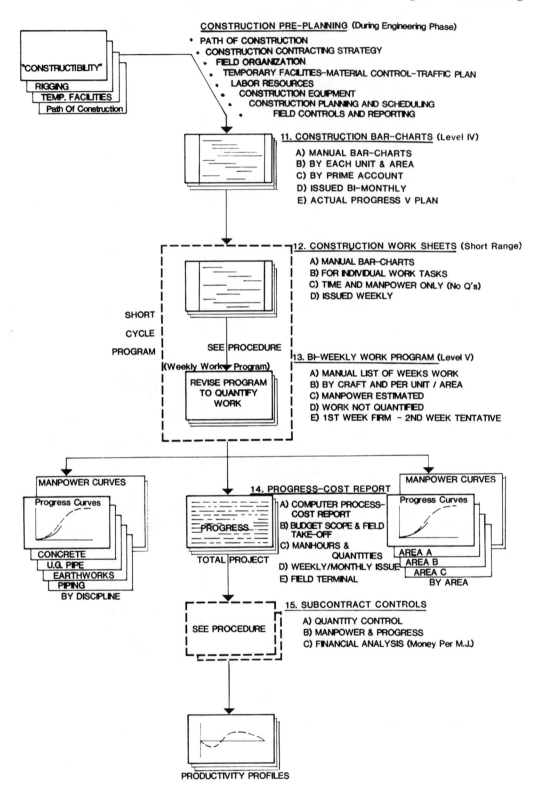

CONSTRUCTION PRE-PLANNING (During Engineering Phase)
- PATH OF CONSTRUCTION
- CONSTRUCTION CONTRACTING STRATEGY
  - FIELD ORGANIZATION
  - TEMPORARY FACILITIES-MATERIAL CONTROL-TRAFFIC PLAN
  - LABOR RESOURCES
    - CONSTRUCTION EQUIPMENT
      - CONSTRUCTION PLANNING AND SCHEDULING
        - FIELD CONTROLS AND REPORTING

"CONSTRUCTIBILITY"
RIGGING
TEMP. FACILITIES
Path Of Construction

11. CONSTRUCTION BAR-CHARTS (Level IV)
A) MANUAL BAR-CHARTS
B) BY EACH UNIT & AREA
C) BY PRIME ACCOUNT
D) ISSUED BI-MONTHLY
E) ACTUAL PROGRESS V PLAN

12. CONSTRUCTION WORK SHEETS (Short Range)
A) MANUAL BAR-CHARTS
B) FOR INDIVIDUAL WORK TASKS
C) TIME AND MANPOWER ONLY (No Q's)
D) ISSUED WEEKLY

SHORT
CYCLE
PROGRAM

SEE PROCEDURE

(Weekly Work Program)

REVISE PROGRAM
TO QUANTIFY
WORK

13. BI-WEEKLY WORK PROGRAM (Level V)
A) MANUAL LIST OF WEEKS WORK
B) BY CRAFT AND PER UNIT / AREA
C) MANPOWER ESTIMATED
D) WORK NOT QUANTIFIED
E) 1ST WEEK FIRM - 2ND WEEK TENTATIVE

MANPOWER CURVES
Progress Curves
CONCRETE
U.G. PIPE
EARTHWORKS
PIPING
BY DISCIPLINE

14. PROGRESS-COST REPORT
PROGRESS
TOTAL PROJECT
A) COMPUTER PROCESS-COST REPORT
B) BUDGET SCOPE & FIELD TAKE-OFF
C) MANHOURS & QUANTITIES
D) WEEKLY/MONTHLY ISSUE
E) FIELD TERMINAL

MANPOWER CURVES
Progress Curves
AREA A
AREA B
AREA C
BY AREA

15. SUBCONTRACT CONTROLS
SEE PROCEDURE
A) QUANTITY CONTROL
B) MANPOWER & PROGRESS
C) FINANCIAL ANALYSIS (Money Per M.J.)

PRODUCTIVITY PROFILES

Figure 5.21 Flowchart of construction scheduling.

A *path of construction* should be developed as early as possible. It will outline the major elements of the construction program from site preparation to pipe erection on an area and subarea basis.

The schedule engineer, in conjunction with owner personnel, should establish priorities for the early and critical construction work, e.g.,

Path of construction (earthwork-concrete-mechanical-piping)
Construction organization-personnel assignments
Detailed layouts for temporary facilities
Labor resource studies-training programs
Labor productivity evaluations and control method
Material handling-logistics studies
Site survey-soil report
Construction equipment requirements
Rigging studies
Construction permits—environmental matters
Site preparation and early fieldwork
Subcontract strategy
Field control procedures
Construction planning and scheduling
Site regulations
Labor contracts and site agreements

5.29 CONSTRUCTION PROGRESS BAR CHARTS

A major method for illustrating construction progress is a bar chart, manually prepared. The bar chart is the traditional technique for adding together progress requirements and achievements of individual areas.

Figure 5.22 shows a construction progress bar chart—process units. It is a typical bar chart used to monitor progress and to evaluate progress requirements which can be used to develop construction control curve (see Figure 5.27). In this example, progress figures for two process units and off sites are combined to determine total planned progress and job status.

Total job progress is computed by aggregating the weighted percentage completion for each process unit and total off site. Weighted percentage completion is a product of the weight and percentage completion for each barline. Weighting is based on budgeted man-hours. The total job progress values obtained are then used to develop the overall project curve. In this particular example, the barlines have been revised to indicate completion 2 months later than originally scheduled. The status of each section is indicated by the position of the progress barline relative to the vertical report dateline.

Percentage requirements for lower-level work activities are generally developed by judgment. Total job progress is the addition, on a weighted basis, of individual lower-level activity progress figures.

Figure 5.22 Construction progress bar chart—process units. O, original, scheduled, numerical percentage; R, revised, scheduled, numerical percentage; A, actual performance (bar versus revised schedule); N, actual numerical percentage; arrow indicates report date.

ITEM	WEIGHT		JAN	FEB	MAR	APR	MAY	JUN	JUL	AUG	SEP	OCT	NOV	DEC	JAN	FEB	MAR	APR	MAY	JUN	JUL	AUG
TOTAL JOB	100	O	31.9	39.4	47.2	53.6	60.4	67.2	73.8	80.3	86	91.1	94.7	97.1	98.6	99.4	99.9	100				
		R	20.2	25.5	31.9	39.4	47.2	53.6	60.4	67.2	73.8	80.3	86	91.1	94.7	97.1	98.6	99.4	99.9	100		
		A	21.5	25.8	30.9	36.9																
		N																				
VACUUM UNIT	35	O	29.7	36.3	44	51.9	60.7	69.4	77.9	85.6	92.2	97	99.3	100								
		R	18.9	24.0	29.7	36.3	44	51.9	60.7	69.4	77.9	85.6	92.2	97	99.3	100						
		A	19.0	24.0	30.0	36.3																
		N																				
FCC UNIT	50	O	34.6	42.3	49.8	55.3	61.1	66.7	72.1	77.6	82.7	87.6	91.6	95.0	97.4	98.9	99.9	100				
		R	22.3	28.2	34.6	42.3	49.8	55.3	61.1	66.7	72.1	77.6	82.7	87.6	91.6	95.0	97.4	98.9	99.9	100		
		A	23.0	26.0	30	34.6																
		N																				
OFF SITES	15	O	28.1	36.8	45.8	51.6	57.5	63.4	69.9	77.1	83.1	89.1	94.4	97.3	99.4	99.8	100					
		R	16.3	20.1	28.1	36.8	45.8	51.6	57.5	63.4	69.9	77.1	83.1	89.1	94.4	97.3	99.4	99.8	100			
		A	22.0	29.0	36.0	45.8																
		N																				

Dependent on level of detail, overall progress can generally be checked or verified with historical experience. It would be unlikely that historical experience could be used for lower-level activities, such as shown in Figure 5.23, construction progress bar chart—work category. This bar chart format is applicable to the scheduling of construction activities by work category in geographic areas. The mechanical erection of an equipment account is shown in this illustration. In addition to a relative weight breakdown, activities are defined by quantities and man-hours. This chart also tracks scope definition as quantities and/or man-hours are revised during field operations. This example shows the work ahead of schedule with overall progress at 37.8% versus a plan of 30%.

5.30 CONSTRUCTION WORK SHEETS (90-DAY SCHEDULE)

Construction work sheets (90-day schedule) should be manual schedules, covering a 2-3 month period of the network program but expanded and modified to show current requirements for the period. The bar charts would show detailed activities, duration, and manpower requirements. Quantities would not normally be shown, as quantities should be used only when the program is about 80% firm. This would be the case with a weekly work program, where use of quantities is essential.

It is important that this "slice" of the detailed network program be updated to reflect changed circumstances and current requirements. Major changes may require an update of the detailed network program.

5.31 CONSTRUCTION WEEKLY WORK PROGRAM

A key element of a successful construction operation, particularly of a large project, is the quality of the short-cycle work program.

Experience to date has clearly indicated that a manually prepared weekly work program, with a 2-4 week look ahead, supported by an overall schedule and detailed estimate, is the most efficient method. It readily adapts to a dynamic construction environment where priorities, man-hour content, site conditions, resources, and weather can change very rapidly.

The essential requirement of a quality short-cycle work program is identifying and itemizing specific pieces of work with the following:

Quantities of measurable units
Application of budgeted unit man-hour rates
Adjustment for current productivity
Manpower assessment
Planning of extra work and rework (man-hours and manpower)
Reconciliation of weekly program to overall plan

CONSTRUCTION PROGRESS BAR CHART – WORK CATEGORY

CODE	DESCRIPTION	WT. OF HRS.	QUANTITIES UNIT	QUANTITIES ORIG. / REVIS.	MANHOURS ORIG. / REVIS.	MANHOURS PERIOD	MANHOURS CUM.	PROGRESS TO DATE ACTUAL %	PROGRESS TO DATE WT. %
	VERTICAL VESSEL	3.8	KG	53,200	500	140	232	94.2	3.6
	HORIZONTAL VESSEL	5.3		70,000	700	60	60	25.0	1.3
	TRAYS FOR D153	1.8		2,500	250				
	DRUM INTERVALS	0.1		500	20				
	FIN FANS	13.8		53,300	1,800	560	560	48.4	6.7
	PUMPS	4.6		11,500	600				
	COMPRESSORS	7.7		15,000	1,000				
	HEATERS	4.6		80,000	600	345	666	100	4.6
	HEAVY STEEL	4.3		23,300	580	258	500	59.8	2.5
	LIGHT STEEL	4.2		10,000	550	223	223	58.1	2.4
	MISC.	1.2		3,000	150				
	ELECT. EQUIP.	4.6		42,500	600				
	OVERALL	56	KG	364,800	7,350	1,586	2,241	37.8	21.2

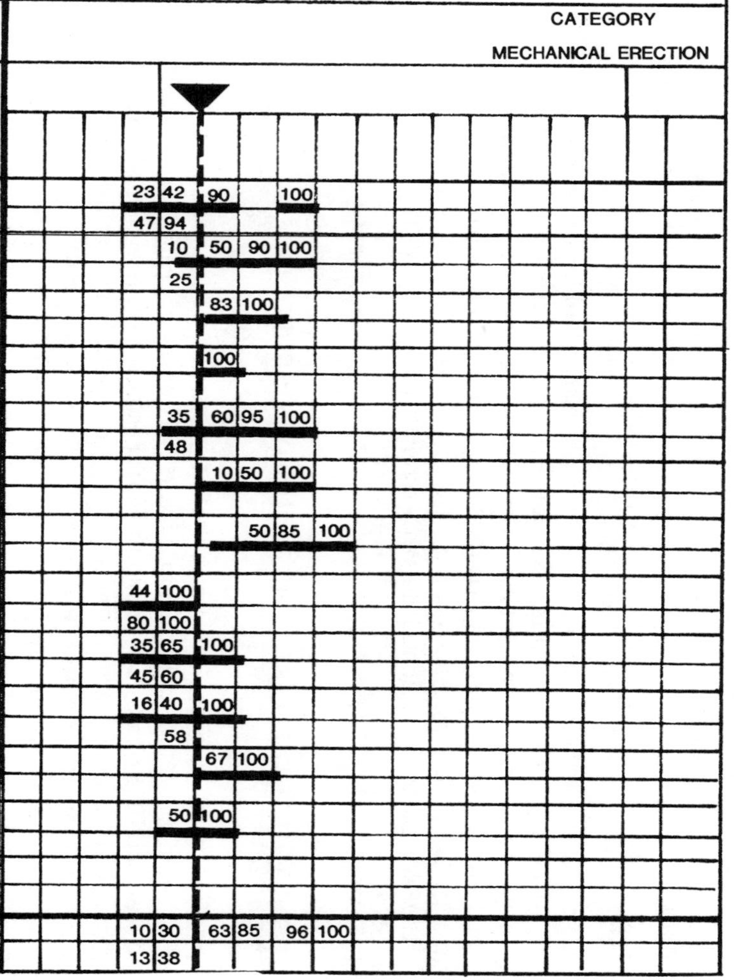

CATEGORY: MECHANICAL ERECTION

PROJECT / JOB NO. / REPORT NO. / DATE

Figure 5.23 Construction progress bar chart—work category.

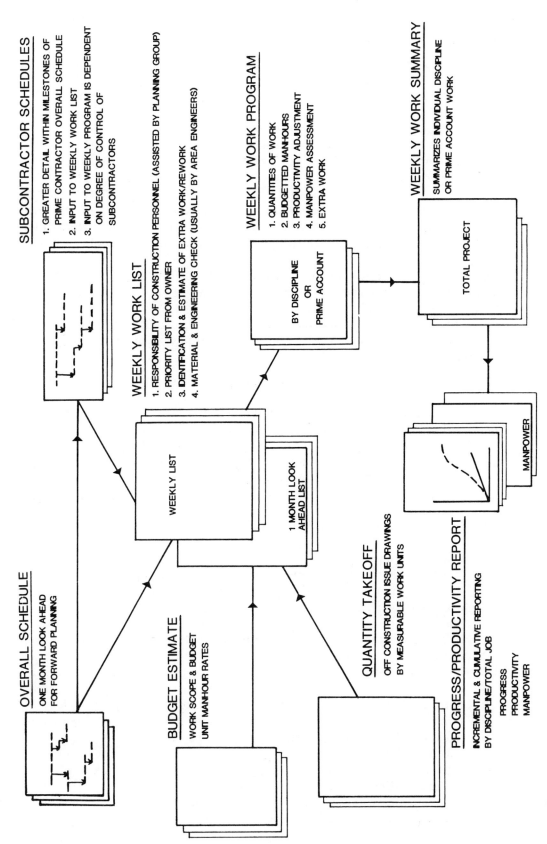

SUBCONTRACTOR SCHEDULES

1. GREATER DETAIL WITHIN MILESTONES OF PRIME CONTRACTOR OVERALL SCHEDULE
2. INPUT TO WEEKLY WORK LIST
3. INPUT TO WEEKLY PROGRAM IS DEPENDENT ON DEGREE OF CONTROL OF SUBCONTRACTORS

WEEKLY WORK LIST

1. RESPONSIBILITY OF CONSTRUCTION PERSONNEL (ASSISTED BY PLANNING GROUP)
2. PRIORITY LIST FROM OWNER
3. IDENTIFICATION & ESTIMATE OF EXTRA WORK/REWORK
4. MATERIAL & ENGINEERING CHECK (USUALLY BY AREA ENGINEERS)

WEEKLY WORK PROGRAM

1. QUANTITES OF WORK
2. BUDGETTED MANHOURS
3. PRODUCTIVITY ADJUSTMENT
4. MANPOWER ASSESSMENT
5. EXTRA WORK

WEEKLY WORK SUMMARY

SUMMARIZES INDIVIDUAL DISCIPLINE OR PRIME ACCOUNT WORK

OVERALL SCHEDULE

ONE MONTH LOOK AHEAD FOR FORWARD PLANNING

BUDGET ESTIMATE

WORK SCOPE & BUDGET UNIT MANHOUR RATES

QUANTITY TAKEOFF

OFF CONSTRUCTION ISSUE DRAWINGS BY MEASURABLE WORK UNITS

PROGRESS/PRODUCTIVITY REPORT

INCREMENTAL & CUMULATIVE REPORTING BY DISCIPLINE/TOTAL JOB

PROGRESS
PRODUCTIVITY
MANPOWER

WEEKLY LIST

1 MONTH LOOK AHEAD LIST

BY DISCIPLINE OR PRIME ACCOUNT

TOTAL PROJECT

MANPOWER

Figure 5.24   Flowchart of construction weekly work program.

The flowchart in Figure 5.24 shows the elements of a typical weekly work program and the flow of information starting with the overall schedule for the month's work, the budget estimate for the work in labor unit man-hours, together with quantity takeoff sheets for detailed scope.

Work lists are then drawn up, usually by construction personnel (assisted by the field planning group) who then ensure that material and engineering drawings are available.

The look-ahead list will be in less detail than the current week's program, and a good system will define 80% work for the second week, 60% work for the third week, and 40% work for the fourth week.

Control of subcontractor work can vary greatly according to contractual agreements, the execution plan, and the capability of the subcontractors. Subcontractors can be controlled on a milestone schedule and manpower basis alone or fully incorporated into the weekly work program.

The field planning group will work with the work list to evaluate required man-hours and manpower and to coordinate prime contractor direct-hire work and subcontract work.

Figure 5.25 is a typical format for a weekly work program. The following explanations refer to the use and function of each column as numbered:

1. Check that all engineering information is available for scheduled work.
2. Check that all material is available for scheduled work.
3. Abbreviated description of work item.
4. Total quantities of measurable units for work item.
5. Budget man-hour rate for this piece of work.
6. Quantities of measurable units for work planned for week.
7. Budgeted man-hours for the planned weekly work. It is obtained by multiplying column 6 by column 5.
8. Extra work and/or rework: Many times, rework has no measurable quantities or man-hour rates. In such cases, the work should be estimated and the man-hours entered in column 8. This is necessary so that a proper manpower assessment can be made.
9. Remarks on priority, constraints, resource requirements, and crew sizes are appropriate. Some contractors use this section to plan by individual day and specify the crew size for each task. Experience shows that this detail is best handled at the foreman level.
10. Planning reconciliation: When the weekly program has been calculated and finalized, it is meaningful to compare the projected output of the weekly program against the overall progress requirement. This should be done for the incremental (weekly) period and for the overall cumulative requirement. The reconciliation can be done at the discipline or prime account level.
11. This number will be total budgeted man-hours for work which has quantities and man-hour rates.
12. This number will be total man-hours for work which cannot be identified with quantities and man-hour rates.

WEEKLY WORK PROGRAM

PROJECT

JOB NO.

REPORT NO.

DATE

WORK CATEGORY

17	TOTAL FORECAST MANHOURS

STATUS		WORK ITEM	SCOPE			THIS PERIOD		EXTRA WORK	REMARKS
ENG.	MATL.		QUANT.	BUDGET RATE		QUANT.	BUDGET HOURS		
1	2	3	4	5		6	7	8	9

PLANNING RECONCILIATION	10		
1. WEEKLY PLAN	%	BUDGETED WEEKLY PROGRAM	11
2. WEEKLY PROGRAM	%	CURRENT PRODUCTIVITY ADJUSTMENT	12
3. PLANNED CUMULATIVE	%	13	% 14
4. ACTUAL CUMULATIVE	%	TOTAL WEEKLY PROGRAM	15

MANPOWER	
WORK TEAM	HRS.
TOTAL MEN	16

Figure 5.25 Construction weekly work program format.

13. It is probable that current productivity will always differ from the productivity level used in the budget unit rate. If the difference is significant, budgeted work (11) should be adjusted to reflect current experience (13).

14. This is the total man-hours required to do the budgeted work after adjusting for current productivity; i.e., 11(13) = 14.

15. Total man-hours required for budgeted work plus extra work; i.e., 15 = 12 + 14. This number is used to calculate the manpower requirements.

16. The manpower assessment, arrived at by dividing the total planned man-hours by the work week in hours. A statistical craft breakdown is then applied to the total manpower figure to arrive at the number of workers by craft.

17. This is the total forecasted man-hours for the discipline or prime account and is required to calculate the weekly program in terms of percent complete; i.e., weekly program % = 15/17.

Note. When manpower is a restraint, either not available or fixed due to a lack of accommodation or saturation, then the calculation process is worked backwards.

Figure 5.26 is a weekly work summary. This document summarizes individual discipline or prime account programs. Planned manhours and total manpower are the same numbers shown on individual work programs marked 15 and 16. The draft breakdown is derived by applying a historical labor standard for appropriate discipline or prime account.

The planning reconciliation provides for evaluation of the weekly program against the overall weekly planned requirement shown on the overall progress curve. Further analysis of manpower and productivity levels of the weekly program versus the overall planned requirement can be made.

5.32 CONSTRUCTION PROGRESS

Curves, as per Figure 5.27, can provide more meaningful analysis of progress than the percentage lines of a construction progress bar chart. Deviations are more recognizable, and trends or recovery plans can be determined more easily.

The planned curve can be determined by judgment, historical experience, and the bar chart evaluation. The best procedure is to use the bar chart evaluation and then use a historical-based standard as a check.

5.32.1 Construction Progress Measurement and Reporting

There are two essential requirements for effective monitoring of a construction program: a quality schedule of critical activities and accurate measurement of construction progress.

WEEKLY WORK SUMMARY

SITE MANAGER _____

WEEK NO. _____
DATE ___ ___ ___

DISCIPLINE OR PRIME ACCOUNT	PLANNED M/HR.	TOTAL MAN-POWER	L	C	P/F	R	W	M/W	I/F	E		
1												
2												
3												
4												
5												
6												
7												
8												
9												
10												
11												
12												
TOTAL												

PLANNED RECONCILIATION

1. WEEKLY PLAN   %
2. WEEKLY PROGRAM   %

TOTAL FORECASTED MANHOUR

3. PLANNED CUMULATIVE   %
4. ACTUAL CUMULATIVE   %
   (LAST PERIOD)

REMARKS:

Figure 5.26 Construction weekly work program summary.

Construction progress control is achieved by closely monitoring progress against a comprehensive set of scheduled construction S curves for each *control area,* as previously outlined.

Engineering work and the initial estimate are normally structured by system, whereas construction is supervised and controlled by area. This will require that the initial estimate be restructured to an area basis prior to the start of construction. This will require careful consideration, as too many areas will be cumbersome and costly, whereas too few may not provide sufficient detail for control of a large project.

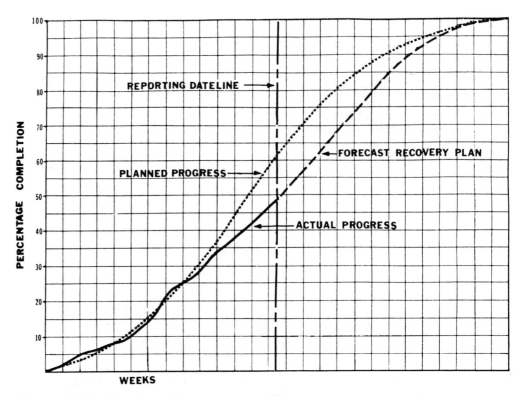

Figure 5.27 Construction progress (S) curve.

There are several techniques for measuring and reporting construction progress. These techniques are usually variations of two basic approaches:

1. Measurement of physical quantities
2. Man-hour assessment

The physical quantity measurement is the preferred method.

Physical Quantity Measurement

Construction progress can be expressed simply as

$$\frac{\text{Physical quantities installed}}{\text{Total scope (quantities) of project}} \times 100\%$$

At the beginning of construction, quantities are often not sufficiently defined to be used as a proper basis for field progress measurement. Budget man-hours should be used until field quantity takeoffs from construction issue drawings are available. This is a developing process, and good judgment is essential to provide a meaningful man-hour budget until quantity takeoffs are completed.

Figure 5.28 shows a typical overall progress report. It lists major accounts and shows man-hours, percent complete, and productivity and forecasts final man-hours. Each prime account is assigned a weighting, shown in column 4, based on the man-hours allocated in the construction budget, column 3.

CODE	ACCOUNT	BUDGET HOURS*	WEIGHT %	% COMPLETE		EARNED HOURS (3+5)	ACTUAL HOURS	PROD'Y $\frac{7}{8} \times 100$	FORECAST $\frac{3}{9}$
				ACCOUNT	PROJECT (4+5)				
1		3		5	6	7	8	9	10
100	CIVIL	440	20	50	10	220	200	110	400
200	STEELWORK	100	4	20	0.8	20	16	125	80
300	MECHANICAL	200	11	10	1.1	20	22	90.9	220
400	PIPING	600	33	5	1.6	30	34	88.2	680
500	ELECTRICAL	160	7						140
600	INSTRUMENTS	200	10						200
700	INSULATION	220	11						220
800	PAINTING	80	4						80
	TOTAL PROJECT	2000	100	–	13.5	290	272	106.6	2040

PROGRESS SUMMARY REPORT

(× 1000)

* BASED ON BUDGET OR FORECAST

PROJECT
JOB NO.
REPORT NO.
PERIOD

Figure 5.28 Construction progress summary.

Each account is further broken down into measurable quantities of work which are given a weight based on the estimated man-hours to install:

Prime Account: 1000—Civil	Cubic Yards (1)	Weight % (2)	% Complete (3)	Weighted % Complete (4)
Foundation for C102	8	20	100	20
Foundation for D104	4	10	50	5
Foundation for P101	2	5	100	5
Foundation for P102	2	5	—	—
Foundation for P103	4	10	—	—
Pipe rack foundations	20	50	40	20
Total account				50

Planned construction S curves are worked up for every area, and an overall construction S curve is developed by combining S curves of each area, based on the weightings of the man-hour budget.

During construction, the total scope forecast can change due to better definition, extra work orders, changes, etc. When scope changes are sufficiently large, a reweighting of construction activities may be necessary.

The percentage completion of each prime account is calculated by totaling the weighted percentages in column 4 of the preceding table. This total is used in column 5 of the summary report to calculate the overall project completion.

The level of detail of quantity measurement and progress reporting varies according to the contractor's work measurement system, the type of contract, and whether construction is subcontract or direct hire.

Man-hour Measurement

By using the man-hour measurement approach, construction progress is expressed as

$$\frac{\text{Man-hours expended}}{\text{Budget man-hours}} \times \text{Efficiency factor} \times 100\%$$

The efficiency-productivity factor in this instance is determined for each category of work by keeping accurate measurements of actual man-hours expended for each unit of work and comparing these with budgeted unit rates. This method can be effective if budget additions and productivity are reflected in the forecast of man-hours.

General Comments

Regardless of the approach used, personnel should be alert to over-booking of progress early in the project. This can be done in a variety of ways, such as giving artificially high weighting to front end activities and making inadequate allowances for back end cleanup work, etc. Extra work orders generated during construction also have the effect of making initial progress assessments artificially high.

5.32.2 Guide to Field Progress Reporting

An accurate assessment of work in progress is essential to get a true picture of progress completion. Good judgment is required to assess the status of part-completed work. This guide covers major categories of work. Each prime account is listed, and work items are broken down into major tasks with recommended percents for completion of the work.

I.   Site preparation and earthwork: report by percent of total cubic yards involved.

II. Earth tank pads
    A. Percent of compacted earth in place   85%
    B. Final dressing   100%

III. Concrete
    A. Report by percent of total cubic yards involved with the following allowances:

1. Rebar in place	20%	(20)
2. Forming complete	70%	(50)
3. Concrete poured	80%	(10)
4. Stripping complete	95%	(15)
5. Dressed and patched	100%	(5)

    B. Piles: report by number in place as percent of total required.
    C. Paving: report by square feet installed against total square feet required.
    D. *Sewers and manholes* (prefabricated)

1. Manholes and catch basins installed by count to	65%	(65)
2. Hookup and connections complete by count	90%	(25)
3. Test and checkout complete by count	100%	(10)

IV. *Steel structures, piping supports, and miscellaneous steel*
    A. Report by tons erected in place   90%
    B. Bolting tension checked and completed   100%

V.   *Buildings* (excluding foundations)
    A. *Shelter type* (no interior work)

1. Steel erected	50%	(50)
2. Walls and roof complete	90%	(40)
3. Checked out complete	100%	(10)

        B. *Masonry type*

1.	Walls erected	30%	(30)
2.	Roof framing complete	50%	(20)
3.	Doors and windows installed	65%	(15)
4.	Interior complete	100%	(35)

VI. *Equipment installation*

     A. *Columns and vessels*

        1. *Shop-fabricated*, no internals

a. Set in place	60%	(60)
b. Secured and grouted	90%	(30)
c. Tested and bolted up	100%	(10)

        2. *Shop-fabricated*, (with trays or internals

a. Set in place	25%	(25)
b. Secured and grouted	35%	(10)
c. Internals complete	90%	(55)
d. Tested and bolted up	100%	(10)

        3. *Field-fabricated:* report by number of pre-fabricated sections or rings and internals installed. Allow appropriate percent complete for partly completed work elements. See Section 7.11 for typical samples of report weighting and format.

     B. *Storage tanks, field-fabricated:* report by base, number of rings installed, roof, and internals from subcontractor erection schedule. Allow appropriate percent complete for partly completed work elements. See Section 7.11 for typical samples of report weighting and format.

     C. *Exchangers*

        1. *Shell and tube* (per unit)

a. Set in place	60%	(60)
b. Secured and grouted	90%	(30)
c. Tested and accepted	100%	(10)

        2. *Fin—tube* (per unit)

a. Set in place	60%	(60)
b. Secured and grouted	90%	(30)
c. Tested and accepted	100%	(10)

        3. *Fin fans* (per unit)

a. Steel structure erected	20%	(20)
b. Housing erected	30%	(10)
c. Fan and driver assembled	50%	(20)
d. Coils installed	70%	(20)
e. Run-in and fan balance	90%	(20)
f. Tested and accepted	100%	(10)

     D. *Heaters*

        1. *Vertical heater* (package unit)

a. Heater set in place	50%	(50)
b. Stack erected	70%	(20)

    c. Secured and grouted 90% (20)
    d. Tested and accepted 100% (10)
  2. *Heater* (field-assembled)
    a. Substructure complete 20% (20)
    b. Refractory installed 55% (35)
    c. Tubes installed   75% (20)
    d. Stack and breeching 85% (10)
      installed
    e. Burners installed 90% (5)
    f. Tested and accepted 100% (10)
  3. *Pumps and drivers*
    a. Pump set in place 40% (40)
    b. Aligned and grouted 90% (50)
    c. Run in and accepted 100% (10)
E. *Compressors and drivers*
  1. *Package compressor* (with driver)
    a. Set in place   50% (50)
    b. Secured and grouted 90% (40)
    c. Run in and accepted 100% (10)
  2. *Package compressor* (with driver separate)
    a. Compressor in place 25% (25)
    b. Driver in place 50% (25)
    c. Unit coupled and 85% (35)
      aligned
    d. Secured and grouted 90% (5)
    e. Run in and accepted 100% (10)

VII. *Piping*
  A. Percent complete in this account can be reported in the following categories by the method indicated:
    1. Fabricated pipe spools: as completed by count, tons or feet
    2. Pipe spools installed: as installed by count, tons or feet
    3. Straight run racked pipe: report by percent of linear feet installed
    4. Underground lines: report by percent of linear feet installed
    5. Steam tracing: report by percent of linear feet installed
    6. Hangers and supports: as completed by count or percent allowance
    7. Hydrotesting: report by subsystem or by holding back 10% of item 2 for hydrotest and punch list work
  B. The preceding is a simplified piping approach. Many contractors have a more detailed approach to measuring completion of pipe erection:
    1. Handling: lay down to work area, percentage basis

2. 2½-in. diameter and below: by feet, screwed or socket weld, by size
3. 3-in diameter and above: fit up and tack, by size, schedule, and specification
4. Weld out: by cubic inches of weld plus per operation
5. Hydrostatic test: percentage basis or by subsystem
6. Punch out: percentage basis (by judgment)
7. Rework: percentage basis (by judgment)
8. Pipe fabrication, pipe supports, and hangers would be similarly treated.

VIII. *Electrical*
A. Power and control equipment: as installed by count
B. Lighting equipment (pole assemblies): report percent installed by count
C. Underground conduit and duct: report percent of linear feet installed
D. Above-ground conduit (power): report percent of linear feet installed
E. Above-ground conduit (lighting): report percent of linear feet installed
F. Power and control wire: report percent of total feet pulled
G. Power connections: report percent of total complete
H. Grounding: report percent of feet installed
I. Lighting wire: report percent of feet installed
J. Push buttons and receptables: report percent of total installed
K. Communications: report by system complete

IX. *Instrumentation of control panels* (including shop-mounted instruments)
A. Install panels   25%   (25)
B. Hook up and connect   85%   (60)
C. Test and check out   100%   (15)

X. *Instruments and instrument materials*
A. Wire and conduit: percent of linear feet installed
B. Pipe and tubing: percent of linear feet installed
C. Field-mounted instruments: percent installed by count
D. Control and relief valves: percent installed by count
E. Racks and supports: percent of linear feet installed
F. Hookups: as completed by count
G. Loop check: as complete by system

XI. *Insulation*
A. Vessels and towers: percent square feet installed
B. Piping: percent linear feet installed

XII. *Painting*
A. Vessels, tanks, towers, and structural steel: percent square feet installed
B. Piping: percent linear feet covered

There are many different contractor systems for measuring completion of construction work. Good systems will be based on quantities, earned value, and a productivity assessment based on actual man-hours versus earned man-hours.

5.33 CONSTRUCTION STATUS REPORT

Figure 5.29 shows a status report by total project or unit-area. In the top section of this illustration are planned and actual cumulative progress curves. Backup data for these curves would normally be obtained from construction progress bar charts. The center section shows planned and actual cumulative productivity curves. Incremental values for each report period are also shown. The bottom section of this exhibit shows planned and actual cumulative manpower levels.

This report monitors the three major variables of construction performance:

Progress
Productivity
Manpower

It enables an overall evaluation of current status and future predictions to be quickly made. It is an excellent management report as it graphically shows the overall status of the project on one piece of paper.

The planned productivity curve should be determined by reference to the productivity profile guidelines in Section 3.23.

The labor histogram will be prepared from the progress curve and man-hour budget. Appropriate allowances should be made for lost time.

For large projects, detailed labor resource evaluations are essential. The evaluation should cover the following:

Local labor pool
Travelers and imported labor
Local practices and regulations
Housing and transportation
Training requirements
Wage rates and allowances

5.34 WORK UNIT TRACKING CURVES

The installation of concrete foundations and the fabrication and erection of spools are generally critical areas of construction and require careful monitoring, especially during the initial stages. The technique shown in Figure 5.30 is recommended. Figure 5.30 shows work unit tracking curves for concrete foundations and spool erection. Monthly and cumulative man-hours per unit concrete installed, or spools erected, are plotted against budget values. Monthly and cumulative quantities completed are plotted. These production rates can also be

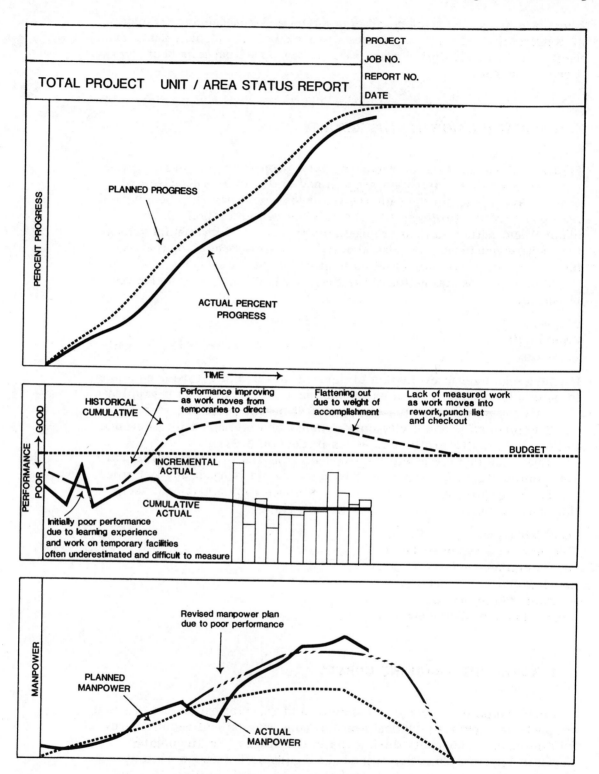

Figure 5.29 Total project unit-area status report.

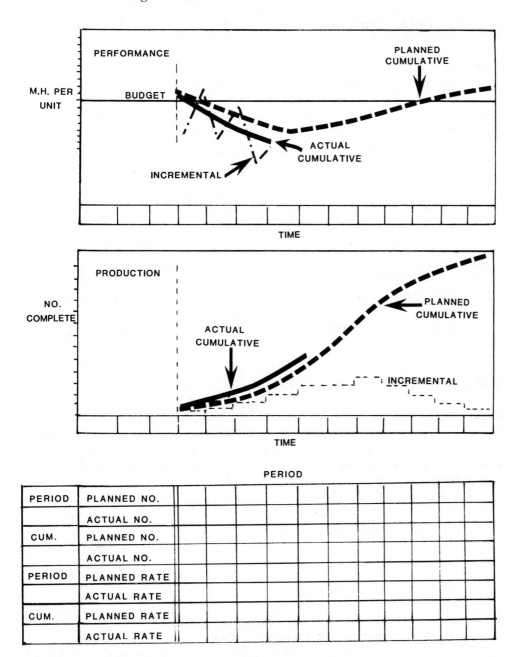

Figure 5.30 Construction work unit tracking curves.

compiled for historical data and used to compare performances of
different projects.

Numerical data for the report period are tabulated at the bottom of
the form. The reporting frequency may be increased from monthly to
biweekly or weekly during the critical periods of control.

This technique can be used for any category of work where installed quantities are easily identified.

5.35 MATERIAL CONTROL

Labor productivity is highly dependent on the efficiency of the field material control system. A major scheduling responsibility is to ensure adequate material supply for the weekly work program. Identification, storage, and issue of materials are the responsibility of field personnel. The tagging and marking of equipment and bulk material and "bagging" of fittings and fixtures are common techniques.

5.36 CONSTRUCTION EQUIPMENT PLANNING

The utilization of construction equipment is dependent on many factors. Good planning is but one of them. Adequate construction preplanning should identify major requirements. Thereafter, the monitoring of numbers of equipment, timing, and effective short-term planning should ensure an adequate supply and proper utilization.

Following are techniques for monitoring construction equipment requirements.

5.36.1 Typical Cost Report (Cranes)

Figure 5.31 shows a typical listing to schedule and monitor construction equipment allocation. All construction equipment, other than small tools, are listed by type and number against a time frame. As cranes are generally the most important item, and they should be separated and individually controlled.

Planned periods should be evaluated against the construction schedule and manpower plan. Numbers and types of equipment should be evaluated against the control budget.

An average crane utilization would be in the 60-70% range.

5.36.2 Overall Cost Analysis

Figure 5.32 shows, graphically, a potential "loss" due to construction equipment requirements being well in excess of those required to support the manpower buildup. The actual requirement is not indicated on this exhibit; it merely shows that mismanagement is probable if the overall monthly equipment cost can be significantly reduced as manpower is increasing. The equipment cost should be compatible with manpower buildup. Equipment buildup should lead manpower buildup so as to ensure labor is not held up at the job site.

Schedule engineers should ensure that the planning and scheduling of construction equipment is compatible with the labor program. This is a difficult task as equipment utilization is variable and dependent on many factors:

EQUIPMENT	SCHEDULE (PLANNED VERSUS ACTUAL)	PURCHASE PRICE OR RENTAL RATE	BUDGET	TO DATE COST	FORCAST PERIOD	FORFCAST COST

PROJECT

JOB NO.

REPORT NO.

DATE

CONSTRUCTION EQUIPMENT COST REPORT

Figure 5.31 Construction equipment list.

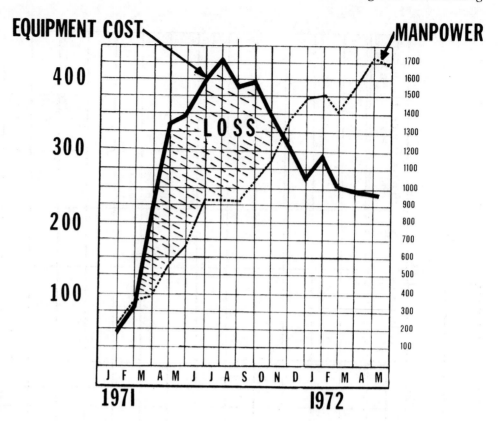

Figure 5.32 Analysis of equipment vs. manpower for boilermakers, pipefitters, and electricians (earthmoving was a subcontract).

Quality of supervision
Size of job site—number of men
Scheduling efficiency
Maintenance capability
Weather

5.36.3 Welding Machine Utilization

Some categories of construction equipment, such as welding machines, have a direct relationship with manpower. Such categories are easily tracked if such tracking is appropriate and required.

Figure 5.33 shows a relationship of number of welding machines to welders. As this is a direct relationship, the oversupply of welding machines was detected and remedial action taken. Welding machines were removed from the job site.

This technique can be used when assessing the schedule for construction equipment. Without additional data the appropriate relationship of welding machines to welders could be 430/340 = 1.26.

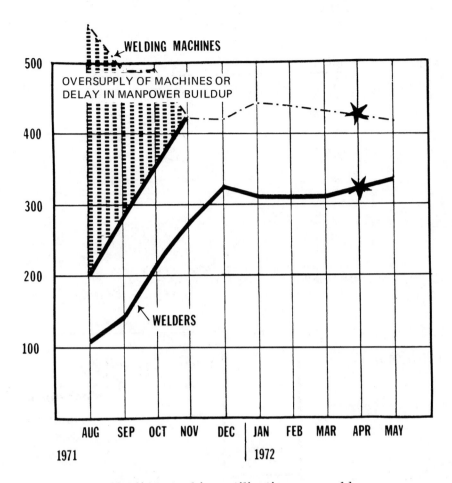

Figure 5.33 Welding machine utilization vs. welders.

5.36.4 Construction Equipment: Time Versus Cost

Construction equipment costs per hour are developed at the job site on an area basis. Here we shall illustrate a large project which has three major control areas: north process, south process, and off sites. Figure 5.34 is a technique to track the total cost per man-hour of construction equipment against time and also to break down the measurement into smaller areas for a greater degree of control. Comparisons of area to area can sometimes be meaningful.

The curve at the bottom of Figure 5.34 shows a typical relationship of overall equipment cost per direct man-hour. This evaluation technique should show an overall reducing hourly cost as direct labor reaches a peak. As labor is run down, the rate will tend to increase— but only slightly if the equipment is efficiently released from the job site. If the rundown rate is the same or higher compared with the buildup rate, then it is probable that equipment is being "held" at the job site. This assumes that an equipment rental agreement has been

CONSTRUCTION - & PER DIRECT HOUR

WEEK ENDING	NORTH	SOUTH	O/S	TOTAL*
21 Dec. 1971	.79	.84	.84	1.19
26 Jan. 1972	.77	.66	.82	1.07
24 Feb.	.74	.61	.76	.91
21 Mar.	.56	.53	.94	.78
25 Apr.	.48	.43	.91	.74
17 May	.49	.35	.64	.69

*Total includes equipment costs for Motor Pool, Central Services, Rigging and other miscellaneous accounts but no hours.

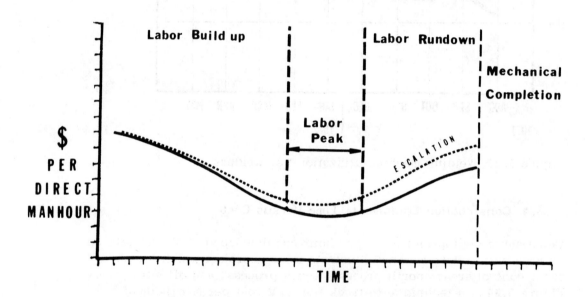

Figure 5.34 Typical equipment cost per man-hour relationship.

reached without escalation for the duration of the project. If escalation is a contractual condition, this should be plotted separately so that one can compare the rundown rate against the buildup rate.

5.37 PIPING CONTROL

As piping erection is usually a major part of construction, an effective control system is essential.

PIPING CONTROL SHEET									REPORT NO. / PERIOD				PROJECT / JOB NO.			
		SIZE - UNIT RATE			SIZE - UNIT RATE			SIZE - UNIT RATE			SIZE - UNIT RATE			SIZE - UNIT RATE		
CODE	DRAWING OR SPOOL NO.	TOTAL Q	THIS PER.	TO DATE	TOTAL Q	THIS PER.	TO DATE	TOTAL Q	THIS PER.	TO DATE	TOTAL Q	THIS PER.	TO DATE	TOTAL Q	THIS PER	TO DATE

Figure 5.35 Piping control report.

Figure 5.35 illustrates a typical control sheet for recording piping quantities installed. The unit of measurement is usually feet of pipe. Five columns are shown for different pipe sizes for the same piece of work. This is necessary as many piping drawings can have several pipe diameters for the same line or piping system. As work is completed, drawings should be marked up, and a weekly tally of quantities installed should be maintained. This control sheet shows the unit rate (man-hours per foot, etc.), total estimated quantities (Q), and quantities this period and to date. Quantities can be easily converted to earned man-hours.

This concludes the chapter on contractor planning and scheduling. It cannot be emphasized enough that the sole function of schedule engineers is to communicate: specifically, to communicate—to management and team members—plans, resources, statuses, analyses, and actions for timely completion of the project. Too often schedules, especially logic networks, appear to be a mass of arrows, lines, and circles. At first sight, engineering and construction managers throw up their hands in horror and resort to the bar charts which they have maintained for just such a situation. When this happens, both the owner and the contractor lose—sometimes for the specific project and always in the long run. Schedule engineers need to be reminded, regularly and forcibly, that "their" schedule is not the end product. Timely completion of the project is the end product.

6

CONTRACTOR COST CONTROL

6.1 INTRODUCTION

In this chapter we shall deal with a contractor's project cost control operation, mainly of reimbursable, phase II projects. Owners would have a project task force working with the contractor on an equal partnership basis. The operation of a contractor home office cost group would be somewhat similar to an owner's group, apart from the estimating operation and a more detailed level of cost control.

Contractors have a capability for detailed estimating, whereas most owners only go as far as a scoping or conceptual estimate. As estimating systems vary so widely, in this book we shall not attempt to cover estimating programs. However, as an estimate is the base for cost control, an estimate review procedure is covered, in detail, in Chapter 4.

It is not likely that contractors would devote significant resources to the ongoing development of cost control methods. For competitive reasons, many contractors develop procedures and methods on existing contracts.

It is a wise owner who will allow some contractor method development on the project. It is a smart contractor who will accept some financial penalty and competitive risk to develop adequate control systems.

On reimbursable projects, it is the owner's responsibility to provide cost and financial objectives which the contractor can support and which are intrinsic to the contractual agreement.

The contractor is responsible for day-to-day control and should quickly establish a quality control system which will gain the confidence of the owner. The system should be cost effective and responsive to the owner's objectives and requirements.

Should owners be vacillating and procrastinating in setting their objectives, then the contractors must insist that the owners provide this information or porpose a program themselves if the owners are incapable.

It is strongly recommended that on reimbursable projects the contractor not develop a cost control program until the owner's financial and control requirements are clearly established.

In Chapters 1 and 2 we commented on owner-contractor relationships, planning the project, establishing objectives, and developing systems. Chapter 4 includes an owner cost control specification. These chapters should be studied in conjunction with this chapter for a full understanding of an effective cost control program—effective, that is, from both the owner and contractor viewpoints.

A successful cost operation requires the owner and contractor to work closely—in harmony and, to the extent possible and practical, with a common set of goals and objectives. It should be recognized that the profit motive on reimbursable projects can result in differing objectives for the contractor.

6.2 COMMUNICATION: A VITAL AND NEGLECTED FACTOR

Too often project cost reports appear to be a mass of numbers. At first sight, engineering and construction managers throw up their hands in horror and resort to intuition or to "bottom-drawer" data which they have maintained for just such a situation. When this happens, both the owner and the contractor lose: sometimes for the specific project and always in the long run. Cost engineers need to be reminded, regularly and forcibly, that "their" report is not the end product.

The best cost engineers keep the following in mind:

Their fundamental purpose is to communicate.
Technical excellence will not compensate for noncommunicating reports.
They cannot work in a vacuum but must make themselves part of the
    daily give-and-take of the project.
They must labor to avoid meaningless reports and poor report formats.
Cost awareness has to be generated and maintained (daily).
Report formats should be well organized for ease of updating and show-
    ing trends.
Criticism should be factual and constructive.
Conclusions and recommendations are essential.
Simplicity is necessary for good understanding.

When the preceding are observed, cost reports and recommendations will have credibility and receive the serious consideration and usage they deserve.

6.3 CONTRACTOR COST CONTROL SYSTEM

Figure 6.1 is a flowchart showing significant elements of a typical contractor's cost control system. Also shown are the major interfaces of the owner in the project estimate, cost trending, and associated owner's costs.

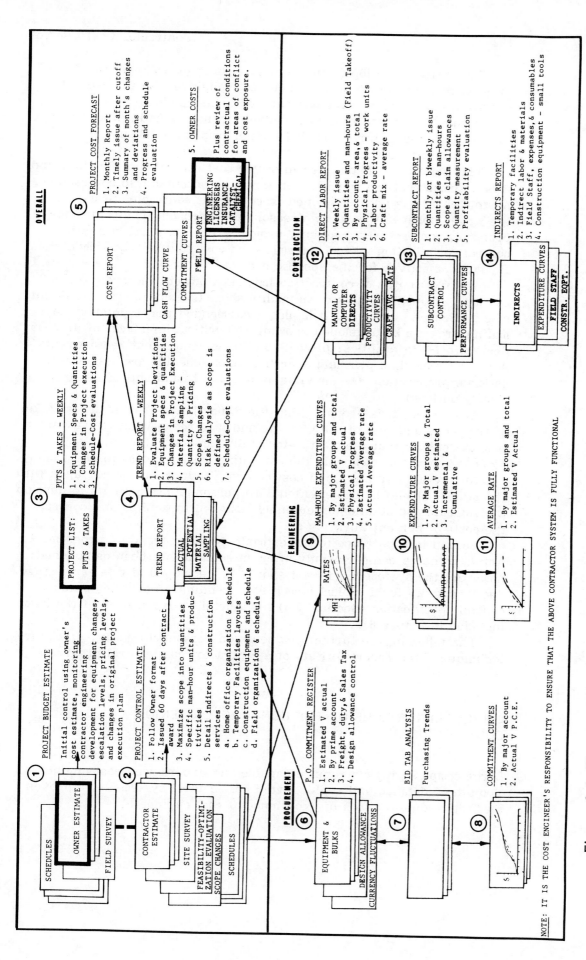

Figure 6.1 Flowchart of contractor cost control system.

The items at the top of the flowchart cover overall control of the project, and the bottom section includes techniques for the separate phases of engineering, procurement, and construction.

It should be noted that cost control techniques and methods are constantly being improved so that "blind compliance" should not be substituted for an intelligent approach.

This same chart is outlined in owner cost control specification, and it is assumed that the specification would be acceptable to contractors. As this chart has been developed from current contractor practices, the writer believes this to be a reasonable approach. The contractor proposal, contractual agreement, project execution plan, and owner control specification should determine the cost control requirements and financial objectives for the specific project.

Within 3 months of contract award, most owners require a budget estimate. A quality estimate, in such a short time, requires assignment of experienced personnel. It is also recommended that a detailed estimating program be developed showing the critical interfaces of process design, off-site facilities, project conditions, and owner requirements. A project execution plan and overall project schedule are essential to estimate preparation. Owner input requirements and approvals should be clearly outlined.

At this time it is probable that the owner has a greater appreciation of the scope and cost of the project, and it is recommended that contractors ensure that their estimators fully tap this information source without having the owner do the estimating work or claim to be so doing.

An overall estimating and cost control program, as agreed upon with the owner, should be implemented with personnel assignments to develop the estimate and additional personnel assigned to monitor and control the costs of current work.

Second in importance to the estimate is a cost trending program. Actual trending can occur only after an estimate has been established; however, the system and format should be developed at this early stage. See Figure 4.4 for a typical format of a trending report. See owner control specification (Section 4.6) for a detailed explanation of the items included in Figure 6.1.

The following are further comments on personnel quality, procedures, techniques, and report formats of a contractor cost control program.

6.4 QUALIFICATIONS OF THE CONTRACTOR SENIOR COST ENGINEER

Large complex projects require capable and experienced cost engineers. Too often, detailed and sophisticated cost control systems have proven ineffective due to a lack of experience of cost engineers.

The following is a recommended list of qualifications for a senior cost engineer:

Education: bachelor degree or equivalent
Five years or more in related industry work
Eight years of estimating and cost control experience
Knowledge of scheduling
Three years of construction (job site) experience
Self-starter, with capacity for teamwork
Good communicator, orally and in writing
Flexible and imaginative approach
Prepared to travel

Large projects require a minimum of 3-4 senior personnel with these qualifications to act in lead positions. Jumbo projects would require a minimum of 5-6. The peak for estimating personnel would probable be 15-20 for a large reimbursable project. The peak for cost personnel, usually when engineering is 70-80% complete and construction 10-15% complete, would probably be 20-25 for a large project.

6.5 CODE OF ACCOUNTS

Effective control requires a detailed breakdown of organization, function, and activity and the subsequent identification of these elements.

A code of accounts, at the prime account and subaccount levels, provides identification. A code of accounts is essential in a contractor's total operation. Six- and eight-figure account codes are common. Account code breakdowns are peculiar to each contractor. Changes to account codes, requested by owners, should be resisted.

As previously outlined, a good work breakdown structure or code of accounts is an essential ingredient of a good estimate. An account code will often go through the entire project from the numbering of the material requisition, the purchase order, and the drawing to the item number of a piece of equipment.

Estimating manuals are based on account codes. Project experience and return data are evaluated and collected by account code.

6.6 ACCOUNTING PROCEDURE

An accounting procedure is an integral part of cost control, as it specifies levels of approval, billing and payment procedures, banking arrangements, accounts numbering systems, and all functions necessary for financial reporting of the project.

The important aspect for cost control is the collection and reporting of commitments and expenditures. This information is necessary to track the status and progress of cost objectives and also to provide a base for developing cost predictions.

An accurate and up-to-date report of commitments and expenditures is essential. On large projects, delayed payments or lost invoices can cause poor cost predictions. Many control techniques are based on unit costs. They can be greatly distorted if the cost to date is inaccurately reported.

Scheduling evaluations also depend on commitment curves where actual values are plotted against planned values.

An important aspect of the accounting program is preparation and presentation of invoices for payment by the owner. These invoices should be accurate and well documented and conform to the owner's billing procedures.

6.7 CASH ADVANCES AND BANK HANDLING PROCEDURE

The major objective of cash advances and the bank handling procedure is to ensure that the project, where appropriate, is funded by the owner.

A cash flow forecast is usually prepared for a 3-month period and then presented to the owner for cash advances on a biweekly or monthly basis. A good forecast should generate a 5% excess requirement. This would be acceptable to most owners.

Most forecasts are manually prepared and evaluate future expenditures for contractor services, equipment and bulk materials, subcontracts, and owner costs.

A common bnaking arrangement is a zero bank account system. This means that contractors will not finance the project and that owners are required to advance sufficient funds, as per the cash flow forecast, to the contractor's nominated bank. Any accruing of interest will be for the owner's account. This procedure should form part of the contractor proposal and specify penalties to the owner for failure to provide timely funding.

6.8 INSURANCES AND TAXES

An ill-defined item of the estimate and also of the contractual agreement can be insurances and taxes. Full evaluations should be made of owner responsibility for insurances and all local and government taxes for which the project will be liable. Environmental and regulatory costs should be fully evaluated insofar as the processing of licenses, permits, and presentations is concerned.

CODE	ITEM/DESCRIPTION	1 COMMITTED TO DATE	2 EXPENDED TO DATE	CONTROL BUDGET 3 INITIAL (AFE) BUDGET	4 APPROVED CHANGES	5 REVISED BUDGET	6 CURRENT FORECAST	7 VARIANCE (6) - (5)
					PROJECT			
					JOB N°			
					PERIOD			
	ALL FIGURES ×	PROJECT COST REPORT			REPORT N° SHEET OF			
1								
2								
3								
4								
5								
6								
7								
8								
9								
10								
11								
12								
13								
14								
15								
16								
17								
18								
19								
20								
21								
22								
23								
24								
25								
26								
27								
28								
29								
30								
31								
32								
33								
34								
35								
36								
37								
38								
39								

Figure 6.2   Monthly cost report.

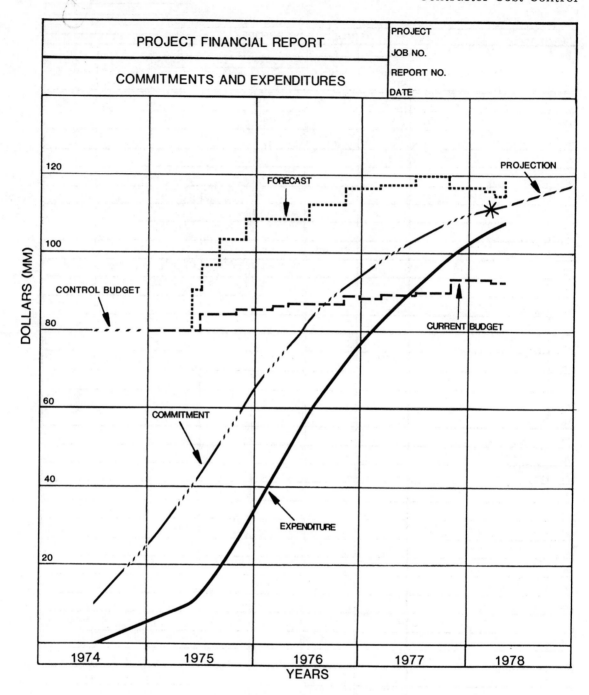

Figure 6.3 Commitment and expenditure curves.

6.9 MONTHLY COST REPORT

Figure 6.2 is a typical format of the monthly cost report. This is a
summary report and should list major items or cost centers. Columns 1
and 2 contain committed and expended costs. Columns 3, 4, and 5 cover
the original budget, updated with approval changes. Columns 6 and 7
carry the forecast and variance of forecast to the current budget.
Currency and currency conversion at the time of appropriation
[authorization for expenditure (AFE)] should be specified.

This same format could be used for detailed as well as summary-
level reports.

The monthly cost report should be a key management document and,
as such, should be timely, accurate, and simple and readily communicate an overall cost evaluation.

6.10 COMMITMENT AND EXPENDITURE REPORT

Figure 6.3 is a typical format for commitment and expenditure curves.
Curve formats are far more conducive to developing forecasts than a
tabular report. A curve shows the trend of performance to date and
can, with past experience and judgment, be developed to a final prediction. This format is particularly efficient, as it shows the development of the control budget and forecast against time.

This example shows an original control budget of $80 million de-
veloped in mid-1974 and, with scope changes, increasing to $94 million
by 1978. The forecast starts at $90 million in 1975 and rises to around
$120 million by 1978. It would be fairly obvious in mid-1975, with commit-
ments of $45 million and a mechanical completion of late 1978, that a
forecast of $90 million would be unlikely. Historical experience would
indicate a straight-line profile to end in 1976, followed by a gradual
rundown to mechanical completion. The status is reported as of April
1978, with commitments of $113 million and a forecast of $118 million.

This technique can be used for detailed elements as well as for the
overall project.

6.11 CASH FLOW CURVE

Figure 6.4 is a typical format of an overall cash flow curve. This shows
a planned curve and an actual cumulative curve, reported on a monthly
basis. A planned curve should be evaluated every month to ensure
accuracy of the short-term (3-month) forecast. A planned curve should
be compared to the overall budget. This curve, plus appropriate backup,
should be presented to the owner for approval on a biweekly or monthly
basis.

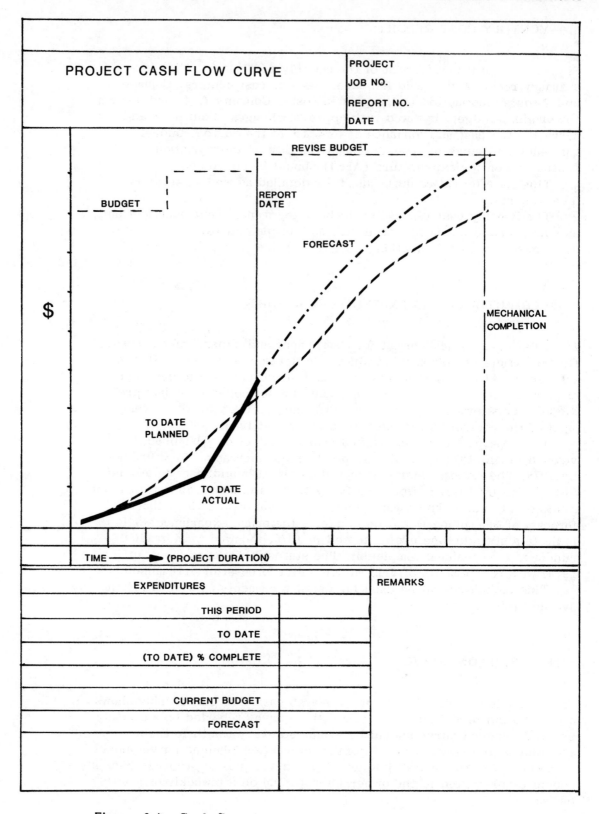

PROJECT CASH FLOW CURVE

PROJECT
JOB NO.
REPORT NO.
DATE

REVISE BUDGET

BUDGET

REPORT
DATE

FORECAST

$

MECHANICAL
COMPLETION

TO DATE
PLANNED

TO DATE
ACTUAL

TIME ────▶ (PROJECT DURATION)

EXPENDITURES		REMARKS
THIS PERIOD		
TO DATE		
(TO DATE) % COMPLETE		
CURRENT BUDGET		
FORECAST		

Figure 6.4   Cash flow curve.

6.12 HOME OFFICE CONTROL

A monthly cost report should list the budget, commitments, expenditures, and forecasts of the contractor home office operation. This would include man-hours, personnel costs, office services, fees, personnel expenses, reproduction expenses, computer expenses, etc. Depending on size and value, individual elements of the total home office budget should be tracked as follows.

6.12.1 Home Office Man-hour Expenditure Curve

Figure 6.5 is a set of incremental and cumulative curves for overall home office man-hours. Planned curves should be developed from the man-hour estimate and project schedule. Actual experience is plotted on a monthly basis. This example shows an overrun against the plan as of month 9. Evaluations of individual elements of the home office confirm that the overrun is irrecoverable; therefore, a forecasted overrun is made. With a curve format, this trend was really discernible in month 6. Depending on the viability of the planned curve, a potential overrun, evident in month 6, becomes a reality by month 9.

However, a man-hour overrun does not necessarily mean a cost overrun. It is possible for an underrun in expense budgets and personnel costs to compensate for an overrun in man-hours. Hence, it is important to monitor man-hour costs.

6.12.2 Home Office Man-hour Rate Profile

Figure 6.6 shows cumulative planned and actual profiles of a home office man-hour rate. This rate represents total home office costs divided by total man-hours. Significant deviation of actual to planned can indicate a potential overrun. Rate overruns can occur because of different a mix of salary levels, unanticipated increases in salary levels, changes in benefits and burdens, overruns in service and expense budgets, and premium costs for overtime.

This example shows an estimated rate of $20 with tracking curves starting at $23-$26, dropping to $17-$18, and finishing at the estimated level. It reflects high-salaried personnel at the start of the project (department managers, project management, process engineers) followed by a lower-priced drafting operation with higher-salaried engineers returning for punch list work and plant start-up.

The planned curve can be developed from historical experience and/ or by evaluating rate curves for each major section, category, or engineering discipline and then adding them together on a weighted man-hour basis. An obvious breakdown would be the following:

Managers
Project engineers
Senior engineers

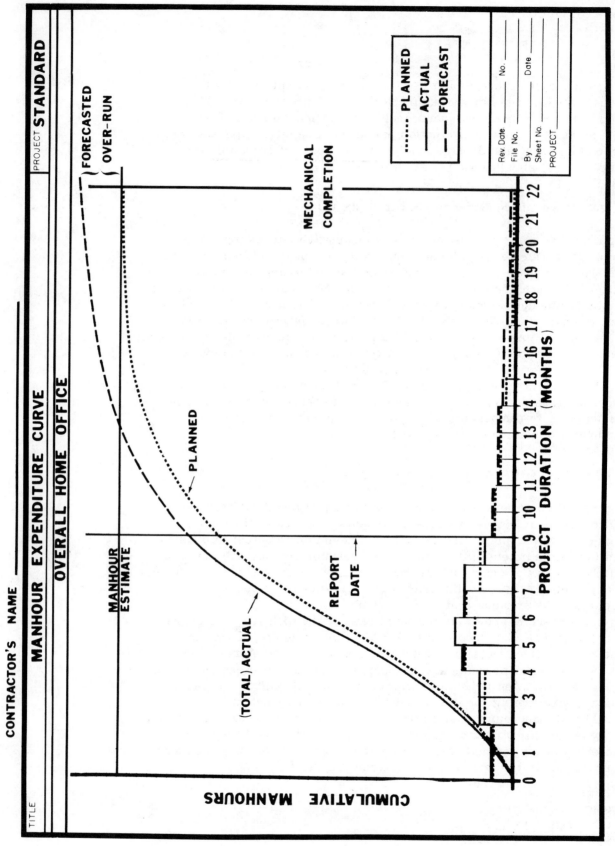

Figure 6.5   Home office man-hour expenditure curve.

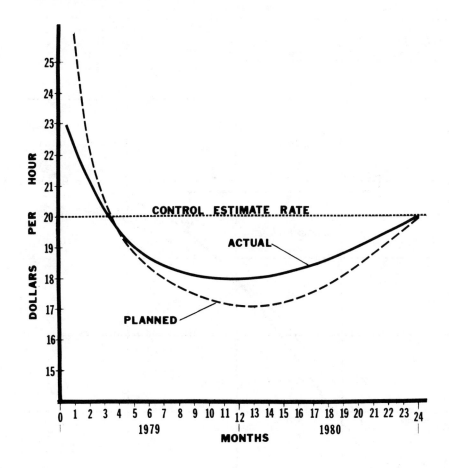

Figure 6.6 Home office man-hour rate profile.

Engineers
Draftspersons
Technicians
Clerical

6.12.3 Home Office Cost Expenditure Curve

Figure 6.7 shows planned and actual expenditure curves of home office costs. Planned curves are developed by judgment and historical experience and can be compiled from profiles of more detailed elements. It is recommended on large projects that individual curves be used to track non-man-hour-related expenses, such as computer, reproduction, communication, and travel-relocation costs.

   This example shows the actual expenditure curve consistently underrunning the planned until the end of 1976 where it continues straight on instead of commencing to run down. A trend was discernible in mid-1976, and, in fact, a forecasted overrun had been made in the third quarter of 1975. A further overrun was made in the first quarter of 1977 due to failure of the curve to commence a rundown.

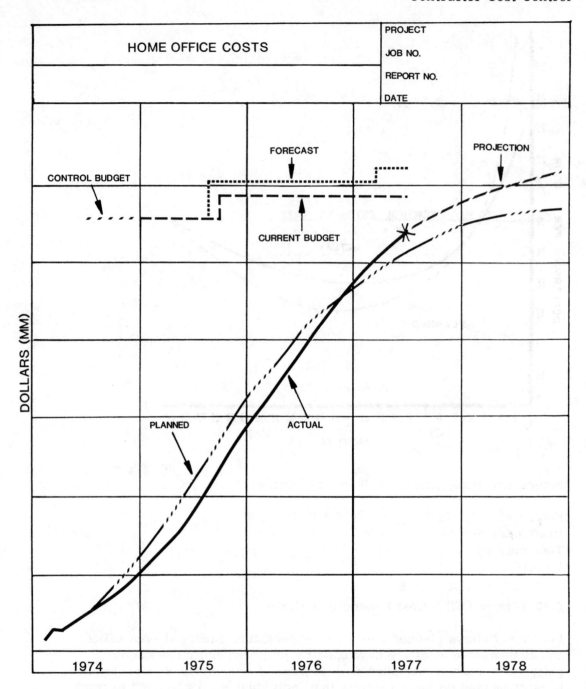

HOME OFFICE COSTS

PROJECT

JOB NO.

REPORT NO.

DATE

Figure 6.7 Home office expense curve.

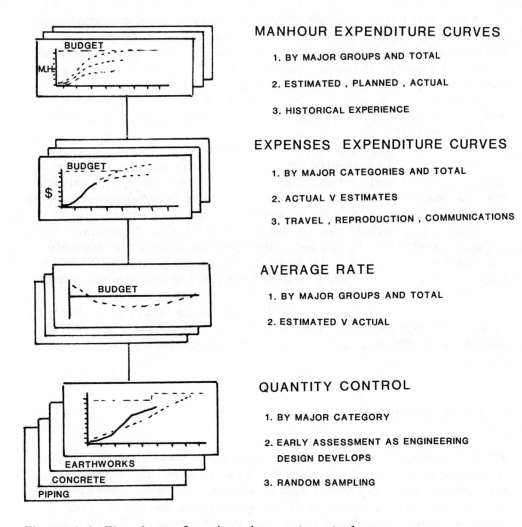

MANHOUR EXPENDITURE CURVES

    1. BY MAJOR GROUPS AND TOTAL

    2. ESTIMATED , PLANNED , ACTUAL

    3. HISTORICAL EXPERIENCE

EXPENSES EXPENDITURE CURVES

    1. BY MAJOR CATEGORIES AND TOTAL

    2. ACTUAL V ESTIMATES

    3. TRAVEL , REPRODUCTION , COMMUNICATIONS

AVERAGE RATE

    1. BY MAJOR GROUPS AND TOTAL

    2. ESTIMATED V ACTUAL

QUANTITY CONTROL

    1. BY MAJOR CATEGORY

    2. EARLY ASSESSMENT AS ENGINEERING
       DESIGN DEVELOPS

    3. RANDOM SAMPLING

Figure 6.8 Flowchart of engineering cost control.

6.13 ENGINEERING COST CONTROL, OVERALL

Scope changes and design developments are likely to occur during the
engineering phase. A major element of control is early identification of
these changes from the engineering budget or control estimate. These
changes would normally be tracked with an overall trending program
and design change log. Occasionally, changes are discovered only when
engineering man-hours overrun.

    Another important element is the monitoring of engineering pro-
ductivity. Comparison against budgeted levels should indicate deviations of man-hours and potential costs.

    As productivity can be measured by cost or scheduling personnel,
further techniques are outlined in Chapter 5.

As an estimate of the total number of drawings and material requisitions is established, an accurate budget should then be available for effective control. The breakdown of engineering into separate control centers is a matter of judgment. The size and number of accounts should be kept to manageable proportions.

Figure 6.8 is an abstract from the flowchart of the typical contractor cost control system. It displays methods by which engineering control can be exercised.

It is in the early engineering phase that value engineering, optimization, and cost trade-offs should be fully utilized. Owner design specifications should be carefully evaluated for conflict with contractor specifications. All differences should be quickly resolved, cost engineers notified of potential cost impact, and cost estimates made.

During this period, cost engineers should ensure effective communication channels with design personnel, provide prompt and accurate cost estimates, liaise with the owner to ensure compliance with owner requirements, and develop a consciousness and spirit of cost control with all groups.

Some contractors attach a coordination group to design engineering to monitor progress, manpower, and productivity. This can result in another layer filtering and refining information used by the cost engineer.

6.14 ENGINEERING CHANGE LOG

The engineering change log should cover all changes from the original scope, including changes to specifications, requisitions, and drawings. All changes, including owner scope changes, should be numerically recorded and a report issued to design groups and the owner. Cost estimates should be made of these changes and included in the trend report.

Due to the broad base of a conceptual estimate, it is not always possible to identify all items as changes. When in doubt, enter the item, as subsequent evaluation will confirm or delete the item.

The major objective of the engineering change log is to track the developing design and costs against the design basis and cost of the conceptual estimate. The objective is not to highlight deficiencies in order to lay blame on the designer, estimator, or owner.

It is recommended that the engineering change log not be used as a device by which to turn all changes into owner change orders. This can be irritating to owners who have usually specified the nature of owner changes. Such changes can, in turn, affect the contractor fee and profit margin.

See Figure 4.4 for a typical format.

6.15 BULKS QUANTITY CONTROL (ENGINEERING)

The tracking of *bulk* quantities (earthwork, concrete, piping, etc.) should be carried out from the process design phase through detailed engineering to mechanical completion. On very large or jumbo projects it is recommended that a small, experienced group be dedicated to this activity.

This requires experienced estimators-engineers to develop quality takeoffs at a very early stage of engineering so that quantity sampling can be instituted during process design and, particularly, during the "layouts" stage after the release of the process design.

6.16 EQUIPMENT BID EVALUATION (TECHNICAL)

Good evaluations and quality bid tabulations are essential for effective cost control. Engineers carrying out technical evaluations of vendor bids and who may be involved in vendor negotiations should be encouraged to review the estimate basis of equipment. Preference choices with accompanying cost penalties should be thoroughly investigated prior to submission for owner approval. Compatibility with existing plant equipment, ease of maintenance, and operating costs are appropriate requirements for equipment selection.

If there are no schedule restraints, commercial evaluations should follow the technical evaluation. This would ensure that purchasing personnel do not waste time with technically unacceptable bids. Obtaining owner technical approval prior to commercial review can also prevent wasting the time of purchasing personnel.

If there are cost deviations involved in the technical review, these items should be brought to the cost engineer's attention.

6.17 ENGINEERING MAN-HOUR CONTROL

Figure 6.9 shows typical examples of man-hour tracking curves. It should be emphasized that this technique does not really control effort or measure performance but indicates a trend and plots a possible outcome.

This example shows an overrun in process design (completed), shows an overrun in the civil plan as of the reporting period, and is on target with piping design but with a different profile. The overall cumulative report is an overrun. Projecting forward at a rundown profile similar to the plan will give a forecasted overrun at completion.

Target curves of anticipated man-hour expenditure should be developed for significant engineering sections. A typical split might be as follows:

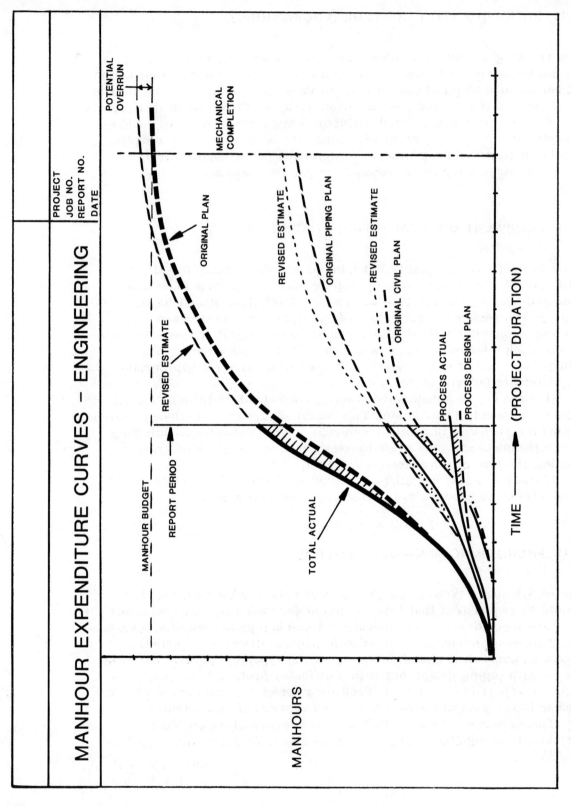

Figure 6.9 Engineering man-hour curves.

1. Process
2. Civil and structural design
3. Equipment and mechanical
4. Piping
5. Electrical
6. Instrumentation

Historical experience can assist in developing good expenditure curves. However, evaluation will depend on the skill and experience of the cost engineer. In practice (especially on large, complex projects), recycling of engineering, causing increases in man-hours, can be due to error or owner changes.

A key to controlling engineering man-hours is quickly establishing a good man-hour estimate and monitoring engineering productivity and expenditure curves.

6.18 ENGINEERING MAN-HOUR RATE PROFILE

Figure 6.10 is a technique to monitor engineering man-hour costs. Refer to Section 6.12.2 for detailes of the profile technique.

6.19 ENGINEERING COST EXPENDITURE CURVE

Figure 6.11 shows planned and actual expenditure curves for engineering costs. A planned or anticipated curve should be developed with judgment, based on the engineering schedule and appropriate historical experience.

This example shows actual expenditures following a similar profile as planned but consistently at a higher level. It is, therefore, reasonable to predict a final overrun with a projection following the same rundown profile but starting from the actual value (overrun) at the month 12 reporting date. This method can be used on small projects where separate curves and man-hour rate profiles are not necessary.

6.20 ENGINEERING STATUS REPORT

Figure 6.12 illustrates a concise, informative format for reporting the status of engineering. The report makes it easy to compare the trends of three significant control elements: physical progress, productivity, and manpower. Such a report could be prepared for each major design discipline.

This report could be produced by a cost or schedule engineer or by a coordination group assigned to engineering. Status reports and

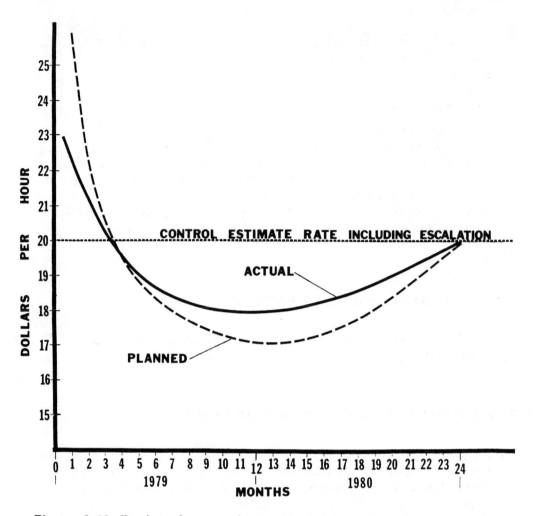

Figure 6.10 Engineering man-hour rate curves.

forecasts prepared by the engineering disciplines should be thoroughly checked by cost-schedule engineers. Evaluation of this information can assist cost engineers in determining the validity of engineering man-hour forecasts.

This example shows progress behind that planned and hence a possible schedule overrun and additional costs. The actual manpower requirement has greatly exceeded the planned level with a resulting low level of productivity. It is most probable that engineering man-hours will overrun substantially.

6.21 PROCUREMENT COST CONTROL, OVERALL

Project purchasing strategy should specify a proposed split of domestic and international purchasing. This should be reviewed and approved by

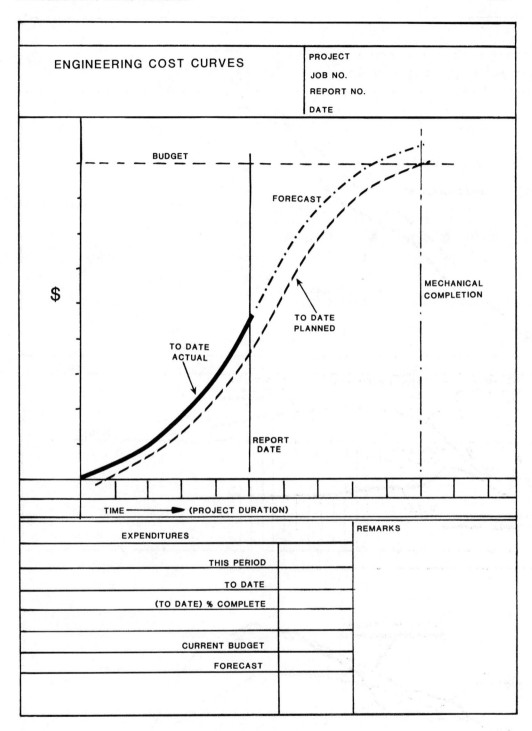

Figure 6.11 Engineering cost curves.

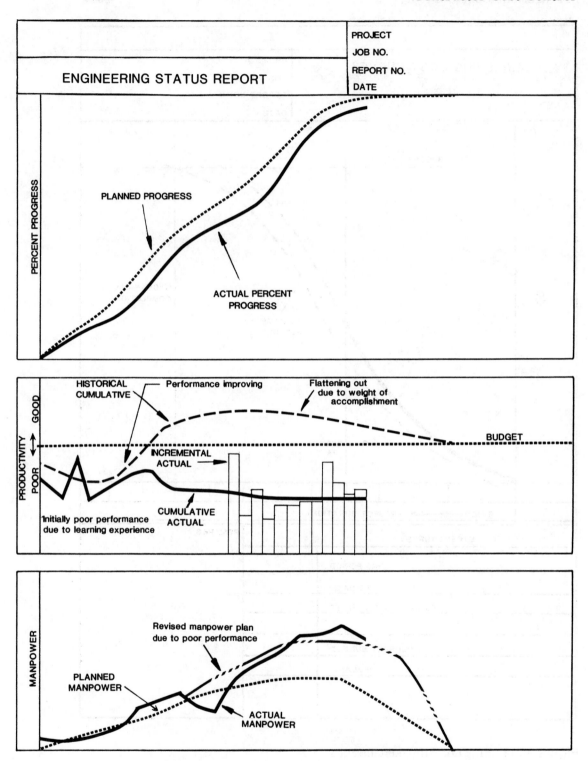

Figure 6.12 Engineering status report.

the owner. In the control budget, escalation rates and design allowances should be established by prime account. Purchasing evaluation techniques should be outlined at an early date and the owner's role in purchasing clearly established. Levels of authority should be developed. Use and coordination of the contractor's overseas purchasing offices should be specified. Project conditions such as schedule acceleration, national purchasing preferences, and owner requirements need to be evaluated for cost impact.

Figure 6.13 is an abstract from the flowchart of the typical contractor cost control system. It displays methods by which purchasing control can be exercised.

A purchase order commitment register should be maintained by prime account and separated for the following major categories:

Firm price equipment orders
Open-ended bulk material orders
Field-purchased materials

Moreover, curves showing actual versus planned commitments should be maintained for these categories.

Generally, low bid items exceeding the control budget by 10% should be thoroughly investigated. Such deviations could signal a "fat" design, poor bid documents resulting in a high bid, tight market conditions, or a poor estimate.

The following should be objectives of a contractor's procurement effort:

Provide timely bid tabs and quality evaluations
Optimize purchase order delivery terms by taking advantage of
    quantity cash discounts and prompt payments
On large projects, maximize the purchase of as many similar items on
    one purchase order as possible to get the best discount terms
Maximize the use of worldwide purchasing
Minimize import duties and taxes (this can be done by requesting
    special waivers from host countries or by reclassifying items to
    lower duty categories)
Minimize freight charges by prudent selection of carriers, consistent
    with schedule requirements (e.g., the use of "nonconference"
    versus "conference" steamship lines)
Make a sensitivity analysis of unit price bids to verify that an apparent
    low bidder is in fact still lowest after evaluating potential quantity
    increases
Check that purchasing manpower levels are adequate
Check that buyers instigate a purchasing policy which uses ethical,
    effective negotiating practices.

Failure to properly observe any of the preceding could result in additional costs.

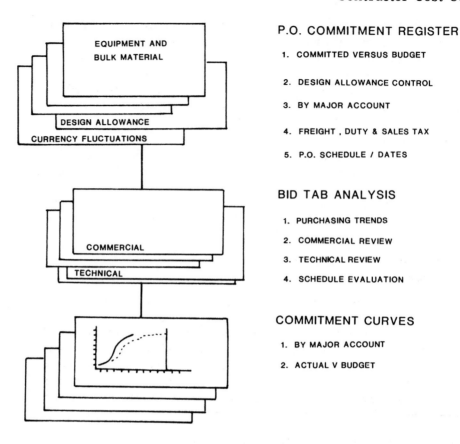

Figure 6.13 Flowchart of procurement cost control.

6.22 PURCHASING PLAN FOR CRITICAL MATERIAL

Refer to Chapter 5 for additional information on the purchasing plan for critical material. Material and equipment on a critical path could require premiums for vendor drawings and premiums for shorter delivery. Alternatively, special expediting arrangements, such as teams resident in vendor shops, can be required. Air freight and special handling could also be required. Such requirements often lead to additional costs.

6.23 BID TABULATION PROCEDURE

The bid tabulation procedure should cover the preparation, control, review, and approval requirements of bid tabulation documents. Levels of approval should be defined; there should be instructions for opening of tenders and evaluations of tender documents; budget comparisons should be made; negotiations philosophy after bid tab preparation and the recommendation basis for selection should be stated. The procedure should require that bid tabs contain information of past knowledge or experience of bidders which may have a bearing on selection.

Bid tabulations are a major source of cost information for cost engineers, and this procedure should require the routing of bid tabs to cost engineers.

6.24 PURCHASE ORDER COMMITMENT REGISTER

Figure 6.14 shows the form of a typical purchase order commitment register. It lists purchase orders placed, date placed, vendor, value, currency, and delivery date. This register should be issued biweekly during the peak commitment stage; later a monthly issue may be adequate. This register acts as a check for the cost engineer that he or she has seen all the purchase orders and latest revisions issued to date. Individual material forecasts by purchasing personnel should be reviewed by the cost engineer. Design allowances should be carefully reviewed against the latest supplement to a purchase order. As engineering advances, so the need for design allowance reduces.

Freight costs, duties, and taxes should be segregated and monitored. Copies of invoices for these charges should be routed through the cost engineer to enable him or her to keep current on forecasting final delivery costs to the job site.

Field purchasing activities should include the issue of a field purchase order register. As this account is difficult to estimate and is often poorly estimated, cost engineers should maintain close scrutiny of field purchasing activities.

6.25 EQUIPMENT COST CURVES

Figure 6.15 is a typical commitment curve for bulk materials and equipment. This curve tracks actual cumulative material commitments relative to a planned profile. This curve will only indicate a trend of total commitment. A significant trend at this stage is an underrun or overrun of actual commitments versus individual control estimate budgets.

The bulk material and equipment commitment curve can be used for two purposes:

As a graphical, overall forecasting tool
As a rough check on the contractor's procurement progress,
    assuming the planned curve reflects the current schedule

Significant deviations of actual versus planned values can provide a trend for cost deviation.

It is recommended that separate curves be drawn for equipment, bulk material, and supply and erect subcontracts.

PURCHASE ORDER COMMITMENT REGISTER

PROJECT
JOB NO.
REPORT NO.
DATE

1	2	3	4	5	6	7	8	9	10	11	12
REQN. NO.	P.O. NO.	DATE PO.	REQD. P.O. DATE	ITEM	VENDOR	COMMITTED	EXPENDED	DESIGN ALLOW.	BUDGET	FORECAST	VARIANCE FORCAST BUDGET

Figure 6.14 Purchase order commitment register.

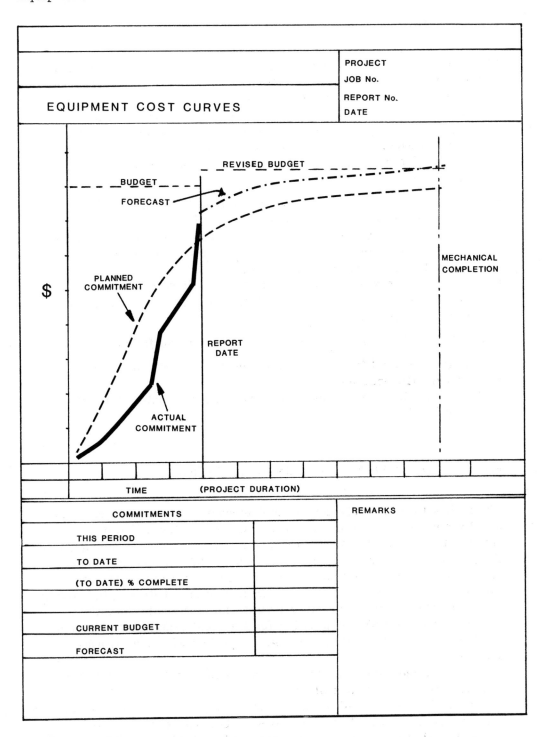

Figure 6.15   Equipment cost curves.

6.26 BACKCHARGE REGISTER

Figure 6.16 illustrates a typical backcharge register. Charges against vendors or subcontractors for extra work incurred by the contractor can have significant cost impact. Backcharges can result from poor vendor-subcontractor workmanship, schedule delays, lack of resources, failure to clean up, etc. Cost engineers should set up a register to record pertinent backcharge data.

Several important points should be observed regarding backcharge administration:

Documentation: All pertinent costs associated with backcharge should be recorded and updated regularly.

Early notification: The vendor or subcontractor should be advised in writing of a backcharge, including an estimate of the associated cost, as soon as possible.

Cost forecast: Cost engineers should heavily discount the actual cost when taking *credit* for *potential recoverable backcharges* in a cost forecast.

The data compiled on this form can be used for the following:

Assess the financial impact on project costs as backcharges are settled with vendors

Highlight "problem" vendors-subcontractors for quality control purposes

6.27 CONSTRUCTION COST CONTROL, OVERALL

The ability to effectively control and forecast construction costs is usually dependent on the quality of the field budget. Too often, sufficient care and attention to the construction scope is missing when the project control estimate is developed in the engineering phase. Lack of attention is particularly evident in a field indirects estimate. Factors are applied to direct-labor costs instead of developing quantity takeoffs. This requires drafting layouts for temporary facilities, developing a detailed organization for the field staff, and preparing detailed construction equipment lists, together with time frame schedules.

Many projects experience overruns in field indirects due to a poor estimate, rather than lack of control.

A widely used technique is an independent assessment, usually by the construction department, of direct-labor man-hours. This is accomplished with detailed quantity takeoffs of all construction issue drawings if the project is on a direct-hire basis. Establishment of the scope for a subcontract job is usually less efficient.

BACKCHARGE REGISTER

PROJECT

JOB NO.

REPORT NO.

DATE

NO.	DATE	P.O. NO.	COMPANY	DESCRIPTION OF BACKCHARGE	WORK ORDER REF.	ESTIMATED COST	ESTD. RECOV.	FORECAST COST	ACTUAL RECOV'D.

Figure 6.16 Backcharge register.

It is difficult to establish detailed (quantity) estimates for small tools, consumables, and field office expenses. A unit or factored basis is a normal method.

The following lists the major elements of a quality construction estimate:

1. Direct field labor
    Quantities updated by field takeoff
    Productivity factor for time and location
    Unit man-hours per work operation
    Handling and rework by factor
2. Indirect field labor (productive and lost time): Factor on direct labor man-hours
3. Field staff
    Organization chart
    Time frame schedule
    Relocation and local living
    Replacement and training
4. Temporary facilities
    Dimensioned layouts
    Quantity takeoff
    Unit rates (dollars per square foot)
    Maintenance by factor
5. Construction equipment
    Listing by category and number
    Time frame schedule
    Unit rates (rental versus purchase)
    Maintenance by factor
6. Small tools and consumables
    Factor on direct labor (dollars per man-hour)
    Loss allowance
7. Field office expenses
    Factor on direct labor (dollars per man-hour)
    Listing for office furniture and equipment
8. Escalation and contingency: by judgment and formula.

Note: Direct material purchase by the field is usually covered by the material estimate.

The major elements of controlling construction costs are early identification of quantity variances, labor productivity, and craft rates and continuous evaluation of field indirects. A quantity field budget, showing clearly defined units of work, is essential.

On large projects, it is recommended that a separate labor *rundown control system* be instituted for the last 20% of the project.

Figure 6.17 is an abstract from the flowchart of the typical contractor cost control system. It displays methods by which construction cost control can be exercised.

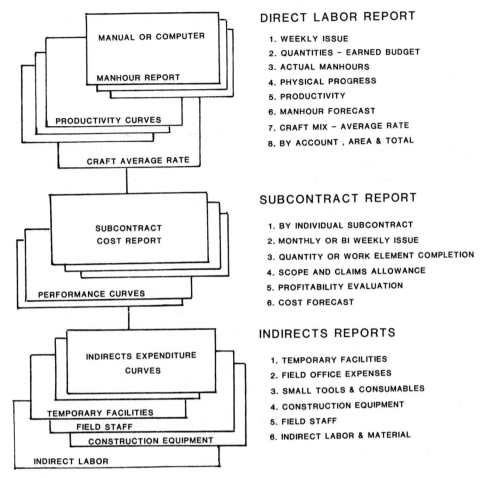

DIRECT LABOR REPORT

1. WEEKLY ISSUE
2. QUANTITIES – EARNED BUDGET
3. ACTUAL MANHOURS
4. PHYSICAL PROGRESS
5. PRODUCTIVITY
6. MANHOUR FORECAST
7. CRAFT MIX – AVERAGE RATE
8. BY ACCOUNT , AREA & TOTAL

SUBCONTRACT REPORT

1. BY INDIVIDUAL SUBCONTRACT
2. MONTHLY OR BI WEEKLY ISSUE
3. QUANTITY OR WORK ELEMENT COMPLETION
4. SCOPE AND CLAIMS ALLOWANCE
5. PROFITABILITY EVALUATION
6. COST FORECAST

INDIRECTS REPORTS

1. TEMPORARY FACILITIES
2. FIELD OFFICE EXPENSES
3. SMALL TOOLS & CONSUMABLES
4. CONSTRUCTION EQUIPMENT
5. FIELD STAFF
6. INDIRECT LABOR & MATERIAL

Figure 6.17 Flowchart of construction cost control.

6.28 RECORDING AND REPORTING EXTRA WORK

Due to the volatile nature of a construction site, change is a constant companion. A field trending system is essential to reflect costs due to changes and extra work.

The following would be typical items:

Specification changes
Design errors
Field errors
Vendor errors
Owner changes
Changed or unusual site conditions

A procedure should be developed to cover extra work initiation, approval and authorization, reporting, and closeout.

A typical procedure and extra work report is covered in Section 7.22.

6.29 MATERIAL CONTROL ON SITE

Failure to properly handle material can result in additional costs. Breakage, damage, and trouble reports should be routed to the field cost engineer for assessment of the cost impact. Small tools and field consumables usually require close attention. Cost evaluations of surplus materials, spares, and start-up requirements should be made as construction draws to a close.

6.30 MACHINERY PROTECTION

Schedule extensions and long schedules can cause additional costs for equipment maintenance. Failure to properly protect machinery can result in serious cost increases and scheduling delays. Vendor recommendations should be written into an overall procedure to protect machinery from the time it leaves the factory to the time of operational acceptance. It is important that vendors be advised of the length of time their equipment will remain unoperated as this could affect packaging specifications, costs, and guarantees. The field staff should inform cost engineers of significant instances of additional protection or winterization requirements.

6.31 MONTHLY PROJECT COST REPORT

Figure 6.18 outlines a typical format for reporting the overall field costs of the contractor and owner. This format covers a situation where work is shared between the owner and contractor and the costs are reported on a single form. Overall cost centers are broken down into direct, indirect, and expense. Each item reported should have an individual cost report, it could be attached to the overall summary. Separate reporting by the contractor and owner could use the same format.

6.32 CONSTRUCTION MAN-HOUR REPORT

Figure 6.19 shows a typical format for reporting man-hours and earned budget value. Progress is measured by budget man-hours. A man-hour prediction is based on the productivity to date versus the man-hours spent to date. Productivity is derived from actual man-hours expended

PROJECT
JOB NO.
REPORT NO.
DATE

PROJECT COST REPORT		CONTRACTOR					OWNER				REMARKS
ITEM	BUDGET	CUM. TO DATE	EXPEND. TO DATE	FORECAST	VARIANCE	CUM. TO DATE	EXPEND. TO DATE	FORECAST	VARIANCE		
1 DIRECT MATERIAL											
2 DIRECT LABOR											
3 DIRECT SUBCONTRACTS											
4 DIRECTS S/T											
5 ENG., SERVICES & FEES											
6 FIELD INDIRECTS											
7 DUTIES, FREIGHT, INSUR.											
8 INDIRECTS S/T											
9 CONTINGENCY											
10 EXTRA WORK											
11 SPARE PARTS											
12 COMM. / START UP											
13 MISC.											
14 CONTRACTOR COSTS TOTAL											
15 OWNER CAPITAL COSTS											
16 OWNER ENG.											
17 LICENSES – ROYALTIES											
18 OWNER MISC.											
19 OWNER COSTS TOTAL											
20 TOTAL CAPITAL COSTS											
21 ASSOCIATED EXPENSES											
22 GRAND TOTAL											

Figure 6.18 Monthly cost report.

SUMMARY REPORT (PRIME ACCOUNT)										JOB NO: REPORT NO: UNIT: PERIOD:

DESCRIPTION	CLASS	MANHOURS SPENT		BDGT. FOR WORK DONE		TOTAL BUDGET	% COMPL.	PRODUCTIVITY		TOTAL PREDICTED MANHOURS
		THIS WEEK	TO DATE	THIS WEEK	TO DATE			THIS WEEK	TO DATE	
EARTHWORK										
FOUNDATIONS										
HEATERS										
↓										
SUBTOTAL DIRECT										
TEMPORARY FACILITIES										
TOOLS & EQUIPMENT										
UNALLOCABLE										
SUBTOTAL INDIRECT										

Figure 6.19 Construction man-hour report.

versus budget hours earned. Indirect man-hours should be shown
separately. Indirect man-hours are not quantity based. It is recommended that an indirects budget or earned value be based on direct
work progress and/or judgment of each major indirect man-hour account.

6.33 CONSTRUCTION BUDGET REPORT

Figure 6.20, an earned budget report, collates quantities as the work is
completed and also predicts total quantities based on a field takeoff made
from construction issue drawings. These quantities are then converted
into an earned value of budget hours, which are then entered on the
man-hour report, as previously illustrated.

6.34 CONSTRUCTION PRODUCTIVITY REPORT (DIRECT LABOR)

Accurate measurement of *overall productivity* is essential to good manpower planning and man-hour-cost forecasting. One widely used method,
called the *earned man-hour* approach, is illustrated in Figure 6.21. This
method requires the following:

Budgeted construction man-hours
Actual man-hours expended (monthly and cumulative)
Physical progress (percent complete, monthly and cumulative)
    or earned man-hours (monthly and cumulative)
Productivity is simply a ratio or yardstick to measure performance
(actual man-hours) versus budgeted or estimated man-hours. Poor per-

ITEM	CLASS	ORIGINAL QUANTITIES	PREDICTED QUANTITIES	UNIT	UNIT RATE	QUANTITIES DONE		EARNED BUDGET		REMARKS
						THIS WK.	TO DATE	THIS WK.	TO DATE	
BY INDIV. WORK CATEGORY										

Figure 6.20 Construction budget report.

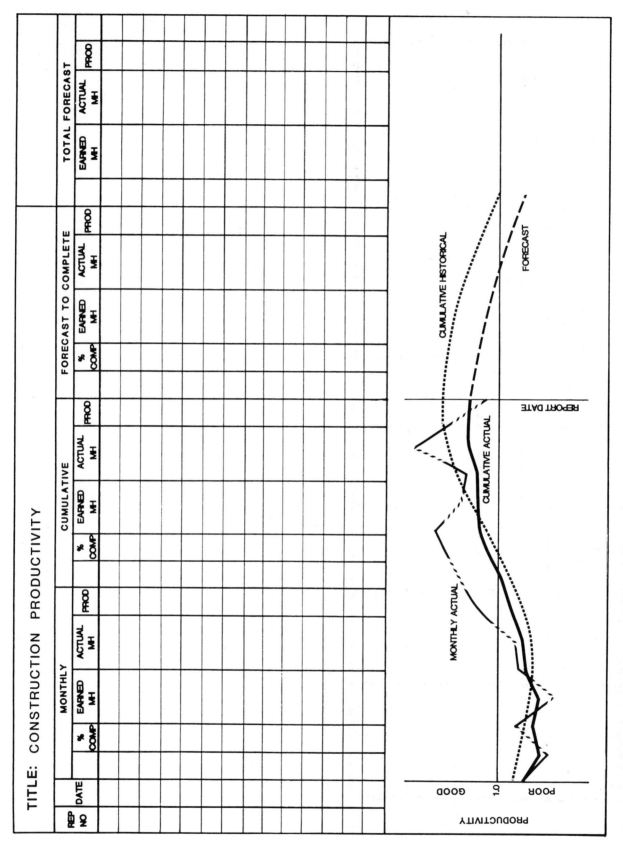

Figure 6.21 Construction productivity report.

formance can be due to deficiencies in the estimate or to poor labor productivity.

From the preceding, productivity is computed as follows:

$$\text{Productivity} = \frac{\text{Earned man-hours}}{\text{Actual man-hours}}$$

The formula is the same for both monthly and cumulative time periods. Good productivity is > 1.0; conversely, poor productivity is < 1.0 by the preceding definition, but productivity can also be measured by an inverse calculation.

Productivity measured by this method is not true or absolute productivity of the labor force. If there is no budget or a bad estimate, then the productivity measurement will similarly be zero or poor. Alternatively, a fat estimate will produce an artificially high productivity which will be no more representative of true productivity than a low estimate. Absolute productivity can only be measured on a unit-man-hour basis. This is often referred to as the work unit, labor unit, or man-hour unit.

6.35 CONSTRUCTION MAN-HOUR CURVE (DIRECT LABOR)

Apart from progress-productivity reports, major control methods of labor costs are the following:

Man-hour expenditure curve
Man-hour rate curve

These curves enable a trend pattern to be readily discerned and a forecast to be made based on the cumulative performance.

Figure 6.22 is a set of incremental and cumulative curves for direct-labor man-hours. Planned curves should be developed from the field estimate and construction schedule. Actual experience is plotted on a weekly-monthly basis. The actual man-hour status is tabulated on the form, together with a current forecast.

This example shows a slight overrun of actual versus planned values. As this trend has been evident for many months, an improvement is not likely, and a final overrun is possible. However, a man-hour overrun does not necessarily mean a cost overrun of the labor budget. It is possible for an underrun in estimated labor man-hour cost to compensate for an overrun in man-hours. Hence, it is important to monitor man-hour costs. This is accomplished with a man-hour rate profile.

6.36 DIRECT-LABOR MAN-HOUR RATE PROFILE

Figure 6.23 shows cumulative planned and actual profiles of the direct-labor man-hour rate. This rate represents total labor costs divided by total direct man-hours. The monthly status is tabulated as shown.

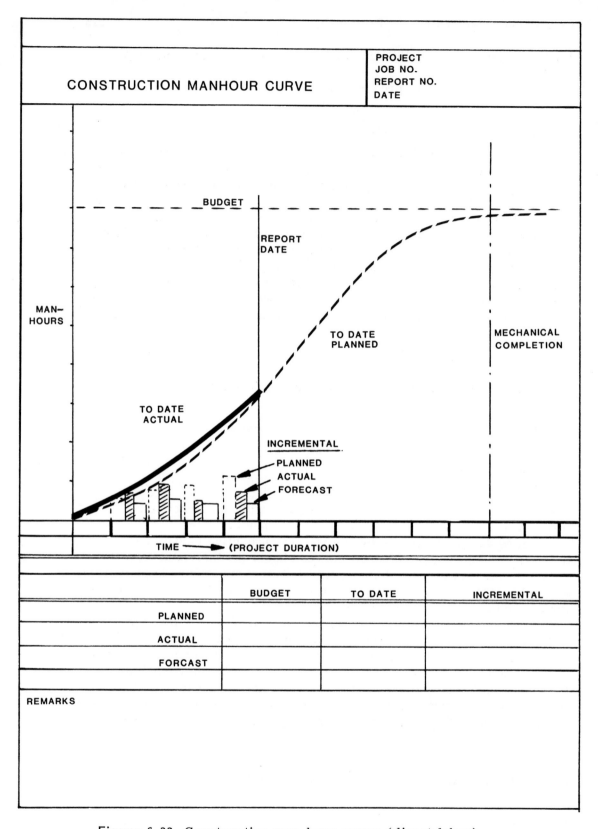

Figure 6.22 Construction man-hour curve (direct labor).

226

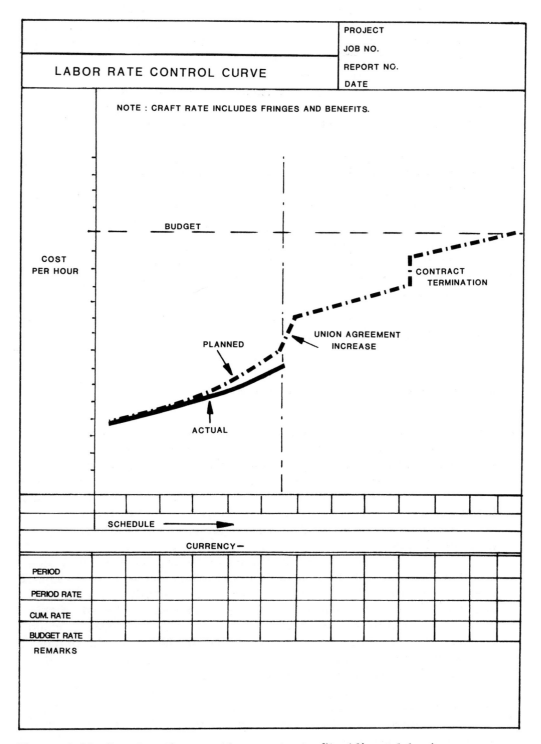

Figure 6.23 Construction man-hour rate profile (direct labor).

Significant deviation of actual versus planned values can indicate a potential overrun. Rate overruns can occur because of different craft mixes, union contract changes, governmental regulation changes, and premium costs for overtime and shift work.

This example shows an estimated level of $14. The curves track reasonable closely for the first 6 months. Abrupt changes in a cumulative profile do not generally occur when the job is well advanced as there is too much weight of past performance to allow instant or abrupt change.

A turndown can indicate release of higher-paid crafts, escalation lower than anticipated, or failure by trade unions to achieve pay demands.

The following profiles are typical of a process plant:

Low at first due to low-skill civil workers (laborers)
Increasing to peak due to highly paid equipment
    operators, millwrights, pipe fitters, and electricians
Then a slight turndown due to lower-paid insulators
    and painters

Man-hour expenditure and rate profile curves could be used to monitor indirect-labor man-hour costs.

6.37 WORK UNIT TRACKING CURVES

Another approach to measuring productivity is recording actual man-hours (incremental and cumulative) against physical units of completed work (e.g., lineal feet of piping, cubic yards of concrete, tons of steel, etc.). These man-hours per unit are an *absolute measure* of productivity in contrast to the relative measure previously outlined. This technique can resolve a problem of budget abnormalities and also enables cost engineers to readily compare performance in different geographical locations.

Figure 6.24 shows typical tracking curves for above-ground pipe erection. Incremental and cumulative performance is monitored. This example shows a budgeted level of 5.4 man-hours/unit and a current cumulative rate of 4.8—currently, a good performance. Based on this performance and judgment of future conditions, a good forecast could be made. As above-ground piping is the major element of the piping account and piping usually represents 35% of a field budget, piping tracking curves are important control tools.

When required, work unit tracking curves should be prepared early in the construction phase. Significant deviations (e.g., ±10%) from the budget should be investigated. A typical list of construction activities and associated work units is as follows:

Civil
    Excavation-backfill: man-hours per cubic yard of soil
    Foundations: Man-hours per cubic yard of concrete

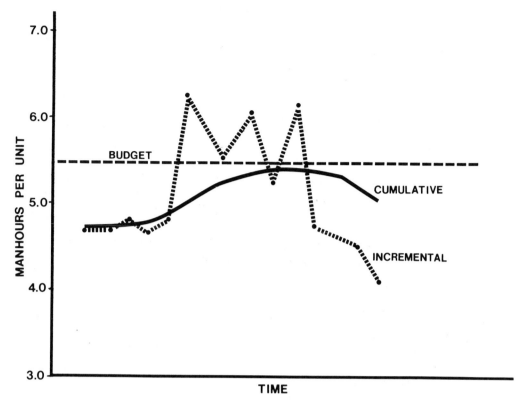

Figure 6.24 Work unit tracking curves (piping).

Fireproofing: man-hours per square foot of surface or cubic yard
  of concrete
Piping
  Field fabrication: man-hours per ton or lineal foot
  Field erection: man-hours per lineal foot (by pipe size) or
    man-hours per ton
Electrical
  Conduit: man-hours per lineal foot
  Wire and cable: man-hours per lineal foot
  Test, connect, and check out: man-hours per connection
Instrumentation
  Install: man-hours per instrument
  Local-remote loops: man-hours per loop
  Calibrate and test: man-hours per instrument
Structural steel: man-hours per ton
Insulation: man-hours per square foot and man-hours per foot (piping)
Painting: man-hours per square foot

Selection of individual work units for control will depend on need,
the size of the project, the amount of money involved, and the ease of
gathering data. This type of data is also very useful for historical
purposes.

6.38 INDIRECT LABOR MAN-HOUR CURVES

As indirect labor budgets are often poorly estimated, tracking curves should be developed for major indirect categories. Figure 6.25 shows a typical indirect man-hour tracking curve. Man-hours and man-hour costs should be tracked separately. A separate curve for average hourly rate could be drawn, or, alternatively, the hourly rate can be entered on the man-hour chart. The monthly status is tabulated as shown, and forecasts are shown. Forecasted man-hours multiplied by the anticipated hourly rate will give forecasted costs.

As is often the case, this example shows a significant man-hour overrun. The overrun started in month 10 and further escalated in month 13. A significant overrun was evident at that time. The hourly rate is also shown to be overrunning.

Indirect labor covers hourly paid labor not directly involved in the construction of permanent facilities; indirect activities can include the following:

Erection of temporary buildings, roads, etc.
Erection and maintenance of temporary utility systems
Site cleanup during and after construction
Materials handling and preservation (warehouse operation)
Scaffolding
Equipment maintenance
Lost time (weather, union allowances, training, etc.)
Welder proficiency tests and other training programs
Tea breaks, walking time, waiting time, etc.

6.39 INDIRECTS COST REPORT (MATERIAL)

Indirect material costs generally do not require curve techniques and can be monitored with a monthly status report. Materials forming part of a subcontract would be handled as part of a subcontract as per methods covered in Chapter 7. Figure 6.26 illustrates a typical monthly status report of field indirect material costs. Individual items are identified by account code; commitments, expenditures, the budget, forecasts, and variances are reported.

6.40 FIELD STAFF CONTROL

In preparing a detailed control estimate, the construction department should provide a field staff organization chart showing all necessary job functions; in addition this department should prepare a listing showing field staff positions, both permanent and local hire, and indicating planned arrival and release dates as well as budget man-hours or man-months. Figure 6.27 shows a typical listing which could be a basic con-

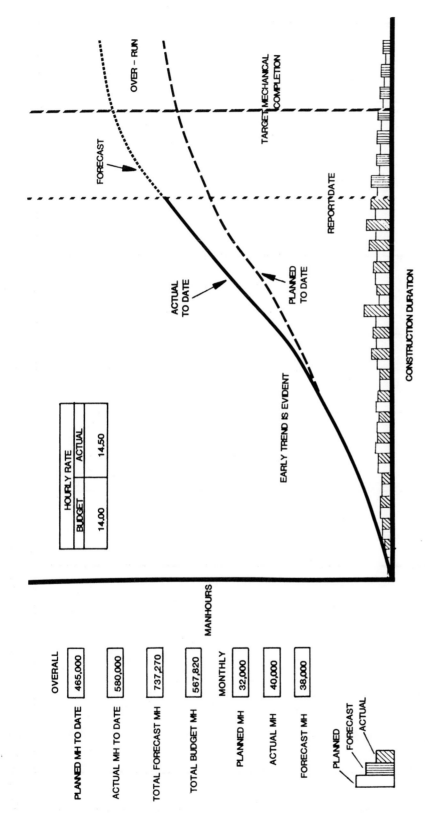

Figure 6.25 Indirect labor man-hour curves (includes labor rate).

CODE	DESCRIPTION	BUDGET	COMMITTED		EXPENDED		FORECAST	VARIANCE
			PERIOD	CUM.	PERIOD	CUM.		
1	2	3	4	5	6	7	8	9

INDIRECTS COST REPORT

PROJECT

JOB NO.

REPORT NO.

DATE

Figure 6.26 Indirect material cost report.

FIELD SUPERVISION LISTING & SCHEDULE

POSITION	NAME	SCHEDULE																		BUDGET $	FORECAST HOURS	HOURLY RATE	FORECAST $

PROJECT

JOB NO.

REPORT NO.

DATE

Figure 6.27 Field supervision report.

trol document for allocation of field supervision. This document should
be constantly updated.

The contract agreement will outline the basis of charging for the
construction staff. On reimbursable projects, these charges are sometimes a source of contention between the owner and contractor due to
differing interpretations of contract conditions. This account is best
controlled on an overall basis with man-hour expenditure and man-hour
rate curves.

6.41 CONSTRUCTION EQUIPMENT COST REPORT

On large projects, the cost of construction equipment can be substantial.
Figure 6.28 serves much the same function as the construction supervision listing. It defines the plan for assigning equipment and provides
for the monitoring and control of that plan during construction. The list
should show actual versus planned arrival and release dates and the
rental rate (or purchase price, if bought) and should compare the total
forecast equipment cost versus the budget.

Timely arrival and release of equipment is of schedule and cost
benefit. Thus, major deviations from the original (i.e., budgeted) plan
warrant close scrutiny.

A detailed evaluation should be made of the construction equipment
rental agreement to ensure that terms and conditions are economically
acceptable. In the United States, rental rates are usually stated as a
percentage of a nationally accepted price list. Factors to investigate are
buy-out conditions for equipment, terms for regular maintenance versus
heavy repair, arrangements and costs for transportation from a particular area, and the date on which the rental will commence.

6.42 CONSTRUCTION EQUIPMENT UTILIZATION

A technique for controlling construction equipment costs is a comparison
of actual costs per labor man-hour against budget and/or a historical
profile. Figure 6.29 is a typical format of control profiles.

This record of monthly and cumulative rental costs against direct
labor man-hours could give an evaluation of equipment commitments in
relation to manpower buildup. This could indicate that equipment was
brought to the site too early or that a projected manpower buildup was
not achieved. In either case, equipment was underutilized.

On large projects, a more detailed approach involves tracking dollar
costs of equipment per direct man-hour by geographical areas. Thus,
the cost engineer can compare areas to evaluate cost differentials.

Finally, this technique can also be applied to specific work activities.
For instance, the cost engineer may want to focus on the utilization of

CONSTRUCTION EQUIPMENT COST REPORT								PROJECT JOB NO. PROJECT NO. DATE		
				BUDGET		FORECAST			COST	
EQUIPMENT	SUPPLIER	MOBILN. COSTS	MONTHLY RATE	NO. OF MONTHS	COST	NO. OF MONTHS	COST	PERIOD	CUM.	
1	2	3	4	5	6	7	8	9	10	

Figure 6.28 Construction equipment report.

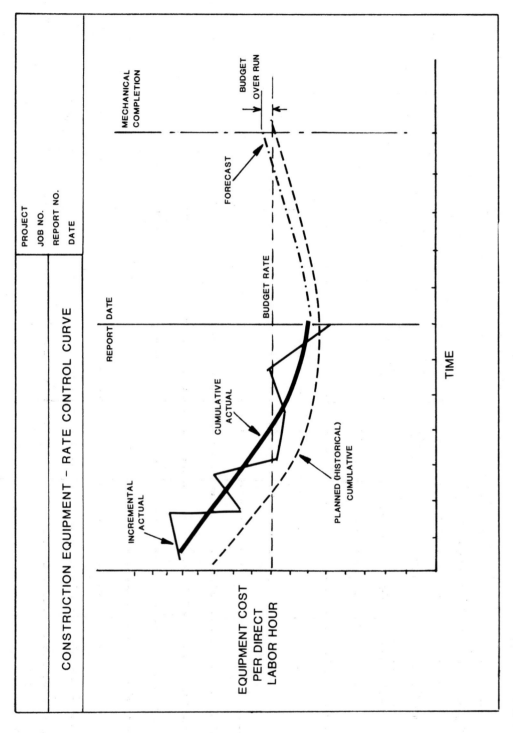

Figure 6.29 Equipment utilization profiles.

welding machines by tracking the number of welding machines relative to the number of welders.

Refer to Section 5.36 for additional information on this technique.

6.43 INDIRECT COST CURVES

For cost elements which are not quantifiable, such as temporary facilities, small tools, consumables, and field office expenses, financial expenditure curves can provide meaningful evaluations. Planned curves, based on history or judgment, could be developed and actual costs plotted against these curves. Figure 6.30 shows incremental and cumulative expenditure curves. Actual costs are plotted against planned costs.

6.44 PROJECT RUNDOWN CONTROL

As construction approaches mechanical completion, an efficient rundown can be difficult to achieve. Complicating efficient completion at this time are design changes, start-up, punch lists, and rework.

On large projects, this situation can be especially serious and lead to increased costs. Moreover, the weight of accumulated performance now obscures incremental performance. Therefore, work can get completed in a haphazard and unplanned manner. It is difficult, as punch lists and completion lists are generated, to ascribe a factual scope of work to a multitude of different items, many having top priority for completion.

A technique for reducing these problems is shown in Figure 6.31. This involves identification of the remaining scope of the work and individually controlling it to completion. This example shows a rundown program for direct labor on a large project.

In addition to field labor, there are other costs to consider:

1. *Material.* At this stage, field-purchased material usually reaches a peak due mainly to design changes and rework. It is suggested that an estimate of these expenditures be made. Planned dollar expenditure curves could be drawn for major categories and actual expenditures plotted.

2. *Subcontracts.* At this state, direct-hire forces could be replaced and the remaining work completed by subcontracts. Often these subcontracts are awarded on a *time and material* basis, making dollar expenditure curves vital in order to retain proper control. There is also the need for closing out the regular construction subcontracts, many of which may require settlement of claims and extras. Resolution of these items requires time and attention, and the subcontract group should not be cut back too quickly at this time.

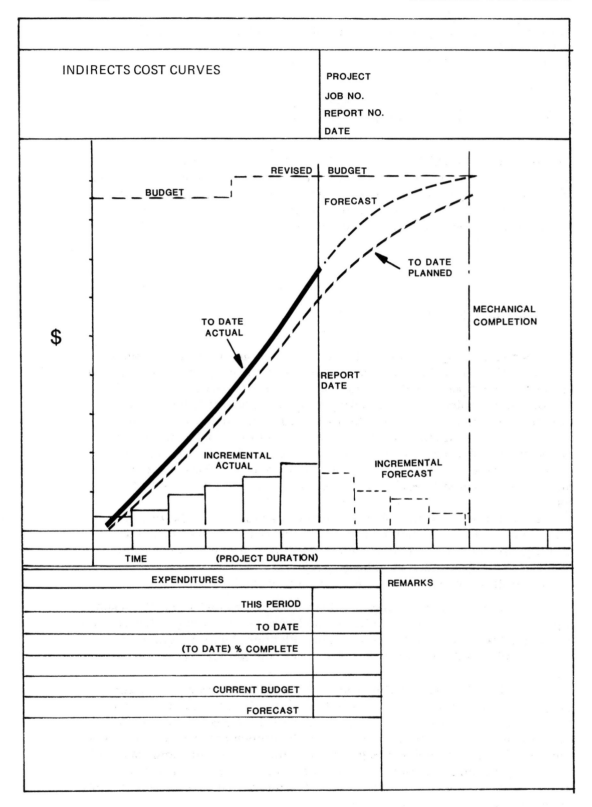

Figure 6.30 Indirect cost curves.

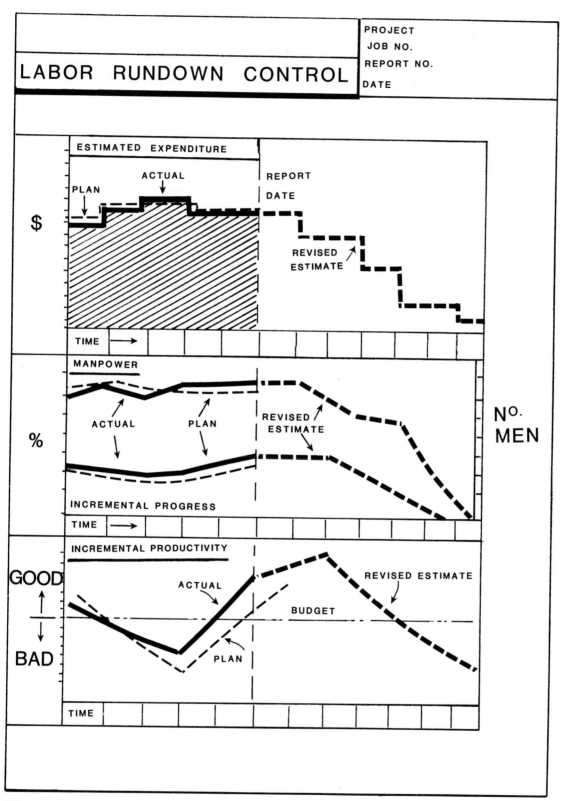

Figure 6.31 Direct labor rundown curve.

3. *Design Changes and Start-up Problems.* A field change log could help identify the scope of this work, and designation of the initiator could assist in a proper allocation of costs.

On reimbursable-type contracts, the prime contractor's scope of work may not include commissioning activities. However, the contractor generally has responsibility for a plant meeting its design performance and so is often asked to assist with commissioning and start-up. Owners believe that design changes required for start-up are the contractor's responsibility as many of these design changes are required for safe plant operation. Thus, on large projects, it is vital that manpower, man-hours, and costs be tightly controlled through the rundown stage.

7

SUBCONTRACT ADMINISTRATION
AND CONTROL

7.1 GENERAL

A quality subcontract administration program would consist of the following:

Fundamentals of administration
Home office organization and objectives
Field organization and objectives
Bid evaluation and analysis

7.2 Fundamentals

1. Direct-hire procedures are not suitable. In the past, most U.S. construction work in the process plant and petrochemical industry was carried out on a direct-hire basis. Due to the advantages of cost and better productivity, more work is now being subcontracted. Large, prime contractors have been slow to recognize the difference in control and the need for revised procedures.
See Section 7.8 for additional information.
2. Lump sum subcontracts require the following:

Adequate change order procedure
Progress measurement
Schedule monitoring
Performance evaluation

There is the concept that lump sum subcontracts require little or no controls and that subcontractors will not provide control information. This is a mistaken concept. It is true that subcontractors will not provide cost data; however, it is a foolish company that does not require progress measurement, schedules, and information for performance evaluation. These requirements should be clearly specified in bid proposal documents. The company should make it clear that the subcontractor's price should reflect these requirements. The requirements often have to be tailored to fit the subcontractor's control capability.

3. Unit price subcontracts are financially based and therefore require full controls for cost and schedule evaluation. The following should be major requirements:

Quantities
Unit rates
Cost and schedule monitoring
Performance evaluation

4. Due to a strong background of direct-hire work, a contractor's field supervision tends to treat subcontractors as poor neighbors or necessary evils. Subcontractors need proper field attention. Previous commitments, contractual considerations, schedule requirements, material supply, construction services, drawing availability, field office-storage areas, joint occupancy coordination, etc., should receive as much attention as the quality of the work. Lack of proper attention can result in failure by a company to meet previously agreed upon commitments, material-drawing delays, poor coordination of multiple subcontractors working in the same area (joint occupancy), unresolved contractual disagreements, poor control of extra work, and inadequate evaluation of performance. All of these can have a significant effect on the overall cost and schedule and result in major claims by subcontractors.

5. Major subcontract agreements often require review and endorsement by company legal personnel. The objective is to check the legal aspects of subcontractor contracts. Sometimes this objective becomes dimmed, and legal personnel become involved in "business" decisions of the subcontract. Business aspects are usually subcontract strategy, conditions of contract, commercial terms, and schedule requirements. This situation should be avoided. Legal personnel rarely have the construction, engineering, and cost experience to make viable decisions. Apart from business considerations, communication channels and personnel responsibilities can be confused when this occurs.

7.3 SUBCONTRACT STRATEGY

Business considerations, project size, and schedule requirements determine, to a large extent, the breakdown of construction work into lump sum, unit price, or cost-plus subcontracts. Due to project size, a further consideration is dividing large scopes of work on an area or functional basis. Area breakdowns are usually more efficient as they provide for a single responsibility, but this requires that subcontractors have necessary skills and experience to handle multiple types of work. One of the earliest subcontract strategy decisions is in the civil work. Should earthwork, concrete foundations, and underground piping be combined on an area basis with a single subcontractor, or should there be three subcontractors each handling the work on a total job basis? Careful consideration of a subcontractor's capability, single responsibility, and interface coordination requirements must be made for an efficient operation. Another element of subcontracting is the question of direct materials as a free-issue item, or supply by subcontractor.

All these variables can affect the ability to schedule and control, and a contractor control system may have to be modified to fit the subcontracting strategy for an effective operation.

A subcontract organization can be a matter of concern. Where subcontracts are the responsibility of the procurement department, necessary input and coordination with construction personnel are often lacking. Similarly, when subcontracts are an engineering function, the involvement of the procurement and construction departments can be too little or too late. It is sufficient to say that all elements of engineering design, purchasing procedures, labor, and site conditions must form part of a subcontract package.

There should also be personnel who are experienced in engineering, business matters, and construction to negotiate subcontracts in the home office and then follow the work to the job site. The continuity of personnel from the home office to the job site is important for a successful subcontract operation. It is essential that engineering, procurement, and construction personnel be properly involved in bid reviews, negotiations, and final bid tabulation.

7.4 SUBCONTRACT PREPARATION

Detailed attention by qualified personnel in the formation of subcontract packages at the very earliest moment is a wise expenditure of time. Too often, lack of attention or a slipping engineering schedule results in subcontracts being awarded with serious business and control discrepancies. The following preparation is essential:

Adequate scope definition
Business-like contractual conditions
Accurate labor regulations and site conditions
Specific control and reporting requirements

Quality subcontract packages require considerable effort and experience in the above-mentioned items. Owners have experienced serious schedule slippages due to contractors failing to recognize the work effort and time required.

For a "fast-track" approach, project schedules frequently require that subcontracts be let on a unit price basis. This is a compromise between lump sum subcontracts, which require full engineering definition, and reimbursable subcontracts, which sometimes are entered into with almost no definition.

For effective execution, unit price subcontracts require high-quality bid packages in which contractual conditions and work unit descriptions are clearly defined. Time and expertise are required to put these together.

See the end of this chapter for typical unit price subcontract formats and work breakdowns.

Figure 7.1 is a standard schedule showing significant activities and durations for a major subcontract on a large project up to and including contract award. Time requirements shown are based on many years of experience. A subcontract preparation schedule can be effective in letting and controlling subcontracts in a business-like, orderly fashion, with due regard to their criticality. At contract award, this schedule completes its work, and control responsibility is then vested in the field construction staff.

An important item of the subcontract package is a *control specification*, which details required control and reporting procedures. It is important that subcontractors fully understand the requirements of this specification so as to provide money and personnel in their proposal to do the work. A much debated item for inclusion in the inquiry package is the amount of schedule information. Too much detail can lead to claims when the schedule is not met, and too little detail will not provide a basis for committing the subcontractor and holding him or her responsible for future performance. A milestone schedule is recommended, together with overall engineering and equipment delivery information. Planned progress requirements can be meaningful, but inclusion of manpower histograms should be avoided.

An overall schedule for all major subcontracts, based on this standard, should be produced as early as possible. Subcontract stragegy discussions between the owner and contractor should provide the information for this schedule.

7.5 HOME OFFICE ORGANIZATION

For companies involved in a significant amount of subcontracting, experienced personnel should be permanently dedicated to handling subcontracts in the home office. Figure 7.2 shows a typical home office organization structure for a fairly large operation. The work can be divided by project or work category (civil-mechanical-piping, electrical, etc.).

It is recommended that a subcontract section be part of the construction department. Some companies have subcontract sections as part of engineering, procurement, and project management groups. Whereas engineering and procurement have some experience in technical and commercial aspects, they rarely have strong construction experience, which is essential for a successful subcontract operation.

A serious problem which can occur with this recommended organization is that construction can be independent and not properly involve engineering and procurement in technical and commercial aspects.

As shown in this exhibit, an essential aspect of an effective subcontract operation is close coordination of construction with other home office groups. These home office functions are the following:

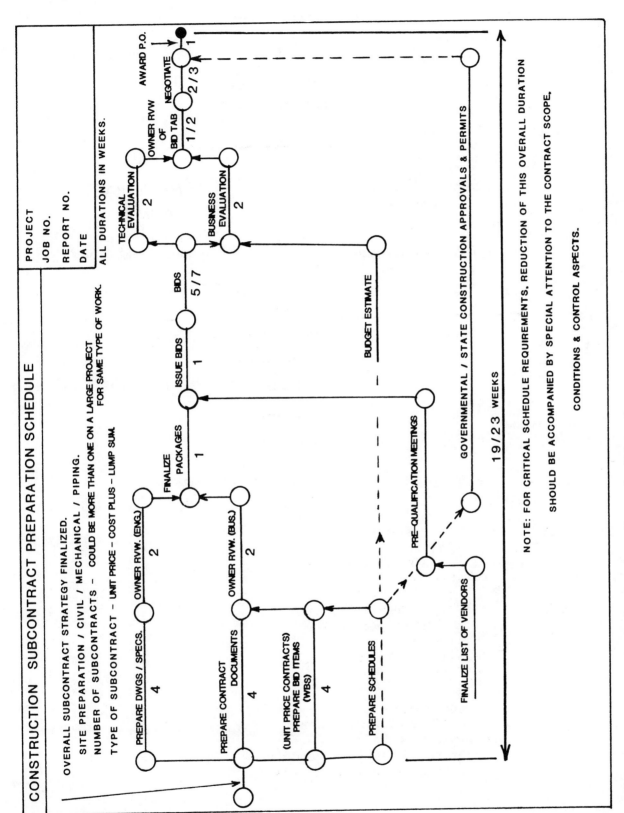

Figure 7.1 Typical subcontract preparation schedule.

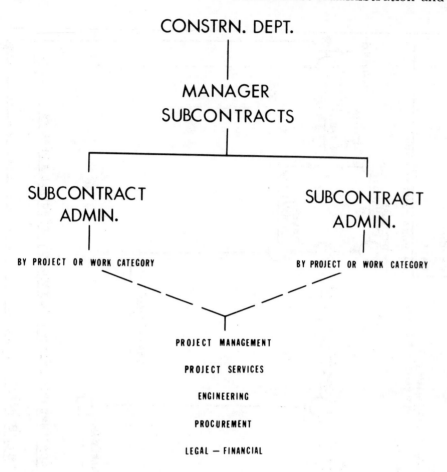

Figure 7.2 Flow chart of home office organization.

Project management
    Strategy
    Cost-schedule objectives
Project services
    Budget estimate
    Cost control specification
    Scheduling specification
    Schedule
    Cost-schedule bid evaluation
Engineering
    Scope
    Specifications
    Work breakdown structure
Procurement
    Commercial terms and conditions
    material control (free issue)

Construction
     Field services
     Site agreement
     Site conditions
     Capability evaluations and surveys
     Specifications (installation)
     Job site visit
     Overall coordination

7.6 FIELD ORGANIZATION

It is vital that there be very close coordination between home office and field subcontract groups. This will avoid attempts by subcontractors to "play off" field personnel against home personnel to get relief or advantage from commitments or conditions previously agreed to or requiring resolution.

It is recommended that subcontracts be negotiated and awarded at the job site at the earliest possible moment. This is generally not possible for site preparation and civil subcontracts as the field organization is not sufficiently developed at that time.

However, selections of field subcontract personnel could be made early so that these personnel could then function out of the home office to handle early subcontracts.

On a large subcontract job, it is essential that the functions of administration, control, and work direction be properly understood and coordinated.

Figure 7.3 shows a typical field functional organization. Allocation of personnel to these functions would depend on number, size, and type of contract. Obviously, reimbursable and unit price subcontracts require more personnel than lump sum subcontracts.

7.7 SUBCONTRACT BID ANALYSIS

It is generally not sufficient to solely evaluate a set of subcontract bids against each other. Comparisons against the budget should be made and an independent, detailed assessment made of the most attractive bid(s). This can give valuable information on the contractor pricing structure, within the body of the proposal, which can be used in further negotiations of the subcontract.

As unit price subcontracts are submitted on a monetary basis, this independent assessment would have to convert from money to man-hours. An adequate assessment could then be made by a comparison of bid unit man-hours to company-estimated man-hours.

The following summarizes a bid analysis program:

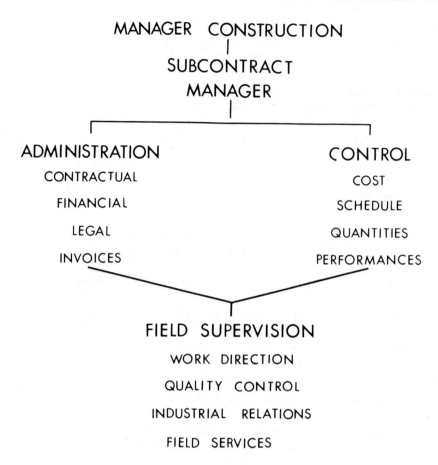

Figure 7.3 Flow chart of field organization.

Bid Analysis

Bid-to-bid evaluation

Evaluation to budget estimate

Detailed estimate-review of bids

    Convert financial units to man-hour units, as follows:

        Labor rate (including benefit allowances)

Construction staff	10-20% labor rate
Construction equipment (earth moving is high cost; insulation is low cost)	10-40% labor rate
Field costs	30-40% labor rate
Overhead and profit	20% labor rate
All-in labor cost	70-120% labor rate

Judgment is required to assess specific percentages from the preceding ranges. Size, work type, and job conditions are significant elements.

7.8 INTRODUCTION TO SUBCONTRACT CONTROL

Traditional contractor direct-hire techniques are rarely suitable for controlling a multiple-subcontract operation. Most subcontractors do not operate with sophisticated control systems, nor do they man their contracts with experienced project control personnel.

Imposition of a prime contractor's system on a subcontractor would require that the subcontractor use an unfamiliar code of accounts, be prepared to code all man-hours to this code of accounts, evaluate the quantities of work completed, assess the progress of partly completed work, and generally provide data for a very detailed and unfamiliar system. This rarely works and generally requires that the prime contractor provide personnel to carry out this work. The cost can be prohibitive even if subcontractors fully cooperate.

On lump sum contracts, subcontractors will generally refuse to provide man-hour data and will provide only a minimum of progress information.

It has to be recognized that subcontractors do not operate with detailed control systems and that the key for success is for a prime contractor to develop a simple, practical method of control and require that subcontractors include adequate personnel costs in their bids to use the system.

The following are essentials for effective control of subcontracts:

1. Good contractual documents and agreements
2. Adequate system for documenting changes and amendments
3. Proper assessment of work scope
4. Effective progress measurement system
5. Effective cost trending and forecasting system
6. Adequate performance measurement system

Most of these elements will generally be the responsibility of the prime contractor--or the owner if the owner is directing the subcontractors.

For the most part this chapter is based on a prime contractor-subcontractor relationship with unit price subcontracts.

7.9 CONTROL SPECIFICATION (LARGE SUBCONTRACTS)

Immediately following contract award, the subcontractor is required to carry out the following functions, prepare reports, and monitor progress as outlined in this specification:

1. *Quantities* (unit price subcontracts)—report monthly
      Report quantities installed by geographical area
      Report quantities installed by total subcontract
      Predict final quantities.
2. *Man-hours*—report weekly: total man-hours by total subcontract
3. *Craft manpower*—report daily: daily workforce report
4. *Scheduling*—report monthly
      Overall milestone schedule-bar chart
      Progress curves (area and total)
      Manpower histograms (area and total)
      Quantity progress curves for major work categories

These reports and progress updates are to be issued 5 days after the cutoff date. Progress curves can be developed on a financial basis and/or a *weighted* man-hour basis.

One of the objectives of this specification is to have subcontractors do the reporting and avoid situations where the contractor and/or the owner has to carry out this function.

7.10 PROGRESS CONTROL

Subcontractors rarely have the capability of sophisticated planning, scheduling, control, and reporting. Therefore, to achieve a successful operation, it is essential to keep control documents as simple as possible. Physical progress should be measured by physical quantities; man-hours should be collected to check on productivity and to assess manpower requirements; work in progress should be accurately identified; scope changes should be promptly recognized; labor availability should be constantly evaluated, particularly on remote job sites or in areas with high concentrations of work.

A key element in measuring progress, evaluating manpower requirements, and predicting completion is the accuracy of the scope in quantities and man-hours. Often an overall progress chart looks like the profile of a mountain range as the actual progress line increases and decreases with time, due to the upgrading of a poor scope evaluation. On large projects, where small scope variations can be significant, quantity takeoffs from construction issue drawings are essential.

Following are exhibits of typical control techniques.

7.11 SUBCONTRACT PROGRESS REPORT

Figure 7.4 breaks down the major operations, on a financial weighted basis, of a tankage subcontract. Individual activities are scheduled, and an overall planned completion curve is drawn based on the man-hours. Physical completion of the activities is measured, and man-hours

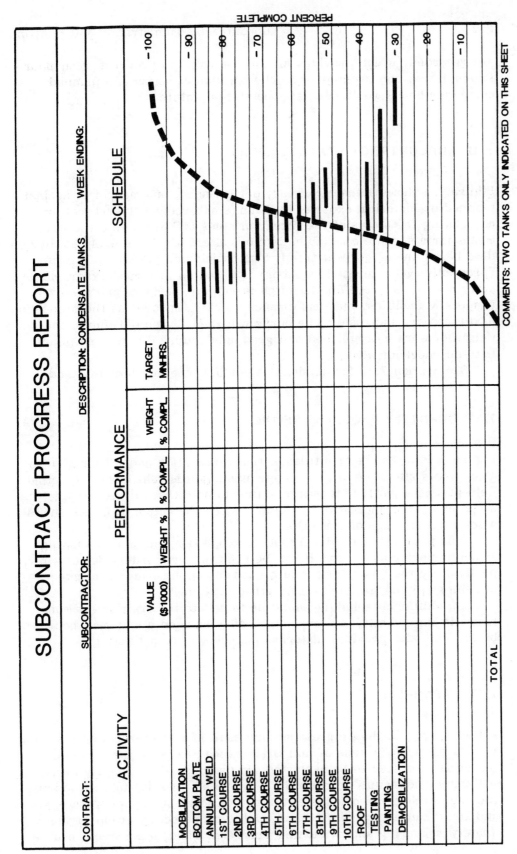

Figure 7.4 Subcontract progress report.

251

are recorded, which provides for an evaluation of progress, man-hour expenditure, and productivity. The addition of actual and planned manpower levels would complete the status picture.

7.12 SUBCONTRACT STATUS REPORT

Figure 7.5 shows actual progress, performance, and manpower against planned or historical experience. This is an excellent visual tool for correlating the status of the three variables and evaluating the requirements for a specific complation date or, alternatively, a likely completion date based on the current trend. The anticipated performance profile (productivity for direct-hire labor) is based on historical experience; early poor results are due to initial learning experience and work on temporary facilities, but performance quickly improves as the proportion of direct work increases. The curve will then flatten out due to the weight of work accomplished and gradually reduce due to final punch list and checkout work.

See Section 7.18 for details of a performance evaluation method.

7.13 QUANTITY PROGRESS REPORT

Figure 7.6 shows the quantities of mass excavation and fill for a large grass roots site. The original scope evaluation is scheduled and actual field progress plotted. It is interesting to note that in this example the scope evaluation increased by 20-30%. Also, the actual progress shows a schedule slippage of 9 months.

This is an efficient visual tool for scope trending and evaluating schedule performance, and it can be used for many categories of work, particularly the "bulks" (it is also good for engineering: concrete drawings, piping isometrics, and structural steel).

An additional technique would be to collate the craft direct man-hours to the quantity and evaluate performance on a unit-man-hour basis. This also provides historical experience for estimating.

7.14 MEASUREMENT

A key element in the progress measurement of subcontracts is quantities. This is particularly true of unit price subcontracts. Lump sum subcontracts also need to be evaluated for progress on a quantity basis.

Many contractors do not maintain detailed quantity takeoffs during the engineering phase. This can lead to a poor estimate of the scope and could cause serious problems for the construction group in adequately measuring and evaluating progress. Field measurement can be

Measurement   253

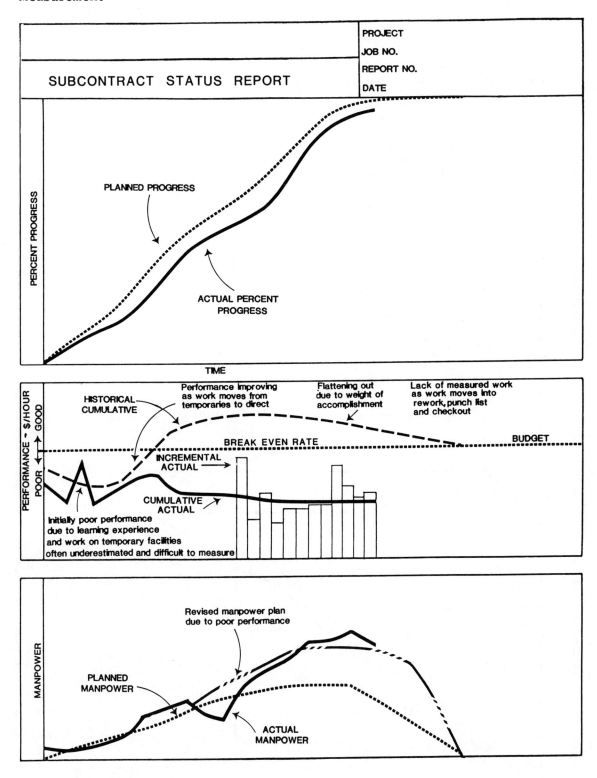

Figure 7.5 Subcontract status report.

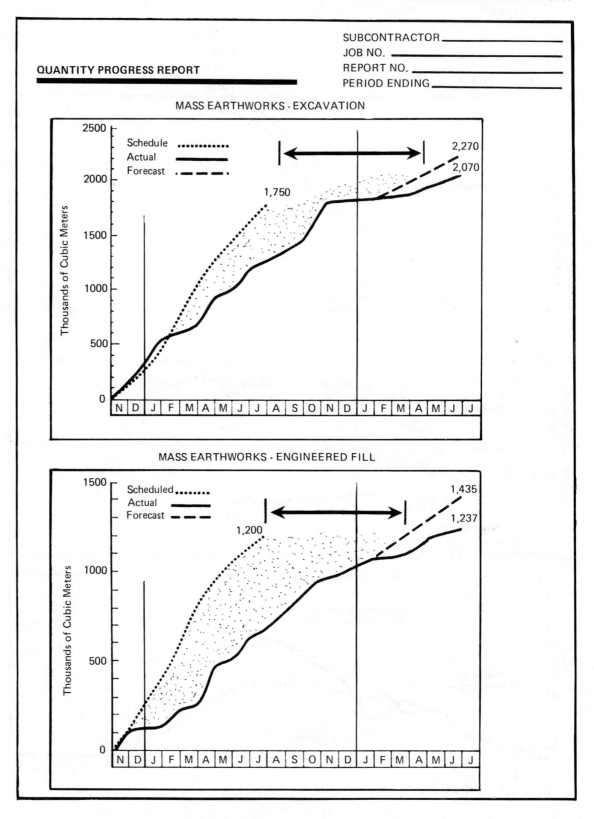

Figure 7.6 Quantity progress report.

greatly facilitated when home office quantity takeoffs are entered on the specific drawings at construction issue. It is then a relatively simple matter in the field, as the work is completed, to use these quantities for payment and measurement of progress, together with field changes as construction proceeds.

To overcome this home office lack of good quantity takeoffs, many contractors have instituted a field quantity takeoff system. As construction drawings are received at the job site, cost engineers, quantity surveyors, and field personnel will take off quantities and maintain a total scope buildup. This will provide for a proper assessment of scope but means that overall construction progress cannot be fully evaluated until field takeoffs are completed. This takes time, and it is often many months into construction before overall progress can be accurately measured.

It is important that field measurement of work in progress be recorded properly on marked-up drawings or quantity lists so that the financial billing of the subcontractor can be adequately checked. It is necessary that the subcontractor's billing be checked to ensure that billing reflects work completed.

At subcontract award, or prior to the start of construction, mutual discussions with the subcontractor on methods of progress measurement and payment should take place. At these meetings, agreements should be reached for the weighted breakdown of lump sum subcontracts and agreements for measuring partial completion of unit prices. The frequency of reporting and the method of measurement is a worthwhile item for agreement at this early date.

7.15 COST CONTROL, OVERALL

The first step in the cost control of subcontracts is evaluation of the contractual documents and contract agreement. In this evaluation one should look for contractual anomalies, pricing discrepancies, and contractor conditions which might lead to future cost exposure. Careful consideration should be given to schedule commitments, warehousing agreements, lay down and material handling requirements, and an evaluation that previously stated commitments by the contractor to the subcontractor can be maintained during the execution of the subcontract. It is particularly important that a review of the schedule commitments of associated interface work by others, job site areas, free-issue material supplies, and services be made as these items often provide the source for major claims by subcontractors.

A log should be maintained of all engineering and contractual changes that have taken place in contractual documents forming part of the agreement with the subcontractor. All changes should be evaluated for potential cost and the appropriate cost trends of such changes recorded. These potential cost deviations should be estimated as definitively as possible for use in future negotiations with the sub-contractor.

Following are exhibits and procedures of typical cost control techniques.

7.16 SUBCONTRACT EVALUATION (UNIT PRICE SUBCONTRACT)

The basic element of all unit price subcontracts, apart from contractual and schedule considerations, is quantities. Experience, particularly of large projects, has shown that takeoffs of early quantities often change as construction progresses. This is often due to better definition of engineering design and the recognition of changes in field conditions bringing improved estimate definitions.

In an evaluation of unit price bids one should consider potential variations in quantities against the pricing structure submitted by the subcontractor.

On several large projects, with different contractors and sub-contractors, owner experience has shown that civil work is greatly underestimated, particularly when it is necessary to let the civil sub-contract in the early design phase to meet schedule. On a fast-track approach, civil subcontracts are often sent out for bids when engineering is only 10% complete. This often results in "guestimates" of quantities.

The following shows a summary commercial breakdown for a civil subcontract, and, as indicated, it would appear that subcontractor A has a bid lower, by $150,000, than subcontractor B. The technical

Technical	Size	Experience	Work Load	Manpower/ Equipment	Supervision
Subcon-tractor A	Large	Good	50%	Sufficient	Adequate
Subcon-tractor B	Large	Good	50%	Sufficient	Adequate

Commercial Summary—$M (Unit Price Subcontracts)	Subcontractor A	Subcontractor B
Earthworks	10,500	8,700
Underground piping	1,800	2,300
Concrete (including framework & rebar)	9,200	9.900

Commercial Summary—$M (Unit Price Subcontracts)	Subcontractor A	Subcontractor B
Buildings	4,500	5,000
Roads (including culverts)	500	750
	26,500	26,650
	0	+150

evaluation shows that all variables are equal for both contractors and hence that the award of the subcontract is solely a question of pricing. Based on this set of figures, a reasonable recommendation would be to award the subcontract to subcontractor A. However, closer scrutiny of the figures shows a wide difference in the earthworks portion of the bids. Subcontractor A has the lowest total bid but the highest earthworks cost. Such a difference is too great to be ignored.

An independent evaluation of the bids could indicate which bid is more reasonable. This independent review should be carried out by converting the quoted work unit costs to man-hour units and comparing them against the prime contractor or owner estimating book. Subsequent negotiations with subcontractors A and B should use this independent review and bid-to-bid comparisons to reach a contract price. It is possible that both subcontractors would still retain the basic pricing structure of their bids so that the wide earthworks difference would remain.

A *sensitivity* evaluation should be carried out to check on the effect on quantity deviations. Experience shows that most quantities, particularly earth-moving quantities, increase substantially from early guestimates. Rarely is there a decrease in quantities on large projects.

The following is the previous bid comparison with an allowance for increased quantities:

	Sensitivity Analysis		
Commercial Summary—$M (Unit Price Subcontracts)	Increase*	Subcontractor A	Subcontractor B
Earthworks	+80%	10,500-18,900	8,700-15,660
Underground piping	+40%	1,800-2,520	2,300-3,220
Concrete (including framework & rebar)	+20%	9,200-11,040	9,900-11,880
Buildings	+10%	4,500-4,950	5,000-5,500

Commercial Summary—$M (Unit Price Subcontract)	Sensitivity Analysis		
	Increase*	Subcontractor A	Subcontractor B
Roads (including culverts)	+10%	500-550	750-825
		26,500-37,960	26,650-37,085
*Typical increase in initial quantities		0	+150
		+875	0

Recommendation: Award to subcontractor B: initially $150,000 higher but with sensitivity evaluation now $875,000 lower

A quantity sensitivity evaluation can greatly change proposal bottom line costs. This particular example shows quantity increases ranging from 10 to 80%.

Experience is essential in determining the amount of potential deviation to these early quantities. The status of engineering, the complexity of the project, knowledge of site conditions, the experience of quantity takeoff personnel, and a viable construction plan are factors in determining quantities of early civil work.

In many cases, quantities are developed by civil designers whose knowledge of construction operations and site conditions is often limited. It is difficult to comprehend that a substantial volume of earth will be moved several times at the same location.

As quantity sensitivity can be a speculative business, it is not recommended that bid quantities be changed to reflect the sensitivity evaluation.

Sensitivity analysis of quantities should be carried out until engineering design is sufficiently advanced to have confidence in the early estimate of these quantities.

7.17 SUBCONTRACT COST CONTROL AND FORECAST

Individual subcontracts should be evaluated and tracked from the original contract price to the final cost forecast. Figure 7.7 shows a typical *tracking* technique and illustrates a form which should be made out for each subcontract. Costs are broken down into material and labor components. The control sheet shows the price of the original contract agreement, accumulates current experience, assesses outstanding work, and forecasts a final predicted total cost. The form is vertically divided into two parts, the top portion being the physical scope of the work and the bottom portion covering financial matters where the physical scope of the work may not have increased. This enables progress measurements to be made on a financial basis of the physical scope of the work.

SUBCONTRACT COST REPORT

CONTRACT FOR :

CONTRACT NO.

CONTRACTOR

ORIGINAL CONTRACT PRICE (LABOR & MATERIAL)

CURRENCY

PROJECT

JOB NO.

REPORT NO.

DATE

ITEM	LABOR		%	MATERIAL		REMARKS
	PREDICTED TOTAL COST	COST TO DATE		PREDICTED TOTAL COST	TO DATE COST	
1 MAIN CONTRACT						
2 WORK OUTSIDE SCOPE OF CONTRACT						
(a) MAJOR CHANGES						
(b) ADDITIONAL BID ITEMS						
(c)						
3 OPEN COST WORK						
4 OTHER (SPECIFY)						
(a)						
(b)						
DIRECT WORK S/T						
5 CLAIMS (SPECIFY)						
(a)						
(b)						
(c)						
TOTAL						

Figure 7.7 Subcontract cost report and control form.

It is necessary to separate labor and material costs to provide allowances for labor claims and conditions which do not affect material prices. The cost engineer must consider all items identified on the form on a factual, contractual, or potential basis. The definition of scope, current conditions, and contractual agreement will largely determine the makeup of the listed items.

Contractor claims will require careful attention. Claims, generally, will fall into the following categories:

Change in "original" quantities
Schedule delays—caused by the owner and/or the prime contractor
Drawing and material delays
Interference by others
Changes in site conditions or site regulations

Most subcontractors will greatly exaggerate adverse conditions and submit inflated claims. Consequently, it is essential that daily logs, schedules, work programs, etc., be maintained for all major subcontracts.

On unit price subcontracts, developed with a minimum of engineering definition, factors of 20%, respectively, for quantity increases and claims should be added to the original contract price (labor only). Should an independent bid evaluation indicate a low bid, a further allowance should be made in anticipation of the subcontractor getting into financial difficulties.

A low bid can result through ignorance of process plant projects and/or site conditions or through a subcontractor "buying the job." There can be occasions when subcontractors will attempt to break into a new area of work or, alternatively, attempt to keep out competitors. Such situations can result in low bids, which, in turn, can lead to serious schedule consequences for an entire project should a subcontractor get into financial difficulties.

Many express the opinion that subcontractors in financial trouble will maximize their field effort to finish early and get out. The reverse is usually true. Subcontractors in financial trouble will generally reduce their field effort to a minimum to contain their losses. This results in low manpower levels and a minimum of construction equipment and supervision and leads to schedule extension. Apart from specialty subcontracts, such as boiler erection, concrete stacks, and tankage, most categories of work require subcontractors to stay to the end of the project. Thus, it is rarely possible for major civil, mechanical, and piping subcontractors to finish early and get out.

In Section 7.8 we shall outline a method by which to assess the financial performance of subcontractors.

7.18 PERFORMANCE EVALUATION

Performance evaluation is a technique to measure and monitor financial performance against man-hours expended by a subcontractor. This should enable evaluations to be made of potential schedule slippage and financial claims where a subcontractor's performance may be causing financial difficulties. If a subcontractor is in financial difficulty due to poor performance, or due to "buying" the work with a low bid, this can lead to schedule and cost problems for the entire project. For direct-hire work, measuring labor productivity resolves this problem. Direct-hire techniques cannot as readily be used to measure subcontracts. When this performance evaluation technique is properly used, it can provide early warning of potential problems.

This technique has been used on large and small projects over the past 10 years and has successfully provided an early warning system for cost exposure and schedule slippage. Early warning provides time to evaluate actions which might alleviate the subcontract situation or at least provide lead time for bringing in other subcontractors.

Performance Evaluation Method

1. Performance factor (labor) $= \dfrac{\text{contract billings}}{\text{man-hours expended}} =$ dollars per man-hour.

2. Assess the subcontractor's operational cost by building up field costs, equipment costs, overhead, etc., onto the base labor cost: = dollars per man-hour.

3. Ensure that billings truly represent work accomplished.

4. Ensure that the man-hour report is accurate.

5. If the subcontract has a material supply, evaluate it for profit on material to add to the profit-loss of the labor element.

6. Efficiency $= \dfrac{\text{performance factor}}{\text{all-in cost}}$.

7. If the cumulative efficiency is less than 1.0, the subcontractor is in a labor loss position.

   This can lead to schedule extensions and claims.

This is a relatively simple procedure and requires up-to-date billings, an estimate of the subcontractor's all-in labor cost, accurate man-hours expended, and an assessment of profit on material supply. Any competent cost engineer would be capable of following this procedure.

A major element of subcontract costs is quantities.

7.19 SUBCONTRACT QUANTITIES

The tracking of quantities from initial takeoffs through intermediate takeoffs to final field takeoffs is absolutely essential. Figure 7.8 illustrates a typical format for controlling quantities. Listed on this form would be all bid items of the contract. Separate sheets should be used for labor and material. The contract column would show quantities of the original contract. The forecast column would show the current assessment of quantities, and the difference between the original contract and the forecast would be entered in the differential column. Thus, the deviation is readily visible. Quantities installed to date, man-hours, and status are also shown.

SUBCONTRACT QUANTITY REPORT				CONTRACT		FORECAST		VARIANCE		TO DATE		
ITEM	UNIT	UNIT RATE		QUANT.	COST	QUANT.	COST	QUANT.	COST	QUANT.	COST	%

PROJECT

JOB NO.

REPORT NO.

DATE

Figure 7.8 Subcontract quantity report.

This report is the base document for "controlling" quantities. It should receive constant attention.

7.20 SUBCONTRACT PERFORMANCE REPORT

Figure 7.9 is a simple tabulation of financial performance per man-hour of each subcontract. In conjunction with the performance curve shown on the subcontractor's status report, these data can provide a good basis for overall cost prediction. Individual performance curves should be developed for all critical subcontracts.

7.21 SUBCONTRACTS FORECAST SUMMARY

All subcontracts should be listed, in total, on the control form shown in Figure 7.10. This form summarizes current cost and forecasted final value and identifies scope, claims, and potential trends. The figures for each subcontract are taken from the individual prediction cost summary reports.

7.22 PROCEDURE FOR FIELD CHANGES AND EXTRA WORK

Figure 7.11 outlines the major elements to efficiently evaluate, report, and estimate field changes and extra work which occur during construction. This is a sample of a field change order form, which has been successfully used on many projects. The objective of this procedure is to identify all changes from approved drawings, evaluate impacts on the cost and schedule, and authorize the work.

Often, field changes and extra work are required on an urgent basis; however, an efficient estimating and authorization procedure need not necessarily delay the work. Too often, owners receive requests on a crash basis where little thought has been given to the need or cost impact of the change.

It is as important to record and control contractor changes as it is owner changes. During the punch list and checkout phase at the tail end of the construction work, owners often require changes to meet operability and safety standards.

Field Changes—Subcontractors—Procedure
(Extra Work Authorization)

General

It is the primary responsibility of the subcontracts administration to maintain the performance of a subcontractor so that contractual commit-

SUBCONTRACT PERFORMANCE REPORT

PROJECT

JOB NO.

REPORT NO.

DATE

P.O. NO.	SUBCONTRACT		$ EARNED PER LABOR MAN HOUR (CUMULATIVE)	ESTD. RATE
	WORK SCOPE	CONTRACTOR		

Figure 7.9 Subcontract performance report.

CONTRACT NO.	CONTRACTOR	WORK SCOPE	BUDGET	ORIGINAL CONTRACT VALUE	CHANGES & EXTRAS	CLAIMS	FORECAST	COMMD.	EXPEND.

SUBCONTRACT SUMMARY REPORT

PROJECT
JOB NO.
REPORT NO.
DATE

Figure 7.10 Subcontract summary cost report.

```
                    FIELD CHANGE ORDER
                    (Contract Amendment)

                                              Number:_____

                                              Date:   _____


To:     Subcontractor

Contract/Purchase Order No. _____ Supplement No. _____


Please proceed with the following change(s):

1.  Description of Change: _____

    _____

    _____

    _____


2.  Reason for Change: _____

    _____

    _____

    _____


3.  Change Requested By: _____

    _____

4.  Estimated Bare Cost $_____ Cost Estimate Attached: _____

5.  Actual Bare Cost    $_____ Sub-contractor Bid Attached: ___

6.  Work Completed on: _____

7.  Remarks: _____

    _____

    _____


8.  Effect on Schedule: _____

9.  Approval and authorization to Proceed:
```

Contractor Initiated By	Contractor Approval	Owner Engineering Release	Owner Subcontract Coordination & Field Approval	Owner Authorization

Figure 7.11 Field change order form.

ments, previously accepted, are achieved. However, contractual commitments of scope, quality, schedule, cost, etc., change; this procedure is used so that work can proceed in a timely, efficient, and orderly manner.

All such changes, whether initiated by the contractor or the owner, shall be identified as *field changes*. They shall be initiated, approved, transmitted, and recorded in a manner designed to minimize the loss of time and extra costs associated with each such change.

1. *Field change order form:* Figure 7.9 is a sample of this form, which becomes the main control document of all changes. This form is reasonably self-explanatory and covers all aspects of scope, cost, schedule, and approval.
2. *This form, fully completed,* together with the subcontractor's bid and the contractor's cost estimate, shall be submitted to the owner subcontracts coordinator, who will process it through the requisite owner sections.
3. *Only with the appropriate signature* in the owner authorization box may this work proceed.
4. *Field changes of costs less than $1000* do not require prior owner authorization; however, it is expected that the same documentation and procedure will prevail so that changes to approved for construction (AFC) drawings and specifications will have owner engineering approval.
5. *The field change order (FCO) should be submitted in duplicate* so that one form may be retained by the owner.
6. *On completion of the work, the FCO will be resubmitted* with items 5 and 6 filled in, and any supporting cost backup should be attached.
7. *It is appreciated that possible urgency of the proposed work* may not give sufficient time for a formal bid to be solicited, so the estimated bare cost (item 4) will be a contractor guesstimate.
8. Particular care should be given to item 8—effect on schedule—so that proper assessment may be made of the proposed change.
9. *It is recommended that the FCO numbering system be tied back* to a cost-schedule geographical area and that the number indicate the number of changes in that area as well as the total number of changes, i.e., if a process unit, 1/1/1. Should the change cover more than one unit or area, then the prefix P for onsites and S for offsites could be used.

7.23 CONCLUSION

Our intent in this chapter on scheduling and controlling construction subcontracts is to present pragmatic control techniques and methods for cost and schedule evaluations. Effective control of subcontracts is demanding and requires personnel experienced in business matters, cost analysis, and schedule evaluation. The best techniques in the world will not ensure an efficient subcontract control operation unless qualified personnel are assigned to the task.

Following are typical work breakdown structures of subcontracts and descriptions of the individual work activities. Contractual, commercial, general, and performance conditions are not included. A complete subcontract package would generally include the following:

Contractual correspondence
Information for bidders
Form of tender
Memorandum of agreement
Terms of insurance
General conditions
Technical provisions
Safety regulations
Description of bid items
Schedule-performance requirements
Control specification

7.24 TYPICAL WORK BREAKDOWN STRUCTURE OF A CIVIL SUBCONTRACT (UNIT PRICE)

7.24.1 List of Bid Items

1.00 General
      1.1 Setup.
2.00 Underground pipe
      2.1 Hydrostatic testing.
      2.2 Install buried cast iron spigot and socket pipe, 6-in. nominal diameter.
      2.3 Install buried cast iron spigot and socket pipe, 4-in. nominal diameter.
      2.4 Install buried cast iron spigot and socket pipe, 8-in. nominal diameter.
      2.5 Install buried cast iron spigot and socket pipe, 10-in. diameter.
      2.6 Install buried cast iron spigot and socket pipe, 12-in. diameter.
      2.7 Install buried cast iron spigot and socket pipe, 14-in. diameter.
      2.8 Install buried cast iron spigot and socket pipe, 20-in. diameter.
      2.9 Coat and wrap joints.
      2.10 Install steel pipe.
      2.11 Weld steel pipe.
      2.12 Install hydrants.
      2.13 Install specialties.
      2.14 Install pipe sleeves at road or bund crossings.
3.00 Underground electrical
      3.1 Install precast inspection pits.

3.2   Install earth electrodes.
3.3   Lay copper earthing tape.
3.4   Install 4-in. pipe sleeves.

4.00   Excavation

4.1   General excavation.
4.2   Machine excavation.
4.3   Hand excavation.
4.4   Machine excavation for underground pipe.
4.5   Hand excavation for underground pipe.
4.6   Overhaul.

5.00   Backfill

5.1   Ordinary backfill.
5.2   Backfilling of underground pipe trenches.
5.3   Granular backfill.
5.4   Sand backfill.

6.00   Demolition

6.1   Break out concrete, over 12-in., heavily reinforced.
6.2   Break out concrete, less than 12-in., lightly reinforced.
6.3   Break out mass concrete, reinforced.
6.4   Break out mass concrete, unreinforced.

7.00   Paving and roads

7.1   Formed upright curbs.
7.2   Unformed inverted curbs.
7.3   4-in.-thick reinforced paving and floors at grade.
7.4   6-in.-thick reinforced paving and floors at grade.
7.5   8-in.-thick reinforced concrete road.
7.6   Lay road subbase.
7.7   Lay crushed stone surfacing.

8.00   Formwork

8.1   Ordinary formwork less than 5 sfca.
8.2   Ordinary formwork greater than 5 sfca.
8.3   Extra over for exposed formwork.
8.4   Formwork for shored surfaces.

9.00   Anchor bolts

9.1   Anchor bolt assemblies less than 20-lb weight.
9.2   Anchor bolt assemblies greater than 20-lb weight.
9.3   Miscellaneous metal accessories to concrete.

10.00   Reinforcement

10.1   Reinforcing rod and mesh--all operations.

11.00   Concrete

11.1   2-in.-thick blinding concrete.
11.2   Install polythene sheeting.
11.3   Pour concrete (up to 5 yd).
11.4   Pour concrete (5-10 yd).
11.5   Concrete bedding and haunching for underground pipe.
11.6   Install precast concrete trench covers.

12.00 Miscellaneous
        12.1 Minor cast-in-place concrete supports.
        12.2 Setting shims.
        12.3 Grouting.

7.24.2 General Comments

It is intended that all work required to complete the following shall be covered by bid items included in this contract: excavations, all concrete foundations and allied works, the complete installation of cast iron underground piping and allied works, and the complete installation of underground earthing cable and associated works.

Concrete foundation work shall be the controlling factor, and the contractor shall note that installation of underground piping and electrical items must be placed in order to ensure maintenance of the schedule.

In the case of excavation and backfill of underground pipe trenches, the contractor shall ensure that trenches are not kept open any longer than essential and to this end shall lubricate and have piping ready for installation as soon as the trench is ready. Any soil subsidence necessitating repairs to the pipe trench, which is the direct result of the contractor failing to meet the stipulated requirements, shall be repaired by the contractor at his or her own expense. Shoring, as required, will be the responsibility of the contractor.

The purchaser will supply and deliver to the site the following direct materials: anchor bolts, reinforcing rod and mesh, and *all* direct material associated with the installation of underground piping, underground electrical, and allied work. These materials shall be stored in the purchaser's designated storage areas, and the unloading, handling, transporting to storage, and storing of these materials shall be the contractor's responsibility. Any costs incurred by others for unloading such material *after* the contractor is established on the site will be backcharged to the contractor.

The remainder of the direct materials as listed on the material tender form are to be supplied by the contractor and quoted for separately on the material tender form.

For the purpose of this contract, the following shall be considered to be indirect materials: tie wires and chains for reinforcing steel; stirrups for supporting base-reinforcing mats, form ties, and similar items; and brazing rods, miscellaneous clips, etc., which may be included in the finished product. They are to be furnished by the contractor, and the cost shall be included in the schedule of bid items and unit prices.

For all work, the unit price shall include all labor costs, including the following: premiums, bonuses, fringes (cash or otherwise), payroll assessments, taxes, insurance, etc.; all tool and equipment costs; all costs of craft supervision, inspection, and services; all sales, excise turnover, and other taxes; any other costs which may

be required for the satisfactory performance and completion of the
work; and the contractor's profit.

The unit rates shall be inclusive of all operations as described in
the description of bid items and shall reflect both labor and material
costs individually. The contractor shall be entitled to no additional
payments whatsoever.

No change in the unit rates will be allowed because of changes
of quantities of the various items, nor because of changes in the
overall scope of the work, except that for a substantial change in the
overall scope of work, the price for setup shall be mutually adjusted.

The price submitted shall be firm for the duration of the work,
and escalation shall not be applicable to labor or materials.

1.1 Setup (Lump Sum)

This item covers the contractor's general expenses in setting up the
project and shall specifically include all temporary buildings and facilities, all overheads, nonproductive field engineering services, administration, and any other indirect costs related to performance of the
work. The contractor's profit, craft supervision, indirect materials,
and all other costs as defined under "General Comments" shall be
included in the unit rates.

The contractor shall be responsible for any clearing, leveling,
filling, compacting, draining, or fencing of the area designated by the
purchaser at the contractor's work and storage area.

This item will be paid for as follows:

1.   On the date of commencement of the work: 30%
2.   At monthly intervals thereafter (subject to actual progress): 10%

2.1 Hydrostatic Testing (Lump Sum)

This item covers all work necessary to hydrostatically and/or pneu-
matically test pipework in accordance with the purchaser's specifications and requirements of all underground pipework upon completion
of installation. The maximum test pressure will not exceed 250 psig.

Included in this item are supply and operation of all pumping
equipment, temporary pipework, fittings, pressure gauges, valves,
blanks, and any other means necessary for testing systems to the
purchaser's satisfaction. Water for testing purposes will be provided
free to the contractor; however, the contractor shall be responsible
for making necessary connections to the source of supply and for
draining systems following satisfactory completion of the tests. All
tests shall be performed in the presence of the purchaser's designated
representative. No test shall be considered complete until the purchaser issues an acceptance certificate to that effect.

Any system which fails under test as a result of the contractor's
negligence or faulty workmanship will be rectified at the contractor's
expense, and that system shall be retested to the satisfaction of the
purchaser.

The arrangement and sequence of tests shall be established by the purchaser. For the purpose of quotation, the contractor shall provide for testing all completed pipework systems.

The price for this item shall not be adjusted for changes in the total scope of work unless the contractor tenders an acceptable proviso for such contingency in the bid.

The pay quantity for this item shall be a lump sum, and for the purposes of progress payments, the contractor and the purchaser, jointly, shall agree on an estimated percentage complete for this item.

2.2-2.8 Install Buried Cast Iron Spigot and Socket Pipe (Linear Feet Plus Each Joint)

This item covers the handling, the hauling from storage, and the installation of underground cast iron spigot and socket pipe, fittings, valves, and accessories, including fitting, aligning, yarning, caulking, leading, and/or otherwise joining or any other operations necessary.

Included in this item is installation of any temporary supports necessary for pipe inspection purposes and final piping supports prior to backfilling.

Excavation and backfill of trenches for piping installed under this item shall be paid for under excavation and backfill bid items.

The lineal feet measurement shall be along the centerline of the pipe and through fittings and valves.

The "each joint" measurement shall be the number of joints of the diameter specified, actually made in installed pipe, and finally tested to the purchaser's specification for connecting pipe, fittings, and valves as required by the purchaser's drawings.

The pay quantity for this item shall be the total linear feet of pipe as finally installed and shall also be on the basis of the number of joints actually installed according to the following bid items:

2.2 Install buried spigot and socket cast iron pipe, nominal diameter 6-in., linear feet + each joint

2.3 Install buried spigot and socket cast iron pipe, nominal diameter 4-in., linear feet + each joint

2.4 Install buried spigot and socket cast iron pipe, nominal diameter 8-in., linear feet + each joint

2.5 Install buried spigot and socket cast iron pipe, nominal diameter 10-in., linear feet + each joint

2.6 Install buried spigot and socket cast iron pipe, nominal diameter 12-in., linear feet + each joint

2.7 Install buried spigot and socket cast iron pipe, nominal diameter 14-in., linear feet + each joint

2.8 Install buried spigot and socket cast iron pipe, nominal diameter 20-in., linear feet + each joint

2.9 Coat and Wrap Joints (Each Joint)

This item covers the coating and wrapping of all welded joints. Work shall include the preparation and cleaning of the joints, application of the coating primer, and final wrapping of the welded joint. Work shall also include minor repairs to coated and wrapped pipe lengths damaged during normal handling and installation. The work does *not* include repairs to extensive damage to coated and wrapped pipe lengths where such damage has occurred during shipment of pipes from the supplier to the site. The contractor shall be responsible for bringing to the attention of the purchaser any such extensive damage, and payment will be made for the repairs on an open cost basis. Failure by the contractor to notify the purchaser of extensive damage may result in the contractor making such repairs at his or her own cost.

Material costs shall *not* be included under this item.

The pay quantity for this item shall be the total number of joints actually coated and wrapped according to the following bid items:

2.9.1   Coat and wrap joints: 3-in. diameter, each joint
2.9.2   Coat and wrap joints: 4-in. diameter, each joint
2.9.3   Coat and wrap joints: 6-in. diameter, each joint
2.9.4   Coat and wrap joints: 8-in. diameter, each joint
2.9.5   Coat and wrap joints: 10-in. diameter, each joint
2.9.6   Coat and wrap joints: 12-in. diameter, each joint
2.9.7   Coat and wrap joints: 14-in. diameter, each joint
2.9.8   Coat and wrap joints: 16-in. diameter, each joint
1.9.9   Coat and wrap joints: 18-in. diameter, each joint

2.10   Install Buried Carbon Steel Pipe (Tons)

This item covers all work required for the proper installation of buried, coated, and wrapped steel pipe and fittings, valves, and extension stems but with the exception of welding, hydrants, and special piping items, which are covered separately.

Work under this item includes handling and hauling from storage, cutting, placing, aligning, making bell holes at joints, supporting pipe and fittings, installing temporary piping supports necessary for pipe inspection purposes, and permanent piping supports prior to backfilling.

Payment for work done under this item will be made only when pipe fittings and valves are properly located and permanently supported in their final position. The pay quantity for these items shall be the total tons of pipe and fittings and valves (excluding hydrants and special piping items) actually installed as required according to following:

2.10.1   Install buried steel pipe: 3-in. diameter, long tons
2.10.2   Install buried steel pipe: 4-in. diameter, long tons
2.10.3   Install buried steel pipe: 6-in. diameter, long tons
2.10.4   Install buried steel pipe: 8-in. diameter, long tons
2.10.5   Install buried steel pipe: 10-in. diameter, long tons
2.10.6   Install buried steel pipe: 12-in. diameter, long tons
2.10.7   Install buried steel pipe: 14-in. diameter, long tons
2.10.8   Install buried steel pipe: 16-in. diameter, long tons
2.10.9   Install buried steel pipe: 18-in. diameter, long tons

2.11 Weld Carbon Steel Pipe (Weld Unit)

This item covers all operations necessary for welding during pipe
fabrication and erection and includes marking, cutting, profiling,
leveling, aligning, fitting up, tack welding, cleaning, chipping, pre-
heating (if necessary), final welding, together with any special welding
requirements, and the final cleaning of welds.

Welding covered by this item is for straight pipes, all types of butt
weld fittings, weld neck and slip on flanges, mitres, welded valves, all
types of reinforced and unreinforced branch welds, socket weld fittings
and valves, all seal welds, and any other fitting or accessory that constitutes and/or requires a finished butt weld.

This item will be paid for on the total number of *weld units* in
accordance with the table entitled "Table of Straight Butt Weld Units"
with the factors for mitres, unreinforced and reinforced branch welds,
and materials other than carbon steel as detailed in note 3 of this table.
The weld unit price shall be inclusive of weld rod and in the case of
reinforced branch welds shall also include reinforcing material.

The contractor shall make the best possible use of straight pipe
lengths in the fabrication and field erection of spool pieces and straight
piping runs. If, in the opinion of the purchaser, the contractor makes
uneconomical welds, the cost of such welds will be charged to the contractor's account.

2.12 Install Hydrants (Each)

This item covers the complete installation of all hydrants complete with
isolating valves and includes the following: material handling, placing,
and orienting of hydrant units; the making of underground joints at
the hydrants; any temporary or permanent supporting required; and all
other operations necessary to perform this work.

The pay quantity for this item shall be the total number of
hydrants, regardless of type, finally installed.

2.13 Install Special Piping Items (Each)

This item covers all operations necessary for the proper installation of
all items defined by the purchaser as special piping items. The work includes material handling, placing, and aligning; connecting to underground piping; any temporary or permanent supports, installation of
gaskets; and all other operations necessary to complete the work.

The work may include, but shall not be limited to, installation of
dresser couplings, dall tubes, all types of strainers, etc.

The pay quantity for this bid item shall be the total number of
special piping items finally installed.

2.14 Install Pipe Sleeves at Road or Bund Crossings (Linear Yards)

This item covers the installation of pipe sleeves at road or bund
crossings.

The work includes material handling, temporary or permanent
supports to hold sleeves in place, cutting, fitting, welding, installation

of seals, placing, and jointing, regardless of whether pipe sleeves or casing pipe will be used.

Excavation or backfilling will be paid for separately.

The pay quantity for this item shall be the linear yards of sleeve or conduit actually installed, regardless of size.

3.1 Install Precast Inspection Pits (Each)

Work under this item covers the precasting, curing, storing, and installation of inspection pits complete with covers where specified and as detailed on the purchaser's drawings. The work includes forming, pouring, and finishing to an acceptable quality; placing precast sections in the proper location; and all other operations necessary to ensure satisfactory installation of inspection pits.

Hand excavation for pits shall be paid for separately.

The pay quantity for this item shall be the total number of individual inspection pits precast and placed in position and complete with a cover according to the purchaser's drawings.

3.2 Install Earth Electrodes (Each)

Work under this item covers the installation of 12 ft × 3/8 in. copper electrodes as specified on the purchaser's drawings. The work includes driving electrodes to the required depth, attaching earth brackets to the electrodes, and coupling earth tape to the brackets. Also included is the backfilling of the inspection pit after installation of the electrodes to the required depths.

The pay quantity for this item shall be the total number of electrodes installed complete with attached brackets and tape and inclusive of backfilling to the required depth and according to the purchaser's drawings and specifications.

3.3 Lay Copper Earthing Tape (Linear Yards)

Work under this item covers all work necessary to lay copper earthing tape below grade level. The work shall include the handling, measuring, cutting, and laying of earthing cables in shallow trenches, clamping as and where necessary. Also included shall be any necessary threading through cable pipe sleeves where earthing tape is required to come above grade. Cable ends must be left coiled in a position so as to prevent damage, a suitable length remaining for connection to equipment busbars, electrodes, etc.

The work under this item also includes any necessary protection of earthing tape to backfill should backfill not commence immediately.

The pay quantity for this item shall be the total length in yards of earthing tape finally laid and secured below grade as called for on the purchaser's drawings.

3.4 Install 4-in. Pipe Sleeves (Linear Feet)

This item covers fabrication and installation of 4-in. pipe sleeves where earthing tape rises above grade and where called for on the purchaser's drawings. The work includes any necessary cutting to nominal 1-ft lengths of 4-in. pipe and the installation of plastic sealing compound after threading of the tape and where tape emerges above grade.

The threading of earthing tape through pipe sleeves shall be covered under item 3.3 and not under this or any other item.

The pay quantity under this item shall be the total length of 4-in. pipe fabricated and installed as pipe sleeves for earthing tape as called for on the purchaser's drawings.

4.1 General Excavation for Foundations and Underground Works (Cubic Yards)

This item covers excavating, loading out, hauling, and stockpiling at a location not more than 500 yd away from the nearest point of the generally excavated area and maintaining good and reasonable temporary drainage of excavated area(s) and stockpile(s).

"General Excavations" shall cover those excavations where the extent to be excavated to any single depth equals or exceeds a horizontal area of 250 yd^2, of any plan shape, measured at the bottom of the excavation.

No general excavation shall be performed without a written instruction from the purchaser to proceed, which shall fully describe the extent to be excavated. The purchaser shall state the limits of excavation, and they shall not be less than 1 yd outside the limits of foundations and underground pipes to be installed later.

The purchaser may direct the slopes to be excavated and maintained at the edges of the excavated areas, and these slopes shall be used for calculating the quantities of this item; however, if the purchaser directs a slope steeper than two horizontal to one vertical, the contractor shall excavate as directed but shall be paid on the basis of two horizontal to one vertical.

The pay quantity for this item shall be cubic yards of general excavation, as described, performed by the contractor as required by the purchaser.

4.2 Machine Excavation for Foundation and Underground Works (Cubic Yards)

This item covers excavating by machine, loading out (if required), hauling, and stockpiling (if required) at a location not more than 500 yd away from the nearest point of the excavated area and maintaining good and reasonable drainage of the excavated areas and stockpiles. All necessary dewatering and shoring of holes shall be included in this item.

"Machine Excavation" shall cover excavation where the extent to be excavated is not considered general site preparation.

The pay quantity for this item shall be calculated from points 18 in. outside of the underground works to be constructed and shall be based on slopes of one horizontal to one vertical regardless of the actual slopes constructed. Where excavations overlap with each other. volumes shall be paid for only once.

Varying and/or sloping bottom depths may be required.

The pay quantity for this item shall be cubic yards of machine excavation, as described, performed by the contractor as required by the purchaser. The contractor shall prepare detailed lists, dimensioned sketches, and calculations for pay quantities for this item. No assessment of progress or interim payments shall be allowed until such information is completed and available for the purchaser's review.

Machine excavation for underground piping trenches shall be paid for under item 4.4 and not under this or any other item.

The excavation and removal of existing above-grade bund walls and tank pads shall be paid for under this item *if* the contractor is directed to do such work by the purchaser.

4.3 Hand Excavation for Foundations and Underground Works (Cubic Yards)

This item covers excavation by hand, loading out (if required), hauling, and stockpiling (if required) at a location not more than 500 yd away from the nearest point of the excavated area and maintaining good and reasonable drainage of the excavated areas and stockpiles.

"Hand Excavation" shall cover those excavations where machine excavation *is not practicable or permissible.*

The pay quantity for this item shall be calculated from points 18 in. outside of the underground works to be constructed and shall be based on slopes of one horizontal to one vertical regardless of the actual slopes constructed. Where excavations overlap, volumes shall be paid for only once.

Varying and/or sloping bottom depths may be required.

The pay quantity for this item shall be cubic yards of hand excavations, as described, performed by the contractor as required by the purchaser. The contractor shall prepare detailed lists, dimensioned sketches, and calculations for pay quantities. No assessment of progress or interim payments shall be allowed until such information is completed and available for the purchaser's review.

Hand excavation for underground piping trenches shall be paid for under item 4.5.

4.4 Machine Excavation for Underground Piping Trenches (Cubic Yards)

This item covers trench-type excavation by machine, dewatering, surface compaction, and the final grading of the trench bed in readiness for the installation of piping. Where excavated material cannot be temporarily deposited near sides of trenches, making allowances for access openings as required, the contractor shall remove excavated material at no extra cost to within 500 yd of the nearest point of excavation.

The pay quantity for this item shall be cubic yards of machine excavation calculated for trenches with vertical sides (regardless of the actual slope), beginning at a point not more than 1 ft outside the outer wall of the pipe and with a depth from the trench bed to grade level.

4.5 Hand Excavation for Underground Piping Trenches (Cubic Yards)

This item covers trench excavation by hand, dewatering, surface compaction, and the final grading of the trench bed in readiness for the installation of piping. Where excavated material cannot be temporarily deposited near sides of the trenches, making allowances for access openings as required, the contractor shall remove excavated material at no extra cost to within 500 yd of the nearest point of excavation.

"Hand Excavation" shall cover those excavations where machine excavation *is not practicable or permissible.*

The pay quantity for this item shall be the cubic yards of hand excavation calculated for trenches with vertical sides (regardless of the actual slope), beginning at a point not more than 1 ft outside the outer wall of the pipe and with a depth from the trench bed to grade level.

4.6 Overhaul (Cubic Yards Per Mile)

This item covers the loading, hauling, and deposition of excavated material to the purchaser's designated spoil heaps where such material has to be hauled distances in excess of 500 yd from the point of excavation. The work also includes the spreading and rough leveling required to maintain spoil heaps in an orderly manner.

The pay quantity for this item shall be cubic yards times miles of overhaul and shall apply to actual quantities performed and agreed upon.

If it is deemed necessary at any time to transport excavated material outside plant limits, the contractor will be entitled to overhaul in accordance with this definition. However, no further payment will be made for this item unless the contractor receives written instructions advising him or her to remove spoil from the plant site.

5.1 Ordinary Backfill from Stockpiles (Cubic Yards)

This item covers loading out from stockpiles not more than 500 yd from the central point of the general area to be backfilled, hauling, placing, spreading, watering or drying, compacting, and the final grading of ordinary backfill in accordance with the purchaser's specification. This material shall be previously excavated earth, if suitable, approved by the purchaser or approved imported backfill.

The pay quantity for this item shall be cubic yards of ordinary backfill actually placed and measured in its final position after compacting. The pay items for backfill shall not exceed the pay limits for any corresponding excavation.

Fill under this item shall be placed in uniform layers not exceeding 18 in. of loose thickness and shall be compacted by rolling each layer with four passes of a Sheeps Foot Roller weighing 7 tons or by other equally efficient and satisfactory approved means.

5.2 Backfilling of Underground Piping Trenches (Cubic Yards)

This item covers careful backfilling in uniform layers not exceeding one
quarter of the smallest diameter of pipe laid, in loose thickness, and
proper compaction of each layer of backfill under, around, and above
installed piping to prevent excessive surface settlement.

Backfill material will generally be that previously excavated and
must be to the approval of the purchaser. Any necessary handling and
haulage from stockpiles not more than 500 yd distant are also included in
this item.

The pay quantity for this item shall be cubic yards of backfill
placed and compacted around pipes, including the volume of the pipe,
for pipe sizes up to and including pipe of 16 in. in outside diameter
and excluding the volume of pipe for larger sizes. The pay quantity
shall be based on trenches with vertical sides (regardless of the actual
slope) and beginning at a point not more than 1 ft outside the outer wall
of the pipe and with a depth from the trench bed to grade level.

5.3 Granular Backfill (Cubic Yards)

This item covers the placing of approved granular backfill as required or
directed by the purchaser and according to the purchaser's specifications. It includes loading out and hauling from stockpiles within 500 yd,
spreading, watering or drying, compacting, and final grading to required levels. The method of compacting granular backfill shall be as
directed by the purchaser and dependent on its application.

Material costs for granular backfill shall *not* be included under
this bid item.

The pay quantity for this item shall be cubic yards of granular
backfill actually placed and measured in its final position after compacting.

5.4 Sand Backfill for Cast Iron Pipe (Cubic Yards)

The work covers handling, hauling from storage, and carefully placing
and compacting sand to a thickness of 6 in. around underground cast
iron pipe as called for in the purchaser's specifications.

The work shall take place prior to and subsequent to the laying of
cast iron pipe.

The contractor shall note that the total volume of sand placed shall
be deducted from the total volume of backfill calculated according to
item 5.2 to ascertain the final pay quantity for that item.

The pay quantity for this item shall be the total volume in cubic
yards of sand placed around underground cast iron pipe in accordance
with the purchaser's specifications.

6.1 Break out Concrete, over 12 in., Heavily Reinforced
(Cubic Yards)

This item covers breaking out and hauling to tip concrete in floor slabs
at grade and below, and any other concrete slabs 12 in. thick and over,
containing more than 2% steel.

The pay quantity for this item shall be the total quantity in cubic yards broken out and disposed of according to the purchaser's instruction.

6.2 Break out Concrete, Less than 12 in., Lightly Reinforced (Cubic Yards)

This item covers breaking out and hauling to tip concrete in floor slabs at grade and below, and any other concrete slabs less than 12 in. thick, containing less than 2% steel.

The pay quantity for this item shall be the total quantity in cubic yards broken out and disposed of according to the purchaser's instruction.

6.3 Break out Mass Concrete, Reinforced (Cubic Yards)

This item covers breaking out and hauling to tip all mass concrete at grade and below. It specifically includes footings for foundations, grade beams, and all other concrete constructions which contain reinforcing steel.

The pay quantity for this item shall be the total quantity in cubic yards of mass concrete broken out and disposed of according to the purchaser's instruction.

6.4 Break out Mass Concrete, Unreinforced (Cubic Yards)

This item covers breaking out and hauling to tip all mass concrete at grade and below. It specifically includes footings for foundations, grade beams, and all other concrete constructions which contain no reinforcing steel.

The pay quantity for this item shall be the total quantity in cubic yards of mass concrete broken out and disposed of according to the purchaser's instruction.

7.1 and 7.2 Integral Curbs (Linear Yards)

These items cover the construction of upright concrete curbs formed integrally with concrete paving or slabs. These items also cover the construction of unformed inverted curbs around the perimeter of certain paving. In either case, however, the area of paving above or below the curbs shall be paid for under the paving item. The work shall include all formwork, the pouring of concrete, and any finishing required to produce a curb of acceptable appearance.

Any reinforcing steel or mesh required shall be paid for under item 10.00. No material costs shall be included under this item.

The pay quantity for this item is linear yards of curbs actually constructed and according to one of the following bid items:

7.1 Formed upright curbs, linear yards
7.2 Unformed inverted curbs, linear yards

7.3 Four-Inch-Thick Reinforced Concrete Paving and Floors at Grade (Square Feet)

This item covers side forming, installations of screed guides, pouring concrete, wood float and broom finishing, construction of all joints, and curing concrete of all concrete paving up to and including a thickness of 4 in. Reinforcing steel or mesh which is required shall be paid for separately.

The quantity to be paid for under this item is the square feet of paving actually installed, including the area under curbs and without any deduction for inserts and blockouts which have an area less than 2 yd^2.

The materials and delivery costs for ready mix concrete, reinforcing steel and mesh, bituminous expansion jointing, expansion joint primer bituminous sealing compound, etc., should *not* be included.

7.4 Six-Inch-Thick Reinforced Concrete Paving and Floors at Grade (Square Feet)

This item is the same as that covered by item 7.3 except that this item is for paving with a thickness in excess of 4 in. and up to and including 6 in.

7.5 Eight-Inch-Thick Reinforced Concrete Road (Square Feet)

The work covered by this item is the same as that covered by item 7.3, except that this item is for the construction of a concrete road 8 in. thick.

7.6 Lay Road Subbase (Square Yards)

This item covers the preparation of a road subbase and includes the preparation of subgrade, transporting, placing, spreading, shaping, compacting, and fine grading of sand or clinker ash, approved by the purchaser, to a final thickness of 4 in.

Material and delivery costs shall *not* be included under this item.

The pay quantity for the item shall be the total square yards of road subbase.

7.7 Lay Crushed Stone Surfacing (Square Yards)

This item covers handling, hauling, leveling, and compacting crushed stone to a nominal thickness of 4 in., waterbonding, and the final compacting of 1-in. fines added for attrition.

Material and delivery costs shall *not* be included.

The pay quantity for the work shall be the total area in square yards.

The contractor shall note that this bid item specifically does *not* apply to any work the contractor may have to do in his or her designated work and storage area. Such work shall be covered under setup, item 1.1.

8.1 Ordinary Formwork Less than 5 sfca (Square Feet
Contact Area)

This item covers all types of formwork for foundations, substructures,
and vertical superstructure surfaces, regardless of height. Specifically
excluded from this item are the following:

Formwork for shored surfaces
Extra over for exposed formwork
Formwork for paving, floors, roads at grade, and curbs
Formwork for minor cast-in-place concrete supports
Formwork for precast concrete trench covers

    This item shall also cover the cutting back and plugging of tie
lines, the repair of minor honeycombs, the chipping of fins, and any
other finishing on concrete surfaces as may be required to yield a
structurally sound structure of satisfactory appearance.
    The quantity to be paid is square feet of contact area as indicated
by the drawings. No allowance will be made for excess formwork against
which conrete is not poured. For pay purposes only, horizontal dimensions will be measured to the nearest inch with no minimum measurement. Vertical dimensions will be measured to the nearest inch with a
minimum pay measurement of 1 ft. Sloping formed surfaces will be paid
at both horizontal and vertical projections, rather than the sloped surface measurement. No payment will be made against this item until
concrete is finished to the purchaser's satisfaction.

8.2 Ordinary Formwork Greater than 5 sfca (Square Feet
Contact Area)

This item shall be the same as item 8.1 except that this item covers forms
greater than 5 ft of contact area.

8.3 Extra Over for Exposed Formwork (Square Feet
Contact Area)

This item covers an extra payment for the use of smooth formwork, such
as plywood or similar boarding yielding a superior finish for all exposed
surfaces (normally above grade) or as directed by the purchaser.
    The quantity under this item represents the approximate area in
square feet of ordinary formwork for shored surfaces requiring a special
finish and does not represent an additional quantity of formwork.

8.4 Formwork for Shored Surfaces (Square Feet
Contact Area)

This item covers the supply and placing of formwork for all heavily
shored horizontal and sloping surfaces more than 6 ft above grade. It
shall include scaffolding or any other means required to support the
formwork.
    This item shall also cover the cutting back and plugging of tie
holes, the repair of minor honeycombs, the chipping of fins, and any

other finishing of concrete surfaces as may be required to yield a structurally sound structure of satisfactory appearance.

The pay quantity under this item is the required square feet of formwork as defined without consideration of any minimum dimensions and with sloping surfaces measured along the slope. No payment will be made against this item until the concrete is finished to the purchaser's satisfaction.

9.00 Anchor Bolt Assemblies (Each Assembly)

All anchor bolt assemblies will be furnished by the purchaser for assembly and installation by the contractor.

This item covers making and installing rigid templates for anchor bolts and the installation of anchor bolt assemblies.

The contractor may be required to dismantle and reassemble anchor bolt assemblies in order to place them in the proper positions. No extra payment will be allowed for such work. However, if the contractor is required to bond, cut, thread, or weld in order to make assemblies fit properly, extra payment shall be allowed for such rework.

The contractor shall protect all anchor bolt threads which project from the concrete by greasing them and covering them with rags securely wired tight.

The pay quantity for this item is the number of anchor bolt assemblies (four separate anchor bolts are counted as four assemblies) installed, and payment shall be based on the following bid items:

9.1 Anchor bolt assemblies up to 20 lb in weight
9.2 Anchor bolt assemblies over 20 lb in weight

9.3 Miscellaneous Metal Accessories to Concrete (Pounds)

This item covers installation of miscellaneous metal accessories such as described below. Accessories used for the convenience of erection and which are furnished by contractor, such as reinforcing, tie wires, and chairs and shuttering ties, are not covered by this item. These are indirect materials, which are furnished and installed by the contractor.

The work under this bid item shall cover the installation of all miscellaneous metal accessories such as but not limited to the following: bearing angles, handrailing, floor grating, chequered plate, sliding plates, support brackets, drains, manhole and catch basin frames and covers, rubbing strips, weir plates, etc.

Material and delivery costs for all miscellaneous metal accessories should *not* be included under this bid item.

Anchor bolt assemblies, reinforcing steel, and reinforcing mesh are not covered by this item.

The pay quantity under this item shall be the actual weight in pounds of the accessories installed.

10.1 Reinforcing Mesh and Steel—All Operations (Pounds)

This item covers all operations involving reinforcing mesh and steel for embedment in concrete and includes but is not limited to handling, prefabricating, cutting, unrolling, shaping, bending, tying into mats or baskets, placing as required, and securing in position.

Material and delivery costs shall *not* be included in this bid item.

The pay quantity under this item is the theoretical weight in pounds of the reinforcing steel and mesh fabricated and placed.

11.1 Two-Inch-Thick Blinding Concrete (Square Yards)

This item covers the placing, spreading, and leveling of a 2-in. layer of blinding concrete.

The pay quantity for this item is the square yards of 2-in.-thick blinding concrete actually placed.

Material and delivery costs for blinding concrete shall *not* be included under this item.

11.2 Install Polythene Sheeting (Square Yards)

This item covers the following: fine grading; the preparation of the subgrade; the handling, cutting (if required), placing, spreading, and leveling of polythene sheeting; and any other operations which may be necessary to install the sheeting to provide an adequate base for *subsequent* paving and flooring.

The pay quantity for this item shall be square yards of polythene sheeting actually placed.

No material or delivery costs shall be included under this item.

11.3 Pour Concrete (up to 5 yd in Height) (Cubic Yards)

This item covers the placing, vibrating, protecting, curing, etc., of concrete up to and not exceeding a height of 5 yd for formed foundations and structures as measured from topside of footings. Specifically excluded from this item are the following:

Concrete for paving, floors, curbs, and roads
Grout, mortar, or concrete for minor items
Concrete for minor cast-in-place supports
Concrete for precast trench covers

The contractor shall furnish and transport the concrete to the forms as required for construction. The material, mixing, and delivery cost of the ready-mixed concrete will be paid for as direct material and not under this item.

The quantity to be paid for under this item is the drawing quantity in cubic yards of required concrete.

11.4 Pour Concrete (5.0-10.0 yd in Height) (Cubic Yards)

The work covered by this item is the same as that described by item 11.3 except that this item is for concrete poured between 5.0 and 10.0 yd in height above topside of the footings. The pay quantity for this item will be measured in the same manner as item 11.3.

The contractor shall note that in single concrete structures that have a total height of column in excess of 5.0 yd, as measured from the topside of the footings, the contractor shall be paid at the unit rate indicated for item 11.3 for concrete poured in the base and at the unit rate indicated for item 11.4 for *all* concrete poured in the column.

11.5 Concrete Bedding and Haunching for Underground Piping (Cubic Yards)

This item covers all operations necessary in placing, protecting, etc., concrete bedding and haunching for underground piping.

The material, mixing, and delivery costs of concrete will be paid for as direct material and not under this item.

The pay quantity for this item shall be cubic yards of concrete bedding and haunching finally placed in position around underground piping.

11.6 Install Precast Concrete Trench Covers (Each)

This item covers the precasting, curing, storing, and installing of concrete trench covers. It includes the following: forming, pouring, and mixing in the coloring material; finishing to an acceptable quality; placing precast covers in the proper location; and all other operations necessary to ensure satisfactory installation of the covers. Reinforcing steel or mesh which is required shall be paid for separately.

The pay quantity for this item shall be the total number of individual trench covers precast and placed in position.

12.1 Minor Cast-in-Place Concrete Supports (Each)

This item covers pipe supports, stair bases, etc., where the volume of concrete per support does not exceed 0.1 yd^2.

Reinforcing steel, if required, will be paid for separately. The mixing and delivery costs of concrete will be paid for as direct material. All other operations required for minor cast-in-place concrete supports, including excavation and backfill, applying epoxy resin adhesive as necessary, forming, placing bolts and other accessories to be embedded in the concrete, pouring concrete, finishing concrete to a quality equal to "ordinary finishing," and any other operations necessary for successful completion of this item, shall be paid for under this item.

The pay quantity under this item is the number of minor cast-in-place concrete supports, as defined.

12.2 Setting Shims (Each Pile of Shims)

This item covers material handling, mixing mortar, placing mortar on foundations, setting shims, and leveling off.

The pay quantity for this item will be the number of piles of shims actually set.

Material and delivery costs for shims should *not* be included in this bid item.

12.3 Grouting (Square Yards)

This item covers the grouting of equipment which has been finally set. The work includes material handling, supplying and mixing mortar, forming, pouring, and finishing by means of grout wash and carborundum stone rubbing to give the best practicable appearance.

The pay quantity for this item will be square yards of grout applied to an average thickness of $1\frac{1}{2}$ in. and finished as directed, with a minimum pay quantity per part grouted of 0.2 yd^2.

The material and delivery costs for sand and cement should *not* be included under this item.

The measurement of this item will be the plan or surface area of each foundation column or plinth receiving grouting, as indicated on the respective foundation drawings.

7.24.3 Materials

General

1. Insofar as possible, firm prices should be given. In cases where definitive information is not fully available, the contractor may be permitted to readjust the quoted prices when final information is available. However, the contractor is expected to make every effort to quote realistic prices and so keep any adjustment to a minimum.

2. The contractor shall note that the following descriptions refer to the supply, delivery, unloading, and storage (if necessary) of materials only. The cost of handling and hauling to the point of construction from storage (if necessary), installation, erection, and/or placing of materials are covered in the description of bid items and shall not be included in the materials price.

3. All materials shall conform to local codes and to the requirements of the technical provisions.

Ready Mix Concrete (Cubic Yards)

This item covers the supply and delivery to the site of a minimum of 4000 $lb/in.^2$ of ready mix concrete for roads. The quantities and qualities of cement, sand, and aggregate shall be as required by the specification.

The pay quantity for this item shall be the total quantity of concrete in cubic yards.

Ready Mix Concrete (Cubic Yards)

This item covers the supply and delivery to the site of a minimum of 3000 $lb/in.^2$ of ready mix concrete for all foundations, paving, and any other concrete work as required. The quantities and qualities of cement, sand, and aggregate shall be as required by the specification.

The pay quantity for this item shall be the total quantity of concrete in cubic yards.

Approved Backfill (Cubic Yards)

This item covers the supply and delivery to the site of approved backfill material.

The pay quantity for this item shall be the total quantity of approved backfill in cubic yards.

Granular Fill (Cubic Yards)

This item covers the supply and delivery to the site of approved granular fill.

The pay quantity for this item shall be the total quantity of granular fill in cubic yards.

Crushed Stone (Cubic Yards)

This item covers the supply and delivery to the site of crushed stone or other material approved by the purchaser. The stone shall be properly sized and designed for waterbonding.

The pay quantity for this item shall be the total cubic yards of crushed stone, measured in place.

Sand or Clinker Ash (Cubic Yards)

This item covers the supply and delivery to the site of sand or clinker ash for use in hardstanding areas and in the subbase for roads.

The pay quantity for this item shall be the total cubic yards of sand or clinker ash measured in place.

Concrete for Blinding, Haunching, etc. (Cubic Yards)

This item covers the supply and delivery to the site of a minimum of 1600 lb/in.^{2} of lean concrete for use in blinding, haunching, etc.

The pay quantity for this item shall be the total cubic yards of concrete.

Washed Sand (Cubic Yards)

This item covers the supply and delivery to the site of washed sand required for grouting, etc.

The pay quantity for this item shall be the total volume of washed sand in cubic yards.

Cement (Tons)

This item covers the supply and delivery of cement required for grouting.

The pay quantity shall be the total weight of cement in tons.

Expansion Joint Material (Linear Yards)

This item covers the supply and delivery to the site of bituminous filler-type expansion joint material in the following sizes:

1. 4 in. wide $\times \frac{1}{2}$ in. thick
2. 6 in. wide $\times \frac{1}{2}$ in. thick

The pay quantity for this item shall be the total length in yards of this material according to the width required.

Expansion Joint Primer (Gallons)

This item covers the supply and delivery to the site of expansion joint material for paving expansion joints.

The pay quantity for this item shall be the total quantity of primer in gallons.

Bituminous Filler Compound (Cubic Wet Tons)

This item covers the supply and delivery to the site of bituminous compound for paving expansion joints.

The pay quantity for this item shall be the total weight of compound in hundredweights.

Steel Shims (Pounds)

This item covers the supply, fabrication, and delivery to the site of steel shims. For the purposes of pricing this item, the contractor shall assume that shims shall be unmachined flat bars measuring $4 \times 2 \times \frac{1}{4}$ in.

The pay quantity for this item shall be the total weight of shims in pounds.

Epoxy Adhesive (Pounds)

This item covers the supply and delivery to the site of epoxy adhesive in accordance with the specifications.

The pay quantity for this item shall be the total weight of epoxy adhesive in pounds.

Manhole Covers, Frames, Chequer Plate, etc. (Pounds)

This item covers the supply and delivery to the site of manhole covers, frames, chequer plate, etc.

The pay quantity for this item shall be the total weight in pounds of manhole covers, frames, chequer plate, etc.

Sliding Plates (Pounds)

This item covers the supply and delivery to the site of sliding plates in accordance with the purchaser's specifications.

The pay quantity for this item shall be the total weight in pounds of sliding plates required.

Coloring Material (Pounds)

This item covers the supply and delivery to the site of coloring material in accordance with the purchaser's specifications.

The pay quantity for this item shall be the total weight in pounds of coloring material required.

Polythene Sheeting (Square Feet)

This item covers the supply and delivery to the site of polythene sheeting for use in the construction of paving, floor slabs, and concrete roads.

The pay quantity for this item shall be the total square feet of polythene sheeting required.

Sand Backfill (Cubic Yards)

This item covers the supply and delivery to the site of sand backfill for use in the protection of underground cast iron pipe.

The pay quantity for this item shall be the total cubic yards of sand backfill required.

7.25 TYPICAL WORK BREAKDOWN STRUCTURE OF A MECHANICAL ERECTION CONTRACT (UNIT PRICE)

7.25.1 List of Bid Items

1.00   General
      1.1 Setup.
2.00   Reactors, towers, tanks, and drums
      2.1   Erect vessels, up to 2.9 tons.
      2.2   Erect vessels, 3-5.9 tons.
      2.3   Erect vessels, 6-9.9 tons.
      2.4   Erect vessels, 10-19.9 tons.
      2.5   Erect vessels, 20-50 tons.
      2.6   Erect vessels, over 50 tons.
      2.7   Install internals, vessel diameter of 0-6 ft.
      2.8   Install internals, vessel diameter of 7-12 ft.
      2.9   Install internals, vessel diameter of 13-18 ft.
      2.10 Load catalysts and packing
3.00   Exchangers, condensers, and air coolers
      3.1   Erect exchangers, 0-2.9 tons.
      3.2   Erect exchangers, 3-5.9 tons.
      3.3   Erect exchangers, 6-9.9 tons.
      3.4   Erect exchangers, 10-19.9 tons.
      3.5   Erect exchangers, 20-29.9 tons.
      3.6   Erect exchangers, 30-50 tons.
      3.7   Erect exchangers, over 50 tons.
      3.8   Erect air coolers.
4.00   Compressors
      4.1   Erect compressor, driver, and auxiliary equipment.
5.00   Pumps
      5.1   Erect pumps and drivers, up to 1 ton.
      5.2   Erect pumps and drivers, 1.1-2.9 tons.

5.3   Erect pumps and drivers, 3.0-9.9 tons.
5.4   Erect pumps and drivers, over 10 tons.
6.00   Structural steel
6.1   Erect rack steel including ladders and platforms.
6.2   Erect equipment steel including ladders and platforms.
6.3   Erect building steel including ladders and platforms.
6.4   Erect sheeting and related items.
7.00   Miscellaneous
7.1   Erect equipment, up to 3 tons.
7.2   Erect equipment, 3 tons and over.

7.25.2   General Comments

This contract covers the complete erection, to an operational state, of items outlined in the list of bid items.

Foundations, complete with holding-down bolts for all equipment, will be provided by others. In addition, permanent shims set at the approximate elevation will be provided integrally with foundations. The grouting of equipment and steelwork will be performed by others.

All equipment shall be checked and accepted by the purchaser prior to release for grouting.

The contractor shall undertake any tests or inspection required by the purchaser other than those undertaken by the material suppliers and will be responsible for any cleaning off, inspection, or similar operation necessary to ensure correct installation of the equipment.

The final installed elevation of the equipment will be found on the plot plans included in "Technical Provisions and Typical Drawings."

The equipment erected under this contract shall be paid for based on the net weight of each equipment item as detailed on drawings or as specified by certified weighbridges.

In the event of large vessels being delivered in sections with no supporting bills of lading, the manufacturer's drawing weight shall be the accepted measure.

All equipment and steelwork paid for on a unit weight basis shall be measured to the first decimal place.

No payment will be made until the equipment item is finally installed to the purchaser's satisfaction. Progress payments, as appropriate, may be agreed to.

The contractor will erect and install particular items of equipment under direction of the equipment vendor's representative in collaboration with the purchaser.

For all work, unit prices shall include all labor costs, including the following: premiums, bonuses, fringes (cash or otherwise), payroll assessments, taxes, insurance, etc.; all tool and equipment costs, including scaffolding and temporary shoring; all costs of craft supervision, inspection, and services; all sales, excise, turnover, and other taxes; any other costs which may be required for the satisfactory performance and completion of the work; and the contractor's profit.

Regardless of quantity variation, the prices will remain firm.

All direct materials under this contract will be furnished by the purchaser and delivered to the site for use by the contractor. The contractor shall be responsible for and include in unit prices the unloading and transport to temporary storage (if necessary) of all material under this contract. Any costs incurred by others for unloading material for this contract after the contractor is established on the site will be backcharged to the contractor.

Existing temporary facilities and utilities (water, electricity) can be used, and the cost of any extra facilities or extensions to existing systems shall be included in the setup cost.

The loading of all catalysts, various packings, etc., and the installation of vessel internals are included in this contract.

1.1 Setup

This item covers the contractor's general expenses in setting up the project and shall specifically include all temporary buildings and facilities, all overheads, nonproductive field engineering services, administration, and any other indirect costs related to the performance of the work. The contractor's profit, craft supervision, indirect materials, and all other costs as defined in "General Comments" shall be included in the unit rates.

This item will be paid for on a lump sum basis, progress payments being made as follows:

1. On the date of commencement of the work: 20%
2. At monthly intervals therafter (subject to actual progress): 10%

2.00 Reactors, Towers, Tanks, and Drums

2.1 Erect vessels, up to 2.9 tons, each item
2.2 Erect vessels, 3.0-5.9 tons, each item
2.3 Erect vessels, 6.0-9.9 tons, each item
2.4 Erect vessels, 10.0-19.9 tons, each item
2.5 Erect vessels, 20.0-50.0 tons, each item
2.6 Erect vessels, 50.1 tons and over, each item

This section covers all work associated with the erection of the preceding items as detailed in the list of equipment. The work also includes the erection and/or installation of internals as described below. For the purposes of definition, the functions of work are given separately.

The work under subcodes 2.1-2.6 includes but is not limited to the following: unloading from trucks, transport to temporary storage (if required), or, alternatively, unloading at the point of erection; rigging and erecting; setting on shims to correct elevation, center lines, and orientation, including scaffolding, wedges, etc.; adjusting bolts in accordance with the technical specifications using torque wrenches where specified; and any other operations necessary to ensure safe and permanent erection.

A rigging study shall be submitted and approved by the purchaser for heavy equipment items mentioned in the list of equipment. This study shall be submitted by the contractor at a later date, but the contractor shall detail types and sizes of mechanical equipment in the erection of equipment under this contract.

Castable lining and refractory brickwork will not be covered under this contract.

The work also includes the following: installing various vessel internals (distributors, bed supports, hold-downs, grids, floating screens, demister pads, etc.):

2.7 Up to 6 ft, 0 in. in diameter, each complete item
2.8 6 ft, 3 in. to 12 ft, 0 in. in diameter, each complete item
2.9 12 ft, 3 in. to 18 ft, 0 in. in diameter, each complete item

2.10 Load Catalysts and Packing (Cubic Feet)

Work under subcode 2.10 covers the installation of catalysts and various packings. The work shall include material handling, loading into vessels including stratification of sizes, the installation of separating grids, and all operations necessary to ensure satisfactory installation. Adequate care must be taken to protect screens and grids already in place when loading catalysts and packings.

The payment for work done under this subcode shall be per cubic foot of catalyst or packing loaded.

3.00 Exchangers, Condensers, and Air Coolers

3.1 Erect exchangers, up to 2.9 tons, each item
3.2 Erect exchangers, 3.0-5.9 tons, each item
3.3 Erect exchangers, 6.0-9.9 tons, each item
3.4 Erect exchangers, 10.0-19.9 tons, each item
3.5 Erect exchangers, 20.0-29.9 tons, each item
3.6 Erect exchangers, 30.0-50.0 tons, each item
3.7 Erect exchangers, 50.1 tons and over, tons
3.8 Air coolers, tons

The work covers complete erection of the preceding items which are detailed in the list of equipment.

The operations to be performed include but are not limited to the following: unloading from wagons or trucks, transport to temporary storage (if required), or, alternatively, unloading at the point of erection; rigging and erecting; setting shims to correct elevation, center lines, and orientation, including any necessary scaffolding; aligning and adjusting bolts in accordance with the technical specifications using a torque wrench (where specified); any additional drilling of structural steel; and locating and attaching platforms and brackets incidental to items.

Included in this item is the erection of pipework or other items (ejectors, etc.) supplied by the equipment vendor, posterection testing, and the running of tests for any such items.

Exchangers, condensers, and air coolers will be delivered tested and complete with the shell heads bolted in position. No provision shall be made in the unit erection rates for removal of heads for inspection. If this is required, it will be paid for on an open cost basis.

Payment shall be per item per ton in the various weight ranges detailed and based on the net weight of the particular item. The price will be firm regardless of whether exchangers fall into the shell and tube or double pipe category. In cases of banked exchangers, the same unit rate will apply for each exchanger in the respective weight range.

4.00 Compressors and Drivers: 4.1 Erect Compressor, Driver, and Auxiliary Equipment (tons)

The work includes but is not limited to the following: unloading from wagons or trucks, transport to temporary storage (if required), or, alternatively, unloading at the point of erection; rigging, shimming, and setting the compressor and any intermediate drive item (reduction gearbox, flywheel, centrifugal clutch, coupling, etc.), turbine, or motor driver; adjusting and all operations necessary to finally align the compressor and driver systems.

Compressors and drivers may be transported in a partially dismantled state. The contractor will perform all the work necessary to fully assemble and erect the complete system according to the equipment vendor's drawings and instructions.

The contractor shall erect, shim, set, and finally install auxiliary equipment (lube oil console, pumps and drivers, circulating oil tanks, bearings, coolers, instruments, support structures, guards, etc.) and pipework supplied by the equipment vendor.

The contractor shall erect, align, install, and test-run equipment under the direction of the equipment vendor's representative in collaboration with the purchaser and thereafter maintain the equipment in a "ready-for-commissioning" state.

Payment shall be per ton based on the net weight of the compressor plus the driver plus the baseplate (if applicable).

5.00 Pumps and Drivers (Motors and Turbines)

5.1 Erect pumps and drivers, up to 1.0 ton, and proportioning pumps, each item
5.2 Erect pumps and drivers, 1.1-2.9 tons, each item
5.3 Erect pumps and drivers, 3.0-9.9 tons, each item
5.4 Erect pumps and drivers, 10.0 tons and over, each item

The work includes but is not limited to the following: unloading of equipment from wagons or trucks, transport to temporary storage (if required), or, alternatively, unloading at the point of erection; rigging, shimming, and setting the pump and any intermediate drive item (reduction gearbox, coupling, centrifugal clutch, etc.) and driver; adjusting; and all operations necessary to finally align the pump and driver system.

If pumps or drivers are transported in a partially dismantled state, the contractor will perform all the work necessary to fully assemble and erect the complete system.

The contractor shall erect and finally install any auxiliary equipment, coolers, instruments, guards, or pipework supplied.

The contractor shall be responsible for test-running the equipment to the purchaser's complete satisfaction and subsequently maintaining it in a ready-for-commissioning state.

Payment will be in the various weight ranges detailed and will be traced on the net weight of the pump, driver, and baseplate.

6.00 Structural and Related Steel and Other Work

6.1 Erect yard steel including ladders and platforms, per ton
6.2 Erect equipment structural steel including ladders, stairways, and platforms, per ton
6.3 Erect building steelwork including ladders, stairways, and platforms, per ton
6.4 Erect sheeting and other related items, per square foot

The work includes but is not limited to the following: unloading from wagons and trucks, transport to temporary storage (if required), or, alternatively, unloading at the points of erection; rigging and erecting; setting on shims to the correct elevation, center lines, and orientation, including any necessary scaffolding; and adjusting bolts in accordance with technical specifications using a torque wrench where specified.

Included in this work is any operation necessary to complete the erection of fixtures associated with structural steelwork in weatherproof shelters, i.e., sheeting panels (all materials), flashing, louvers, steel doors, gutters, roof trusses, clips, etc.

Structural steelwork will be delivered, fabricated, and marked in the normal manner for erection. Platforms, columns, davits, beams, bracing, ladders, grating, and handrailing may require assembling and fitting on the site before erection.

Payment will be per ton for steelwork in the three categories detailed and per square foot for cladding and sheeting inclusive of flashing, gutters, and all other related items.

7.00 Miscellaneous and Special Equipment

7.1 Erect miscellaneous equipment, up to 2.5 tons, per ton
7.2 Erect miscellaneous equipment, 2.5 tons and over, per ton

The work under this section covers the complete erection of miscellaneous and special equipment which may include but is not limited to the following:

Propeller-type tank mixers
Emergency generators
Instrument air driers
Chlorinators
Weatherhoods and silencers
Coalescer
Air blower silencers

Miscellaneous small mixing tanks
Chain- and motor-operated hoists
Injection systems, etc.

The work includes material handling, transport to temporary storage (if required), or, alternatively, unloading at the point of erection; rigging; shimming where necessary; setting at correct elevation, center lines, and orientation; bolting; and any other operation necessary to ensure complete erection of miscellaneous equipment.

Payment shall be per item or ton in the weight ranges as defined.

8

ENERGY: COST AND SCHEDULE CONCEPTS

8.1 INTRODUCTION

Costs and schedules are highly dependent on the availability of resources, project size, complexity, and prior experience (data base).
Current energy predictions for the United States and for the world
indicate a future lack of resources, increasing size and complexity of
projects, and very little experience, particularly with synthetic fuels
and offshore producing facilities.

In this chapter we shall briefly cover construction aspects of the
U.S. domestic energy industry, illustrating that the major problem is
not a shortage of natural energy resources but the inability to build
producing facilities to the degree required. Lack of a comprehensive
energy policy and restrictive regulations have restrained the petroleum
industry from providing adequate and timely facilities.

In 1973 OPEC increased oil prices sharply and abruptly. In the rest
of the free world, most governments reacted rationally. They worked
closely with the oil companies to make the problem manageable. But they
did not try to shield their people from higher prices, and there was no
effort to hunt for scapegoats. Instead, those governments moved to
accelerate exploration for oil—witness the North Sea—and to develop the
only other energy option available to most of them: nuclear energy.

In the United States, on the contrary, politicians and others, in-
clusing television, labeled the whole situation a hoax prompted by the
oil companies. The U.S. government set up an allocation system that
created shortages of gasoline at stations in some areas and surpluses in
other areas—while forbidding oil companies to shift a single gallon on
their own.

If this sounds familiar, it is because it is what happened again early
in 1979 with gasoline sent in the wrong volumes to the wrong places at
the wrong times by government dictate, greatly worsening a rather
modest shortage.

Energy supply and demand are significant factors in the cost of
facilities. Thus petroleum plant costs and schedules need to be viewed
against the total energy picture.

In today's world, energy is the lifeblood of a modern industrial
nation. The creation of a synthetic fuels industry, virtually from

scratch, to meet U.S. long-term energy requirements will require a major effort. Technological advances, governmental incentives and support, reductions in red tape, and large investments will be necessary to provide facilities to reduce the dependence on imported energy. However, the major problem may not be financial but environmental. If the proposed Energy Mobilization Board becomes a paper tiger, then development will be slow. In addition, it will take time to develop the necessary infrastructure for a coal-based synthetic fuels industry.

To produce 2.5 million barrels of synthetics from coal would require 375 million tons a year more coal. And to replace 4 million barrels of oil a day with synthetics derived from coal would require mining *600* million additional tons of coal a year—that is, nearly doubling 1980's coal production.

It should also be noted that the U.S. refining capacity is now running close to 75% of its capacity. There is some spare capacity as refineries can run at 90% of capacity. However, further expansion of conventional plants is required in addition to the development of synthetic fuels. Existing plants need "upgrading" to produce additional gasoline from the same barrels of crude, and additional facilities are required to handle heavy, sour crudes.

As for nuclear power, there were 68 nuclear plants operating in the United States in 1979. They accounted for nearly 4% of total energy demand and 12-13% of the country's electricity. There were 94 additional reactors under construction. Since those 94 are larger on average than those already operating, they would roughly triple the present nuclear electricity-generating capacity. If all 94 of them were in operation now, along with the other 68, nuclear power would be furnishing 12-13% of total energy demand and 35-38% of U.S. electricity. The Three Mile Island incident has, of course, raised some question of whether to permit completion of all these plants, much less initiate new ones.

It seems highly likely that the overwhelming majority of the growth in U.S. energy demand for the rest of this century will be for electricity. Nuclear power is uniquely suited for this job.

We are facing a massive construction program in the next 20 years if we are to maintain a reasonable standard of living. Changing and remote areas of engineering-construction operations and massive increases in size and complexity of projects have thrust effective planning, cost analysis, and scheduling to the forefront.

Considering the potential transition to synthetic fuels and further expansion of conventional plants, the following question needs to be considered: "Are there sufficient resources?"

There are serious concerns about equipment manufacturing capacity, the availability of engineers, and construction craft skills. Financial and schedule objectives of such projects should reflect both previous experience and current economic conditions if projects are to be successfully executed.

The following exhibits outline energy reserves, supply and demand, synthetic fuels development, and associated elements affecting costs and schedules. This information is not intended to be a detailed, in-depth review of the energy scene. My intent is to alert project control personnel to the potential need and overall conditions of the energy industry.

I firmly believe that such information can add to the capability of estimators, cost engineers, and schedulers in recognizing the scope and
conditions of energy projects. There are many projections of future energy requirements, and I have presented a scenario which I developed
in 1979. I have updated the projections of supply and demand with the
actual experience of 1979 and 1980. The "bottom line" is that we have
reduced imports, reduced demand, increased domestic production, reduced the GNP, and increased unemployment. There is a direct relationship among GNP, energy requirements, and employment.

8.2 NORTH AMERICAN ENERGY RESERVES

8.2.1 U.S. Energy Reserves

Figure 8.1 shows the location and size of known, recoverable reserves.
These data are from the Institute of Gas Technology and general industry sources. Remote areas, such as northeastern Utah (the asphalt
ridge) with concentrations of coal, shale oil, and tar sands, have a
high potential for future development. *However, such remote areas will
entail additional costs due to a lack of local resources and an established
infrastructure.*

At 400 billion tons, the United States has the largest reserves of
coal in the world. Domestic usage in 1980 was about 750 million tons a
year.

The present (1980) consumption of domestic oil and gas at 17.6
million barrels per day (bpd) (equivalent) will probably last about 10-15
years based on current reserves. Future discoveries will give additional
time. However, most experts agree that future discoveries will not meet
the anticipated demand and that U.S. reserves of oil and gas will last a
further 20-30 years but at reducing levels.

Oil company planners believe that production of crude oil from currently producing domestic fields will drop from about 8.6 million bpd in
1980 to about 5 million bpd in 1999. The "planners" also anticipate that
by 1990 future discoveries of "easy crude" will not meet the increasing
demand, even allowing for a future reducing level of gasoline
consumption.

Based on current experience, it appears that "political considerations" may not allow nuclear energy to bridge the "gap." Hence, costlier
synthetic fuels and increased coal usage will have to be developed, in
bulk, over the next 15 years.

Due to more favorable environmental aspects, the best bet for synthetic energy is thought to be the production of oil and gas from coal.
As shown, the large U.S. coal reserves could provide the United States
with a 100-year bridge but at a cost, as synthetic fuels from coal is the
more expensive route.

Thereafter, nuclear fusion and solar energy could take care of the
long term. For the short term, solar energy, in the form of home heating, is not a significant contributor to the U.S. total energy requirements. Consider solar energy from this perspective. If you could heat

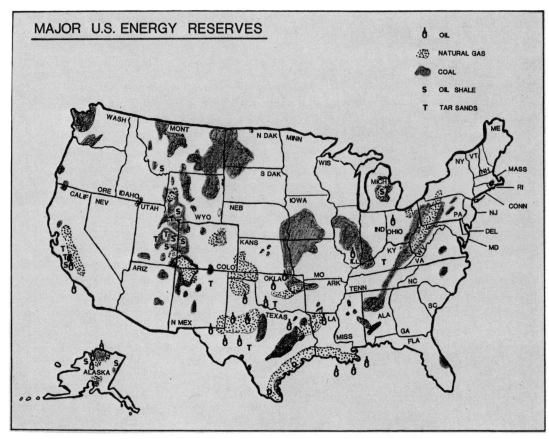

NOW:	EQUIVALENT BARRELS (BILLION)	NUMBER YEARS AT CURRENT USAGE	
OIL	30	10	
GAS	40	15	
FUTURE:			
OIL SHALE	70	12	FUTURE DISCOVERIES
TAR SANDS	5	1	AND IMPORTS ARE
HEAVY OIL	3	1	NOT CONSIDERED.
*COAL (SYNFUEL)	400	70	
*ASSUME 50% COAL RESERVES USED FOR SYNFUEL		**100 YEARS**	
OTHER:			
COAL	200 BILLION TONS	250	
NUCLEAR	1 BILLION POUNDS URANIUN	?	
SOLAR	ELECTRIC CURRENT (PHOTOVOLTAICS)	?	

Figure 1　Major U.S. energy reserves.

a million homes in the United States and also furnish all their electricity
year-round by solar power, you would be displacing less than 0.3% of
U.S. energy consumption from all sources combined.

8.2.2 Canadian (Alberta) Key Energy Reserves

The development of Alberta's oil sands has been in progress for more
than 20 years (see Figure 8.2). In the past 5 years, the work has
greatly accelerated. Two new projects were started in 1980: Shell's tar
sands project at Fort McMurray and Imperial's heavy oil project at
Cold Lake.

As the Canadian and Alberta governments are insisting on a maximum
Canadian content, it is already apparent that Canada's resources, particularly of engineering personnel, are stretched thin and will continue
so for the foreseeable future. Conflicts between federal and provincial
governments on energy programs can further impact on cost and
schedule. U.S. investment and capital projects programs can also be
seriously affected by proposed new regulations.

8.3 U.S. ENERGY CONSUMPTION BY RESOURCE

Many factors affect consumption, and it is now apparent that future consumption cannot continue to increase at the same rate as in the immediate
past.

From a sociological viewpoint, the U.S. economy needs to absorb
from 1.5 million to 2 million new entrants into the work force from 1979
to 1985, and if unemployment is to be held to the 1979 level, the United
States needs economic growth averaging 3.5% a year. This would require
an annual increase of 2.2% in energy supplies. This growth was not
achieved. As a result, unemployment increased in 1980.

Figure 8.3 shows the 1978 consumption by resource and predicts
requirements for 1990 based on a 2.2% growth per year. This growth is
half that which the United States experienced in the period 1960-1973;
1979 consumption was little different from 1978.

This 1990 scenario shows that a shortfall in domestic oil and gas
supply could be made up from increased imports, domestic coal, and
nuclear power. Nuclear power is essential for the short and long term,
and it has been estimated that the current contribution of about 4%
should increase to 11% by 1990 (equivalent of 5 million bpd). President
Carter's plan to replace imports with 2.5 million bpd of synthetic fuels
by 1990, itself an extremely difficult task, will not meet this 1990 requirement based on restraining imports at current levels. Conservation
can have a significant effect on this scenario. Domestic oil products
were reduced 7.7% from 1979 to 1980. Oil imports were reduced from 6.4
million to 5.2 million bpd (18%).

A major consideration in rapidly developing synthetic fuels is the
question of the capacity of equipment manufacturers and engineering
designers. The industry could run into the same supply bottleneck of

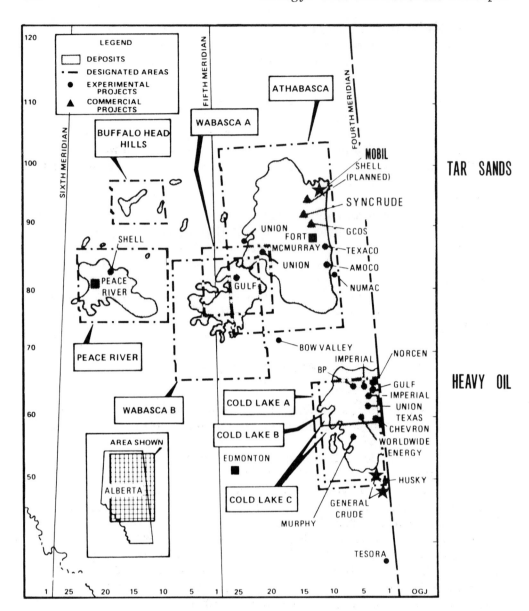

Figure 8.2 Alberta's oil sands and heavy oil reserves. Alberta's total oil sands and heavy oil reserves approach 1 trillion barrels, of which over 300 billion barrels are considered recoverable. The map indicates the locations of key reserves. Source: Energy Resources Conservation Board.

the early 1970s when orders poured in from the nuclear industry, the Middle East, and the domestic petrochemical industry.

   To produce 1.5 million barrels of *synfuels* from coal, Fluor Corporation projects that it will soak up about 40% of the nation's compressor capacity, 30% of the pump-manufacturing capacity, and so forth. Inflation in the cost of these items, too, is obviously a danger, and this, in turn, *would keep the tab for a plant moving up the cost escalator.*

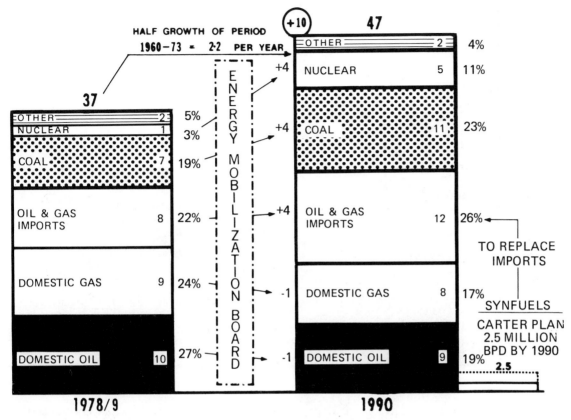

Figure 8.3 U.S. energy consumption by resource (million barrels per day oil equivalent).

Figure 8.4 shows a forecast of U.S. consumption and supply of oil and gas. Gas has been converted to an oil equivalent. This forecast takes current usage (1978-1979) of 19 million bpd, as shown in Figure 8.3, and predicts a 50% drop in production from existing fields to 10 million bpd by 1990.

Assuming future discoveries of oil and gas resources come in at rates somewhat above recent levels, supplies could still be below annual production rates. As shown, this would produce a declining reserve base, with a net loss of 2 million bpd, and could lead to decreasing production levels. As shown, consumption for 1979 and 1980 fall below the "consumption scenario." It is probable that consumption levels will increase as the nation's GNP improves and unemployment is reduced.

If conservation levels are also reduced, then we again face the return of shortages and/or limited supplies. Current discoveries of gas and future exploration forecasts look promising. However, governmental regulations and policies are still uncertain. The ultimate effect could then be a requirement for increased imports. Based on current uncertainties of overseas supply, this would hardly be a wise move.

The alternative is to develop all forms of domestic energy resources, increase conservation, and provide a comprehensive governmental energy policy which deals equitably with industry and the consumer—and *to do it quickly*.

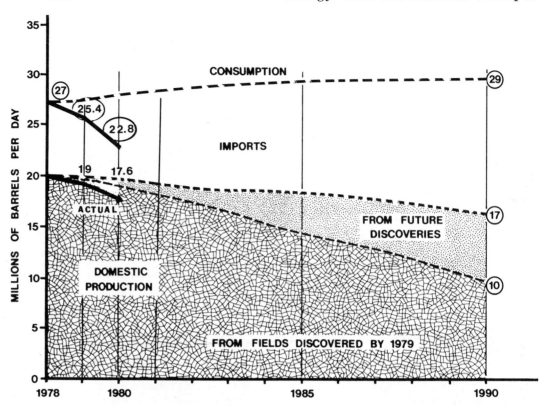

Figure 8.4   U.S. oil and gas consumption and supply (gas converted to oil equivalent).

8.4 DEVELOPMENT OF SYNTHETIC FUELS TECHNOLOGY

Figure 8.5 outlines the current state of technology and illustrates that coal conversion to gasoline may be a good bet for the future. Gasification techniques are well established, and the *methanol to gasoline* process has been proven with pilot plants.

Tar sands plants are in operation in Canada; unfortunately U.S. reserves are small. Massive tailings and settling ponds are required. These, plus environmental aspects, would provide significant problems. Technology, however, is well established and commercially proven. No commercial plants are presently planned for the United States.

Oil shale has significant environmental problems, mainly huge piles of rubble. The process also requires a large amount of water. One and a half tons of rock can produce 1 barrel of oil. To produce 1 million barrels of shale oil a day would require mining more than 550 million tons of shale a year. Because of environmental restrictions, infrastructure requirements, and the limited availability of water, the maximum production of shale oil in the United States will probably be limited to between 1.5 million and 2 million bpd—and this, too, is years away. Commercial development of shale oil will probably require building demonstration plants prior to large-scale operations. This will add to the costs. Plans for three commercial plants in the United States are presently being developed.

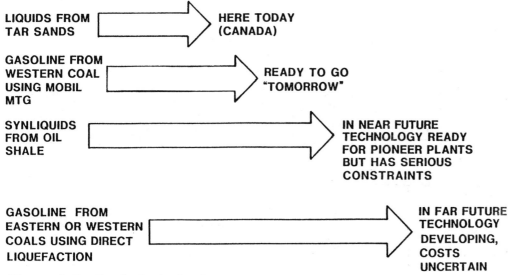

Figure 8.5   Synfuels technology.

Direct coal liquefaction is the least developed technology of synthetic fuels. The reaction process requires very high pressures and temperatures. Pilot plants and demonstration models will be necessary prior to large commercial operations. Again, this will add to the costs.

Heavy oils, though small in reserves, require established processing techniques, mainly hydrocracking; however, "enhanced" recovery techniques will add to the cost.

8.5 COAL TO GASOLINE CONVERSION

8.5.1 Typical Process

Figure 8.6 shows a block flow diagram of Lurgi gasification-methanol synthesis with a Mobil methanol to gasoline process unit. Coal gasification techniques have been established for many years, and the Mobil methanol process has been successfully operated in 1976 in a pilot plant at Mobil's research facility in New Jersey.

Other processes are the ICI process for gasification-methanol synthesis and the Fischer-Tropsch process for methanol to gasoline conversion.

This block flow diagram indicates that a coal mine, utilities plant, and many process units are required for a coal to gasoline plant—by any definition, a jumbo or megaproject.

8.5.2 Schedule Evaluation (Normal Versus Accelerated)

Figure 8.7 shows a feasibility schedule for a coal to gasoline plant. An accelerated basis is compared with an owner's normal project strategy of a phase I for process design, cost estimate, and schedule followed by a phase II for full execution. This schedule is a summary of a more detailed

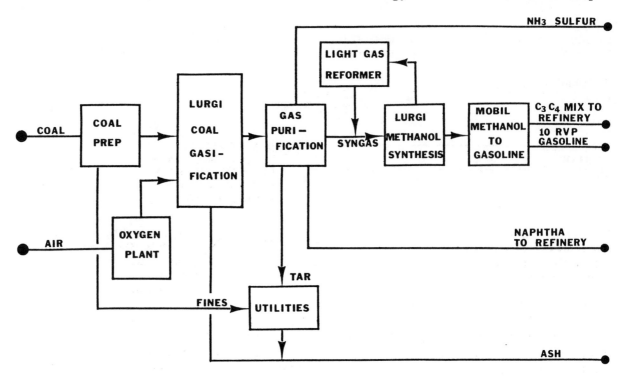

Figure 8.6   Block flow diagram of coal to gasoline.

schedule which considered overall schedules for each major process unit.
The coal mine has not been considered.

The schedule range is 66 months (accelerated) versus 91 months
(normal). The accelerated case requires a radical change from current
experience where environmental aspects require 2-3 years from application to permit issue.

Notes 1-4 outline the overall basis of the schedule. Schedule durations have been established by the historical experience of large process plants adjusted for the "jumbo size factor." Refer to Figure 3.21
regarding construction parameters for jumbo projects. That chart will
provide an overall construction schedule based on the number of construction man-hours. Obviously, a schedule difference of 25 months has
a considerable effect on costs.

This summary schedule is an effective tool for senior management
reviews. It has high visibility and clearly demonstrates the schedule
difference for two project strategies.

8.5.3 Schedule Plus Manpower

Figure 8.8 is the "normal schedule" shown in Figure 8.7 but now includes cost, man-hour data, and manpower loading. This exhibit gives
an even better appreciation of project size as well as schedule. Considering escalation, the project cost would be in excess of $5 billion.
Estimated man-hours and an 8-year schedule would give peak manning
levels for the owner of 80, contractor engineering of 950, and craft
labor of 6300. The schedule and costs comprehend a construction camp

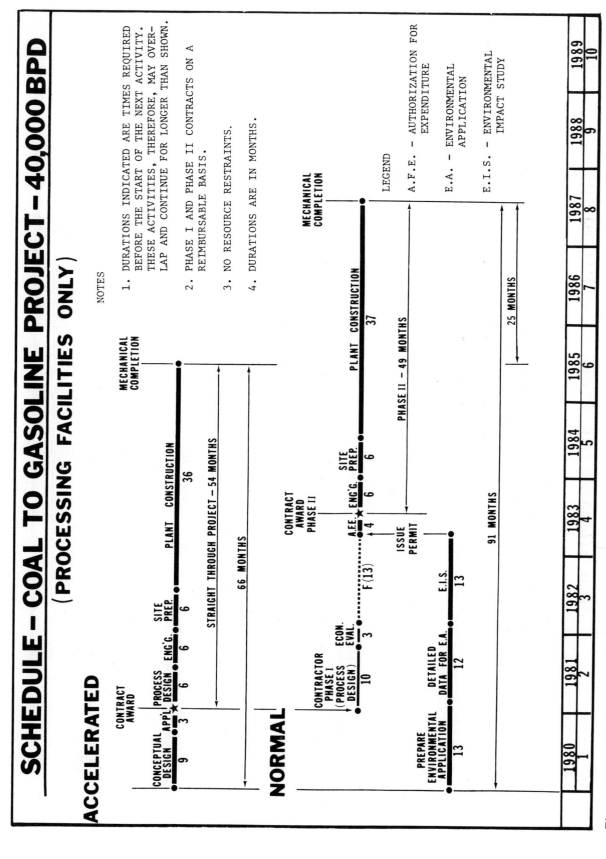

Figure 8.7 Coal to gasoline schedule (two bases).

307

COAL TO GASOLINE PROJECT – 40,000 BPD

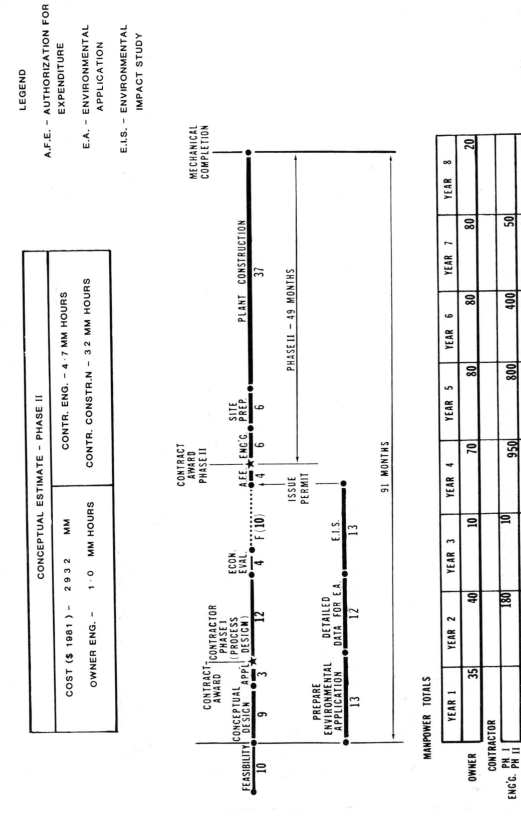

Figure 8.8   Coal to gasoline schedule (costs, man-hours, manpower).

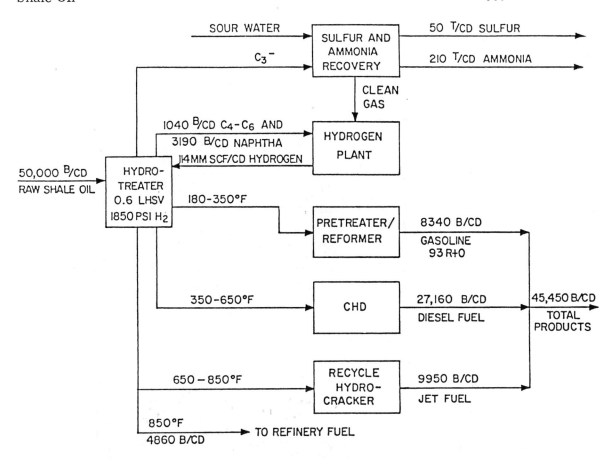

Figure 8.9 Block flow diagram of shale oil.

job due to limited resources and the lack of infrastructure at the job site location.

8.6 SHALE OIL

8.6.1 Block Flow Diagram: Products Plant

Figure 8.9 shows a block flow diagram for a shale oil products plant and promotes an appreciation of the complexity and number of process units. Hydrotreaters and hydrocrackers are among the most expensive process units. Not included is the shale oil mining operation.

8.6.2 Mechanical Design

Figure 8.10 is a sketch of the current design of retorts used for separating oil from kerogen. The present development has small-diameter retorts in use in a pilot plant. Commercial operations will require much larger-diameter retorts, and the mechanical design of these vessels is a critical factor in the development of shale oil.

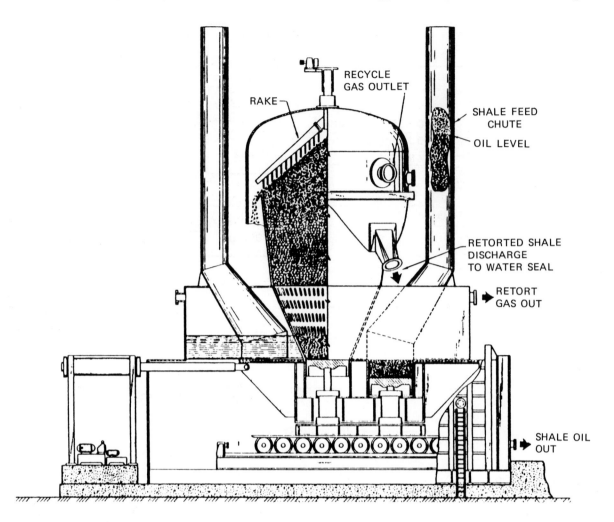

Figure 8.10   Typical shale oil retort.

8.6.3 Schedule

Figure 8.11 shows a feasibility schedule for an oil shale plant. This overall schedule is based on building a demonstration plant prior to large-scale commercial operations. The commercial plant would consist of a further four 10,000-bpd trains identical to the demonstration plant but modified as a result of testing out. As the end product is raw shale oil, a pipeline and processing plant (small refinery) would be required for finished products, probably gasoline, diesel fuel, and jet fuel.

This schedule assumes a raw shale oil facility in Colorado and a processing plant at Joliet, Illinois with an interconnecting pipeline.

The schedule assumes a phased project approach of the following:

Feasibility
Conceptual design
Process design (phase I)
Detailed design-procurement-construction (phase II)

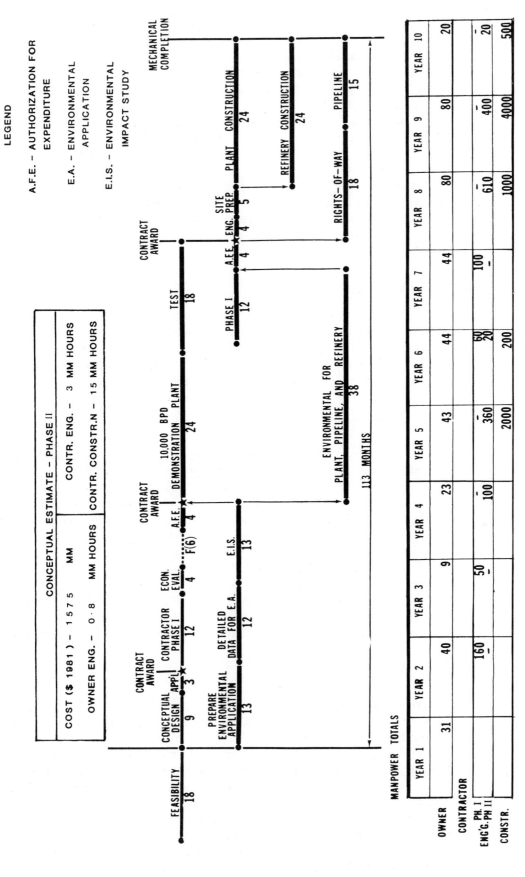

Figure 8.11 Shale oil schedule (costs, man-hours, manpower).

The contracting strategy is fixed fee-reimbursable. Resources are not restrained. Durations are based on the historical experience of large process plants. Refer to Figure 3.21 for guidance on the overall construction schedule.

Considering escalation, the project cost could be in excess of $3 billion. Estimated man-hours and a 10-year schedule would give peak manning levels for the owner of 80, contractor engineering of 600, and craft labor of 4000.

It is probable that a construction camp would be required for the raw shale oil plant due to lack of local resources and infrastructures.

This schedule format gives good overall visibility and is recommended for reviews with higher management.

8.7 TAR SANDS

With operating plants in Canada, tar sands are the most developed of synthetic fuels. Due to the massive size of current tar sands' projects, these projects have the highest capital costs; however, unit costs are favorable due to large throughputs in the range of 100,000-200,000 bpd.

8.7.1 Block Flow Diagrams

Figure 8.12 shows a typical processing scheme for a tar sands plant. As can be seen, this is a very large processing operation in addition to a massive mining operation. Key process units are cokers (multiple), and a critical mining item is the gigantic excavator (dragline), having a *bite* of 80 yd^3. These machines take about 12-18 months to manufacture and an additional 12-18 months to erect at the job site. Three of these would generally be the required minimum.

Figure 8.13 is a block flow diagram of the Syncrude Tar Sands Project and shows a sketch of the mining operation plus a flow diagram of the process plant. This plant is meant to produce 129,000 bpd of synthetic crude, and the overall scope is outlined in man-hours, man-power, and quantities of major items—by any standards, a jumbo project.

8.7.2 Schedule

Figure 8.14 shows an overall schedule based on a fixed fee-reimbursable contracting strategy and phased approach as per previous synfuel schedules. The one difference is Canadian environmental requirements.

Considering escalation, the project cost could be in excess of $8 billion. Estimated man-hours and a 10-year schedule would give peak manning levels for the owner of 110, contractor engineering of 1200, and craft labor of 7000.

Due to a requirement by the authorities for maximum Canadian content, engineering would necessitate multiple offices; the equipment manufacturing capacity could be overloaded and engineering skills in short supply. A construction camp would be required. The schedule

TAR SANDS - PROCESS BLOCK FLOW
(BITUMEN UPGRADING)

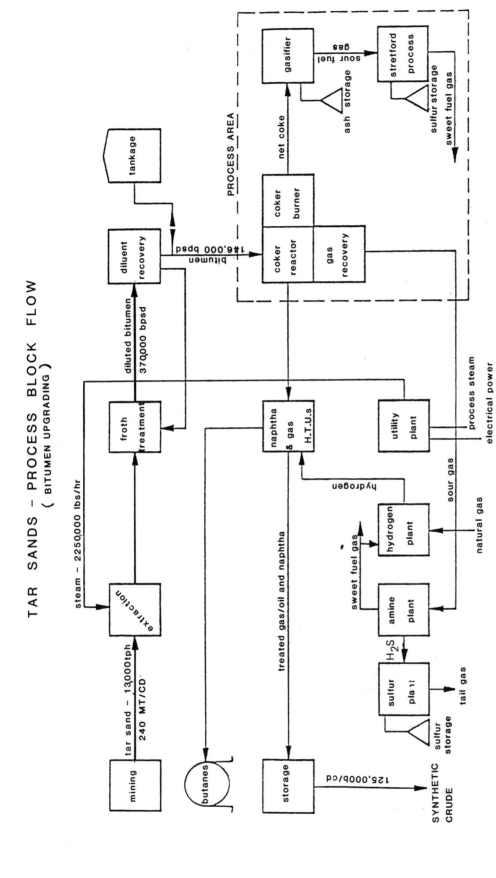

Figure 8.12 Block flow diagram of tar sands.

313

SYNCRUDE TAR SANDS PROJECT
ALBERTA CANADA 1972 - 1978

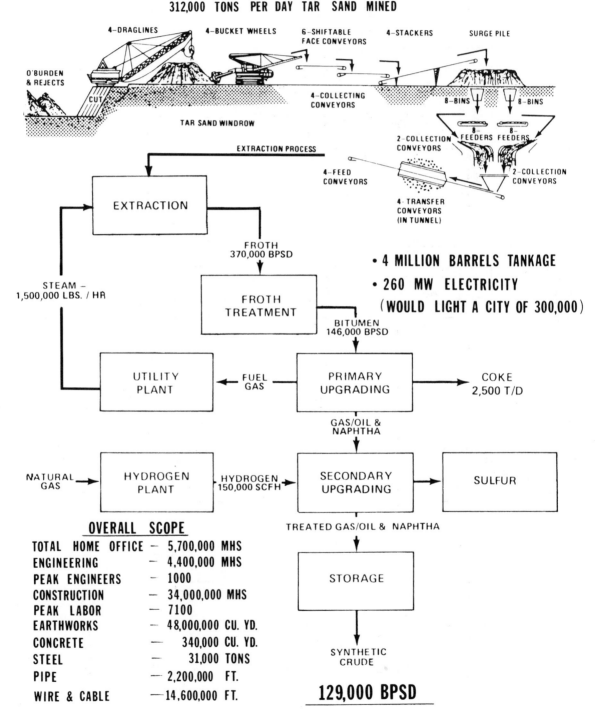

SYNCRUDE PROJECT: MINING

93 MILLION TONS PER YEAR TAR SAND AND OVERBURDEN

312,000 TONS PER DAY TAR SAND MINED

- **4 MILLION BARRELS TANKAGE**
- **260 MW ELECTRICITY**
  (WOULD LIGHT A CITY OF 300,000)

OVERALL SCOPE

TOTAL HOME OFFICE	—	5,700,000 MHS
ENGINEERING	—	4,400,000 MHS
PEAK ENGINEERS	—	1000
CONSTRUCTION	—	34,000,000 MHS
PEAK LABOR	—	7100
EARTHWORKS	—	48,000,000 CU. YD.
CONCRETE	—	340,000 CU. YD.
STEEL	—	31,000 TONS
PIPE	—	2,200,000 FT.
WIRE & CABLE	—	14,600,000 FT.

129,000 BPSD

Figure 8.13   Block flow diagram plus quantities of tar sands.

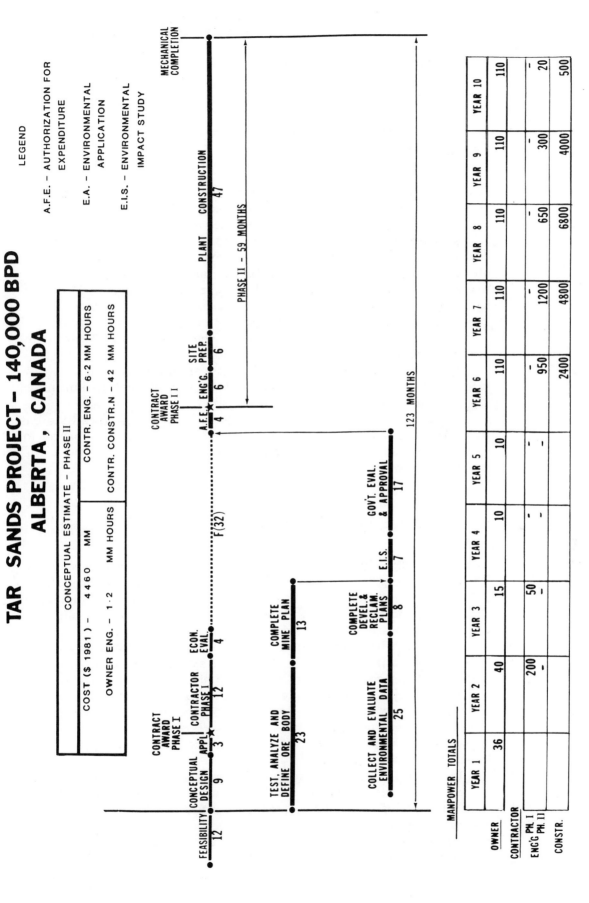

Figure 8.14   Tar sands schedule (costs, man-hours, manpower).

315

reflects this situation; engineering resources will probably be a critical item.

8.8 COST DIFFERENTIALS OF SYNTHETIC FUEL
VERSUS CONVENTIONAL REFINERY

It is difficult to generalize on the comparative costs of conventional refineries versus synthetic fuel plants as no two plants are ever identical. However, several key differences are apparent.

New technology is a significant factor. The mechanical design of coal gasifiers, coal reactors, fixed beds versus fluid beds and shale oil retorts needs to be developed for the larger vessels that are required for commercial operations. Hence, current projects will have to use smaller vessels and many more of them. This adds costs.

Schedules are longer due to size and complexity.

Plant locations are in remote areas, where there is no local infrastructure to support the construction phase.

Project management and control responsibilities are greatly enlarged due to the size, complexity, and division of work to multiple engineering offices and prefabrication sites.

Figure 8.15 represents differentials on an order to magnitude basis. Directionally, the numbers are correct. It is apparent that, barrel for barrel, the cost of a synthetic fuels plant can be more than twice that of a conventional refinery.

8.9 CRUDE OIL AND GASOLINE PRICES

The data outlined in Figure 8.16 come from general industry sources. They show the price of OPEC crude oil and U.S. gasoline from 1973 to 1981. The price of crude oil is the most significant factor in determining the financial viability of synthetic fuel plants. Governmental allowances and incentives are also significant.

Apart from unproven technology, plant size and location provide major variables in determining the cost of synthetic fuel plants. Accessibility, local resources, and environmental and governmental regulations impact the schedule, which, in turn, affects the project cost.

Coal costs vary greatly, depending on the btu content and whether the coal is deep- or strip-mined. Transportation costs and railroad capacities are major considerations. Economic factors and government incentives are significant.

Figure 8.16 shows the tremendous price increases of OPEC oil in the early and late 1970s. Accurate cost and schedule evaluations require that forecasts of future price trends be made. Supply and demand, which are generally determined by industry need and price levels, also have a major impact on inflation. The OPEC cartel, however, can determine crude pricing levels and supply by edict. This is a major problem facing a synthetic fuel industry. At any time, a significant reduction in the

ENGINEERING
   NEW TECHNOLOGY AND SIZE   **INCREASE 50-70%**

FIELD LABOR (MHR's.)
   SIZE AND CAMP JOB   **INCREASE 20-30%**

CAMP COST
   REMOTE LOCATION   **$50-100 MILLION**

PROJECT MANAGEMENT
   & CONTROL   **INCREASE 50-80%**

ENVIRONMENTAL
   LAND, AIR, WATER   **VERY LARGE**

SCHEDULE
   PHASE II ONLY   **INCREASE 40-60%**

Figure 8.15   Cost differentials: synthetic fuel plant vs. conventional refinery. The cost increments shown can be only a rough guide since the numbers will vary widely depending on the type of project, location, engineering development, phased approach, contracting conditions, schedule, and execution strategy.

price of OPEC oil can make a synthetic fuel plant uneconomic, with the obvious result of affecting a company's economic viability.

8.10 REFINING AND DISTRIBUTION COSTS

Apart from plant capital costs, the costs of refining and distribution are major elements in determining economic viability.

Figure 8.17 illustrates U.S. cost and pricing elements of a gallon of gasoline. This is an average breakdown of costs. There would be significant variations for individual companies as crude oil prices depend on domestic versus overseas supply; refining and distribution costs depend on the efficiency of plants; the marketing system and the size of the operation can significantly reduce unit costs. Owners' profit, shown as 5%, varies domestically versus overseas operations (higher) and can be influenced by *inventory gains*. Dealers' margins, shown as 11%, face severe competition and have been reduced compared to 1979. Governmental price controls would generally allow around 14%. Data for this chart come from general industry sources.

8.11 DOES THE UNITED STATES HAVE THE RESOURCES?

Of great significance to a cost estimate and schedule is the question of resources. Material supplies, design engineers, project control personnel,

	OPEC CRUDE (Dollars per Barrel)	U.S. GAS (cents per Gallon)
1973	2.41	37.3
1974	10.95	52.8
1975	10.46	57.5
1976	11.51	58.3
1977	12.09	61.6
1978	12.7	64.9
1979	18.0	80.0
1980	32.0	$1.23
1981 (1st quarter)	35.0	$1.25

Figure 8.16   Crude oil and gasoline prices. The OPEC price is as set by Saudi Arabia and the U.S. gasoline prices are averages for the year. The 1981 prices are for the first quarter.

construction equipment, and craft labor are major resources. Industry forecasts show a future shortfall of design engineers and a current shortfall of project control personnel.

Figures 8.18 and 8.19 show the overall requirements for 1 synthetic fuel plant and 20 synthetic fuel plants. Figure 8.19, based on general industry cost estimates, outlines overall investment, engineering, and construction manpower requirements for 20 synthetic fuel projects. These projects would provide 2 million bpd.

At an approximate cost of $2 billion per plant (1979 dollars), completion of the 20 plants by 1990 would require about 24,000 designers and a construction force of 120,000. The investment cost (1979 dollars) would be in excess of $40 billion. With escalation, the investment could be $80-$100 billion.

These numbers can only be a rough guide as costs and manpower requirements will vary widely depending on schedule, location, and the type of project. However, this rough analysis does outline the large engineering manpower and construction labor requirements for a rapidly expanding synthetic fuels program.

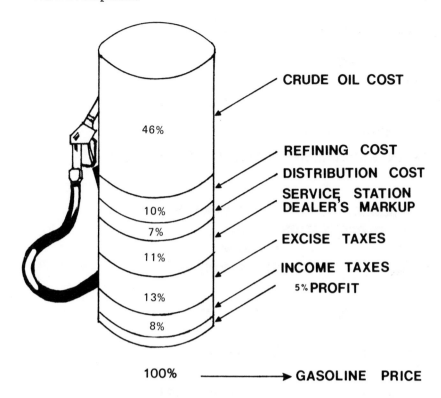

CRUDE OIL COST

REFINING COST
DISTRIBUTION COST
SERVICE STATION
DEALER'S MARKUP

EXCISE TAXES

INCOME TAXES
5% PROFIT

46%

10%
7%
11%

13%

8%

100% ⟶ GASOLINE PRICE

Figure 8.17   U.S. gasoline pricing, 1980.

8.12 COAL DEVELOPMENT

Figure 8.20 outlines major environmental problems which are impacting
costs and the expansion of the coal industry. Acid drainage from
abandoned mines, sulfur dioxide emissions, and calcium sulfite wastes
are major problems.

An added concern is the question of carbon dioxide. Compared with
oil and gas, coal gives off much higher levels of carbon dioxide. While
there is no general concensus, scientists point out that high levels of
carbon dioxide in the earth's atmosphere can cause a "greenhouse
effect."

For the period 1979-1980, the coal industry had an excess capacity
of about 100-150 million tons/year. Demand has been reduced due to a
reduced growth rate of utility companies and increased costs, making
U.S. exports of metallurgical coal less competitive.

Major improvements in the coal industry over the past few years
and the move to increased strip mining are solving the environmental
problems outlined in this exhibit. The coal mine health and safety act
has significantly improved safety, health, and working conditions;
however, permitting requirements are still a very lengthy business.

Apart from the requirements for a synthetics fuel industry, additional coal will be required for new coal-fired power stations and for
transferring from oil to coal on existing stations.

WHAT ARE THE RESOURCES
FOR

1 SYNTHETIC FUEL PLANT AT 100,000 BPD
PHASE II ONLY
(DETAILED DESIGN, PROCUREMENT, CONSTRUCTION)

SCHEDULE (PHASE II)	50/60 MONTHS
(EXCLUDING A DEMONSTRATION PLANT)	
ENGINEERING	50/60 MONTHS
CONSTRUCTION	37/45 MONTHS
PROBABLE COST (1979 $)	2/3 BILLION
ENGINEERING HOURS	4/6 MILLION
DESIGN ENGINEERS	1200/1500 (PEAK)
CONSTRUCTION HOURS	30/40 MILLION
CRAFT LABOR	6000/8000 (PEAK)

Figure 8.18   Resources for one synfuel plant.

8.12.1 Strip Mining Facilities

The majority of coal projects are surface strip mines where critical paths are generally through mechanical handling equipment and supply and field assembly of the very large coal excavators. Figure 8.21 is a sketch of a typical layout for strip mining facilities. It shows the type of facilities provided and their relationships and relative scale. It can be helpful in showing the overall scope for the development of feasibility schedules.

8.12.2 Strip Mine Schedule

Figure 8.22 is a basic project master schedule covering engineering, procurement, and construction of a surface coal mine. As such, it is equivalent to a phase II standard schedule for process plants. This schedule shows a 28-month overall project duration, with 20 months for construction, and ends with coal production. This schedule assumes that feasibility, environmental, and permitting requirements are complete.

DO WE HAVE THE RESOURCES
FOR

20 SYNTHETIC FUELS PLANTS, EACH AT 100,000 BPD
BY 1990

PROBABLE COST (1979 $)	**40 BILLION**
	2 MILLION BPD
ENGINEERING HOURS	**80 MILLION**
DESIGN ENGINEERS	**24,000**
CONSTRUCTION HOURS	**600 MILLION**
CRAFT LABOR	**120,000**

Figure 8.19   Resources for 20 synfuel plants.

Apart from environmental aspects, critical paths are through mechanical handling equipment and supply and field assembly of large coal excavators.

This schedule is for guidance only; the notes and qualifications should be read carefully. Deviations from the assumptions should be evaluated and their impact upon the project duration assessed.

The schedule shows critical paths for the following major components of a strip mine:

Railroad
Plant facility
Power supply and distribution
Mining equipment
Operations staff

As many of these projects will be located in the Mountain West (Utah, Colorado, Wyoming) the schedule assumes a significant amount of winterization to enable a reasonable work effort during winter. Outside work during winter should be discounted as per note 1.

It has also been assumed that design and purchasing activities for one shovel were completed during phase I. This will allow a purchase commitment to be immediately made by the prime contractor or owner upon the award of the phase II contract. One shovel is required to remove overburden prior to coal production. An alternative to this strategy

BRUCE MANSFIELD COAL
FIRED GENERATING STATION
SHIPPINGPORT. PA.

SCRUBBER WASTES
CALCIUM - SULFITE SLUDGE

DEATHS FOR UNDERGROUND MINING - 1 in 5300

"BLACK LUNG DISEASE" - ANNUAL COAL TAX OF $1 BILLION PLUS

ACID DRAINAGE FROM ABANDONED MINES (STREAMS/RIVERS)

SULFUR DIOXIDE - SCRUBBERS (94% EFFECTIVE)

           "SCRUBBING" APPLIED TO LOW-SULFUR COAL

PARTICULATES - FABRIC FILTERS (BAGHOUSES) (99% EFFECTIVE)

CALCIUM SULFITE - HUGE SLUDGE PONDS (DISPOSAL)

CARBON DIOXIDE - "GREENHOUSE EFFECT" - AGRICULTURE

(CO_2 IN OUR ATMOSPHERE ACTS AS ONE-WAY FILTER FOR

ENERGY FROM SUN)

FOR SAME AMOUNT OF HEAT, COAL VERSUS OIL = +24% CO_2

           COAL VERSUS GAS = +76% CO_2

   WARMING OF THE EARTH

   MELTING OF POLAR ICE CAPS

   FLOODING OF SEACOAST CITIES

Figure 8.20 Coal development problems.

is to remove overburden with traditional earth-moving equipment (pans, scrapers, dozers, etc.). However, this will add costs.

As many of these facilities will be located in remote areas, without local resources and an established infrastructure, operational staff requirements and housing are major considerations.

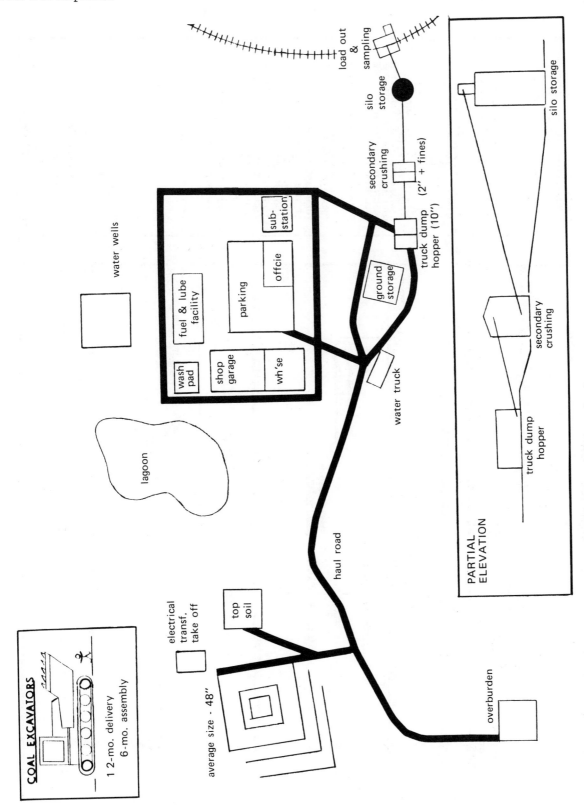

Figure 8.21   Coal development—typical layout (strip mine).

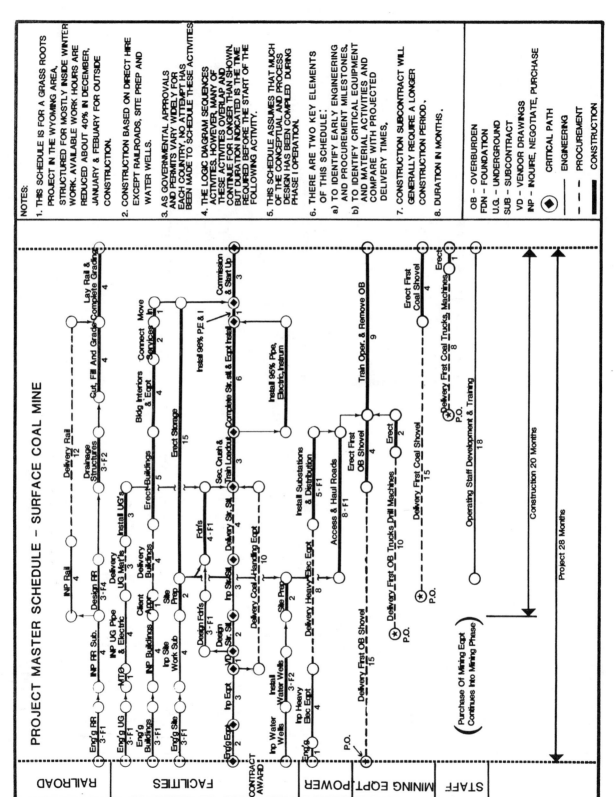

Figure 8.22   Coal development—typical schedule (strip mine).

8.13 URANIUM DEVELOPMENT

Uranium projects are divided between mining and leaching operations. A mining operation entails sinking a shaft, installing a headframe, and developing an underground station and mining levels. A major difference from a coal operation is in the mechanical handling of uranium ore, which, due to a small amount of radioactivity, requires a *water slushing* technique to handle the ore.

Uranium leaching, however, is a relatively recent technology, and a detailed explanation is included at the end of this chapter.

The varying project phases, feasibility-phase I-phase II, are similar to process plant projects, and explanations are given in Section 1.3.

Environmental and governmental regulations for uranium projects are in a constant state of flux and must be individually reviewed for each project.

8.13.1 Uranium Mine Layout

Figure 8.23 depicts a typical layout and facilities for an underground uranium mining operation. It illustrates the overall scope and complexity of the activities to be considered when preparing feasibility schedules. A mining operation provides the ore for the milling and extraction process shown in Figure 8.24.

Where satisfactory conditions exist, uranium can be extracted directly from the underground reservoir by leaching. This process should not be confused with the mining, milling, leaching, extracting, and drying procedures shown in Figures 8.23 and 8.24.

8.13.2 Uranium Mill Layout

Figure 8.24 depicts typical equipment, the layout, and the overall scope for a uranium milling, leaching, extraction, drying, and packaging plant. This illustration can be a useful guide when preparing feasibility schedules for these facilities.

In all cases of uranium projects, governmental and environmental regulations must be individually considered as they impact heavily upon the schedule.

8.13.3 Schedule for Uranium Mine and Mill

Figure 8.25 covers phase I and phase II for a mining and ore treatment facilities project. The facilities included are shown diagrammatically in Figures 8.23 and 8.24.

For the mine, phase I, which includes selection of a contractor for phase II, is 9 months, and phase II is 30 months. An additional 16 months are required before the mine becomes operational. The overall duration is 55 months. The critical path is through the purchase of hoisting equipment, the installation of the headframe, and the sinking of the shaft. For facilities in a remote location, a construction labor

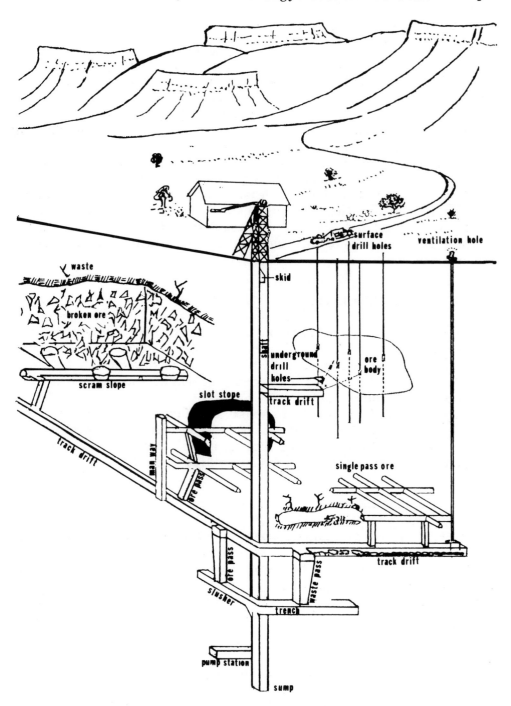

Figure 8.23   Uranium development—typical layout (mine).

camp would generally be required. Early completion of plant permanent housing could provide accommodation for the owner and contractor project staff personnel. Mine operations would generally be carried out by the owner.

For the mill, phase I is 9 months, and phase II is 25 months. An additional 3 months are required for commissioning. The overall

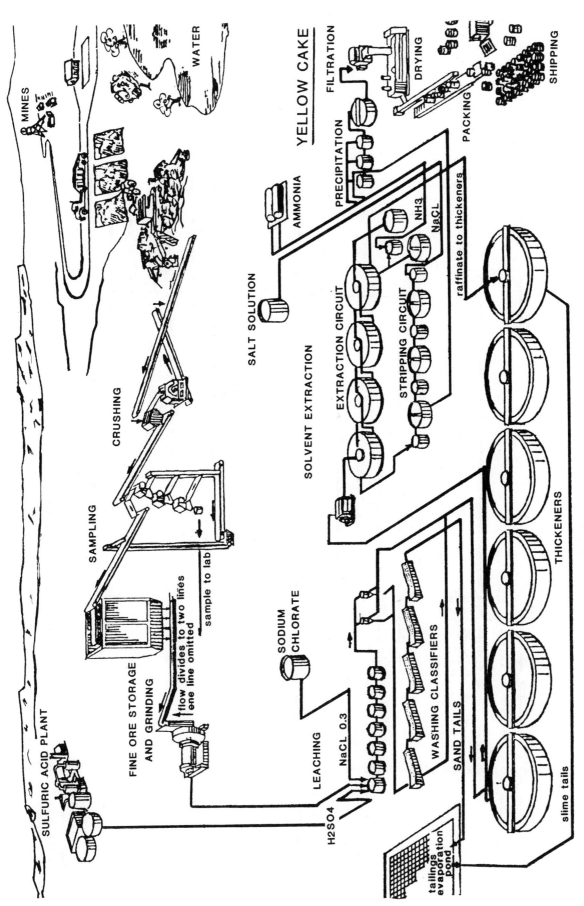

Figure 8.24 Uranium development—typical layout (mill).

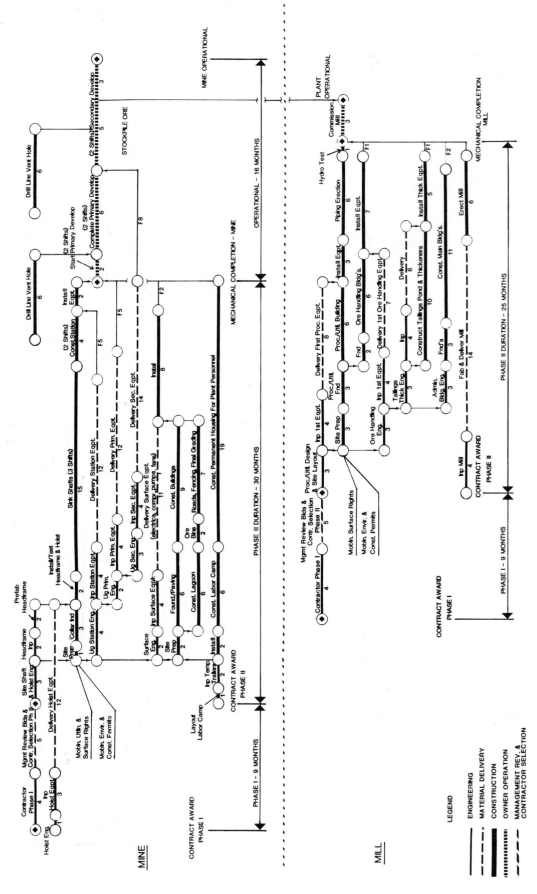

Figure 8.25   Uranium development—typical schedule (mines and mills).

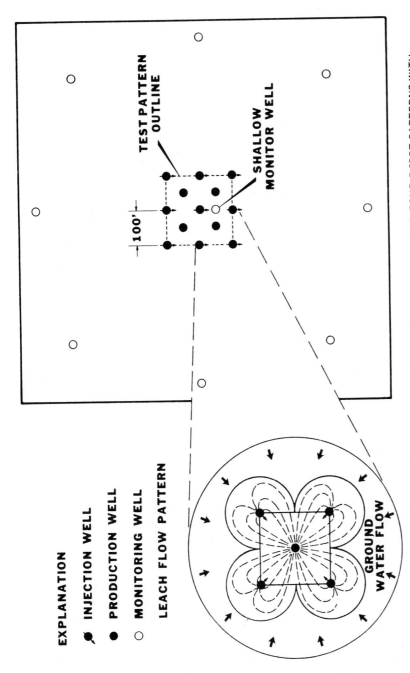

THIS EXHIBIT SHOWS **A Co**'S PROPOSED PILOT TEST CONFIGURATION USING FOUR 5-SPOT PATTERNS WITH ONE SHALLOW MONITOR WELL WITHIN THE INJECTION-PRODUCTION WELL OUTLINE. THE LEACH TEST AREA IS SURROUNDED BY MONITOR WELLS COMPLETED IN THE MINERALIZED ZONE TO BE LEACHED.

THE ENLARGEMENT SHOWS THE FLOW PATTERN FOR A SINGLE 5-SPOT WITH LEACH SOLUTIONS FLOWING ALONG THE PRESSURE GRADIENT FROM INJECTION WELLS TO PRODUCTION WELLS.

Figure 8.26   Uranium development—typical well configuration.

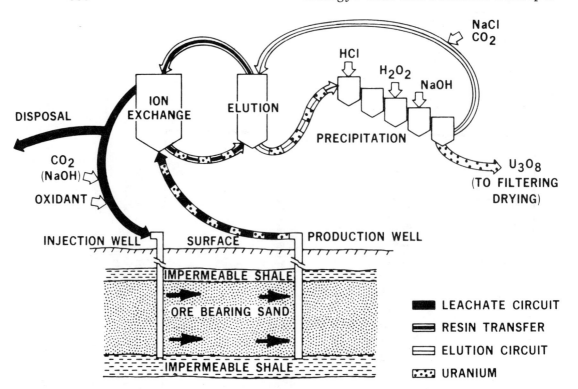

Figure 8.27   Uranium development—in situ leaching process.

duration is 37 months. Where milling and mining facilities are jointly
required, the relationship of plant and mine operational dates is shown.
The critical path is generally through design, delivery, and erection of
the process equipment and associated piping. The durations are typical,
and the schedule is for guidance only.

8.13.4 In Situ Leaching

Ore deposits were originally carried into place and dissolved in alkaline
groundwaters containing oxygen. When the water flowed into sand for-
mations containing hydrogen sulfide or organic material, it lost its
oxygen, and uranium precipitated as a coating on the sand grains. In
situ leaching seeks to reverse this process by putting uranium back into
solution and pumping it to the surface through production wells.

A typical arrangement for a production field is shown in Figure 8.26.
Production wells are surrounded on four sides by injection wells. Non-
toxic leach solutions in very dilute form (about 3000 ppm dissolved salts)
are pumped down the four injection wells and drawn up from the
production well. By keeping production levels slightly above injection
levels, the producing well becomes a pressure sink that draws the
uranium solution plus some surrounding groundwaters toward it. By
increasing or decreasing the pressure differential between the production and injection wells, the movement and flow of solutions can be
tightly controlled.

Some designs use a ring of monitor wells surrounding the pattern
area. They would be sampled regularly to make sure no leachate is

escaping. A shallow monitor well could be drilled in the aquifer (water-bearing formation) just overlying the test grid to detect any vertical leachate excursions. Such excursions are unlikely because the ore zones are typically bounded by shale barriers on both sides.

If any excursions are found, production in the affected area would be increased relative to injection until the water quality is back to normal. Since only a small portion of the aquifer is being treated and leachate concentrations are so dilute, any possible excursion would have only a very minor impact on the water quality in the surrounding area.

Solution pumped out of the producing wells is sent to an ion exchange column which absorbs the uranium (Figure 8.27). The product is transferred to an elution column that strips uranium from the ion exchange material and then to precipitation tanks where a series of non-toxic chemicals causes the uranium to precipitate. After further separation, solids from the precipitation are filtered, dried, and packaged to produce yellowcake. The barren leachate is pumped back down the injection well for reuse. About 97 or 98% of the water used in the process is recirculated, making the in situ leaching process essentially a closed system.

Restoration

When in situ leaching is finally completed in an area, the injection wells will be shut in and the leach zone flushed with natural groundwater by simply withdrawing water through the production wells. This water is purified in an electrodialysis unit (salt removal), and the restored water, with about 80% of the volume withdrawn, is reinjected into the aquifer. The concentrated brine stream, the remaining 20%, is pumped to the waste disposal pond. These restoration operations would occur simultaneously with leaching in another part of the ore body. The bottom of the wells opposite the ore-bearing formation will then be plugged with concrete and the upper part filled with heavy mud and capped with 10 ft of concrete.

Waste Disposal

While nearly all the produced water is recirculated, there is a small excess of production over injection, typically 1-3%, needed to help control the underground flow of leachate. For a 1 million lb/year plant, excess production will amount to about 50-120 gal/min (gpm). Following uranium removal by ion exchange, this excess production is sent to waste disposal ponds, which are lined with double layers of heavy plastic liners to prevent leakage and monitored by surrounding shallow wells. These ponds also receive a small volume of backwash waters, 20-30 gpm, which are used to clean the ion exchange columns and filters. The brine stream for restoration sent to waste disposal might amount to 30 gpm. Some of the chemicals, primarily sodium chloride, used in processing the uranium solution into yellowcake also come to these ponds.

The waters in these waste disposal ponds contain, in the range of 3000 ppm, total dissolved solids (primarily sodium chloride, sulfate, bicarbonate, calcium, magnesium, and silica) and are slightly alkaline (pH 7-8). Very low concentrations of some heavy metals may also be present in these waste solutions. If the ore has a high lime content, precipitated calcite will settle to the bottom of the pond. This solid residue will contain low concentrations of radium-226 coprecipitated with the calcite, and while not a radiation hazard, the solids must be permanently disposed of in an environmentally safe manner.

In southern Texas, waste solutions are concentrated by evaporation, and excess liquid is pumped to a deep disposal well and stored in a formation containing nonpotable (high-salinity) water. The relatively small amount of solid residue will be buried according to Texas Department of Health Resources regulations.

8.14 NUCLEAR POWER

Figure 8.28 shows the location of existing and planned nuclear plants under construction and a cost comparison of nuclear, coal-fired, and oil-fired plants. The cost comparison is for a plant to be completed in 1985.

If the nuclear industry is not allowed to expand, future U.S. electrical energy requirements may be met only with increased oil imports and conventional oil-fired power stations.

The direct costs for nuclear plants are higher than for coal- and oil-fired stations; however, operating costs are lower. Nuclear plant costs are further increased by lengthy permitting requirements which add considerably to the overall schedule.

Expansion of the nuclear industry is presently constrained by a reduced demand for electricity and concern over safety aspects. While operating procedures need to be improved, major safety reports over the past 5 years generally agree that safety is not a major problem. As shown in this exhibit, the safety record (deaths per year) of the nuclear industry is better than most industries. These "risk" statistics were presented by Lord Rothschild in the 1978 BBC Dimbleby lecture. He presented a table showing the average person's current risk of death each year from various causes.

There is much to be learned from Three Mile Island to improve on the already remarkable safety record of the nuclear industry. This obviously must be done expeditiously, and adequate waste-disposal sites must be developed, because it is highly unlikely that the United States can balance its supply and demand of energy in the next 10-20 years without a much larger contribution from nuclear power.

Fusion technology could provide a significant portion of our energy requirement in the next century, but this is uncertain. Other nations are building liquid metal fast breeder reactors (LMFBRs) capable of producing more fuel than is consumed. To avoid the separation of plutonium, President Carter deferred reprocessing of spent reactor fuel in the United States and delayed the development of the LMFBRs. The United States needs to continue research and development of various breeder technologies, however, or risk the ability to influence the direction of nuclear development.

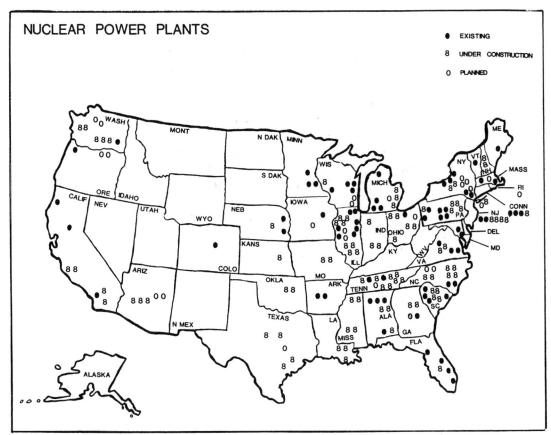

NUCLEAR POWER PLANTS

- ● EXISTING
- 8 UNDER CONSTRUCTION
- 0 PLANNED

COST COMPARISON (1985)	CONSTRUCTION COST	OPERATING COST
NUCLEAR	$ 1050 PER KW	3.7¢ PER KW-HOUR
COAL FIRED	$ 860 PER KW	4.3¢ PER KW-HOUR
OIL FIRED	$ 745 PER KW	7.3¢ PER KW-HOUR
SOLAR	$20,000 PER KW	- -

SCHEDULE - 10-12 YEARS - REGULATORY APPROVALS/PERMITS

SAFETY - POLITICAL AND PUBLIC CONCERN.

		DEATHS PER YEAR	
QUARRYING	-	1 IN	3100
COAL MINING	-	1 IN	5300
TRAFFIC ACCIDENTS	-	1 IN	7500
INFLUENZA	-	1 IN	18,000
CONTRACEPTIVE PILLS	-	1 IN	50,000
NUCLEAR	-	1 IN	50,000

(MAJOR REPORTS ON NUCLEAR SAFETY - RASMUSSEN, FORD)
(FOUNDATION AND LEWIS REPORT (NRC).)

WASTE STORAGE A PROBLEM

FUSION TECHNOLOGY - FEEDSTOCK IS WATER
- CONTAINMENT OF HIGH TEMPERATURES

Figure 8.28 Nuclear development—costs, safety.

This concludes the chapter on energy projects. It is not intended that this chapter cover, in detail, all aspects of energy and energy projects. However, it is our intent to briefly outline the major elements of the current-day energy situation.

Costs and schedules have to reflect present-day conditions. Supply and demand should be understood by cost and schedule engineers as their estimate, cost forecast, and schedule can be directly affected. Energy politics are also a fact of life and should also be reflected in the project execution plan. Resources are another major factor, and a good estimate, quality forecast, and realistic schedule should reflect current and future availability of resources.

9

OFFSHORE (NORTH SEA) PRODUCING PLATFORMS

In this chapter we shall mainly cover the scheduling of North Sea platforms. Cost control techniques would be similar to those covered in Chapters 4 and 6 for process plants.

Due to the following unique conditions, scheduling relationships and durations for offshore platforms are different from onshore process plants.

9.1 NORTH SEA SCHEDULING: INTRODUCTION

New and changing technology, a hostile environment (the North Sea), marine construction on a massive scale, and a minimum of experience and data provide the background to planning and scheduling a North Sea offshore platform.

As a result, the first generation of North Sea platforms experienced a considerable degree of last-minute innovation and were built without full scope definition and little appreciation of the complexities of offshore construction work.

The oil industry was breaking new technological barriers in terms of the size and complexity of production facilities. Because of the urgent need to bring these first fields on-stream, companies were tackling many of the problems during construction and installation stages. Equipment and designs were constantly being revised. Cost and schedule overruns were a common experience, and it was not until 1976 that realistic criteria and appropriate techniques had been developed to control these large and complex projects.

Field development designs vary greatly: a single platform for drilling, living, and producing or multiple platforms to separately cover these functions. Platform designs also vary from concrete gravity structures to steel jackets, with topsides of integrated decks, totally modular construction, or combinations of both. Production takeoff facilities, depending on the site location, can be by pipeline or tanker. Government regulations and agencies and partner and joint venture relationships add a further dimension that must be recognized by the planning and scheduling effort.

In this chapter we shall present concepts, guidelines, and general data on North Sea platforms.

9.2 MAP OF NORTH SEA GAS AND OIL FIELDS

Figure 9.1 shows the location of and lists the major gas and oil fields in the United Kingdom and Norwegian sectors. Also depicted are existing and proposed oil and gas pipelines for connecting various fields and transporting products ashore.

The majority of the fields are owned and developed by joint venture groups. The process by which agreement on the percentage of ownership is reached is called *unitization* and is based on the estimated capacity that each partner's "block" has in the reservoir. One of the joint venture partners, usually the partner with the largest share of the field reserves, is selected as the operator of the field. This entails designing, building, and operating the producing facility. The project execution of a facility will usually require reviews and approvals by a committee of the joint venture partners.

9.3 EXPLORATION AND APPRAISAL

Figure 9.2 illustrates a typical exploration and appraisal program for a North Sea block. Detailed seismograph surveys of block 9/13 were commenced immediately following award of the license. Drilling on the first wildcat well, situated in 390 ft of water, was started in May 1972. This well, 9/13-1, found oil in Jurassic sandstone at 10,000 ft and was tested in September 1972 at a daily rate of 3400 barrels of oil. In July 1973, 9-13/2 was also found productive, indicating a commercially viable field. The decision was taken, therefore, to initiate development planning. Subsequent drilling at wells 9/13-5 and 9/13-6 extended the productive area.

The exploration program in block 9/13 has, over a period of 4 years, involved 1000 mi of seismic surveys and the drilling of 12 exploration and appraisal wells using floating rigs. The geology of the block is complex and seismic interpretation unusually difficult, presenting problems in finding and delineating productive areas. The wells drilled have consequently shown varying results: some successes and some disappointments.

Discoveries separate from the field accumulation have been made by well 9/13-4 to the southwest, indicated to be small, and by wells 9/13-7 and 9/13-12 to the north, which require further appraisal drilling to determine their extent. Each of these wells is located about 5 miles from the platform.

Drilling will establish in due time the full potential of the block and also yield information on which to base decisions on viability and methods of future development for those accumulations beyond the reach of the field platform.

As one potential method for handling outlying productive wells, a practical test of subsea completion equipment is being conducted on well 9/13-1, the field's discovery well, situated about 2000 ft from the platform. Fixed permanently to the well are a base and master wellhead valve assembly to which is connected a replaceable module containing all

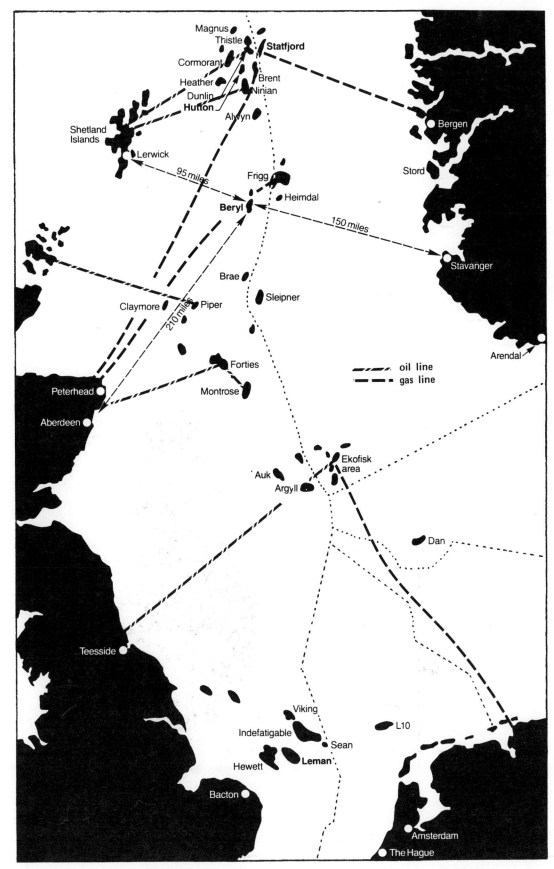

Figure 9.1 Map of North Sea gas and oil fields.

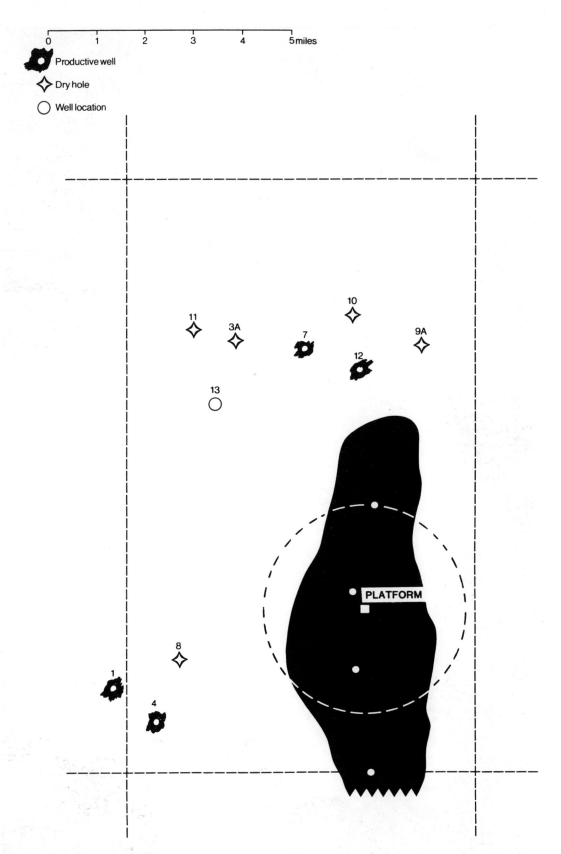

Figure 9.2   Sketch of exploration-drilling program.

the well control gear. This module can be raised and lowered from a floating rig whenever necessary for maintenance or replacement. The operation of the well when producing is controlled and monitored from the platform to which the wellhead is connected by a multiconductor electrical cable. The oil from the well flows through a flexible pipeline on the seabed to the platform.

Undoubtedly, subsea completion equipment will be greatly developed in the future as discoveries are being made in greater and greater water depths.

9.4 FIELD DEVELOPMENT CONCEPT

Analyses of development alternatives and economic factors in 1974 indicated the field was not of sufficient size to justify the costly installation of a subsea pipeline and shore terminal at a distant landfall. Viable alternatives were thus limited to those involving tanker loading in the field. Since loading operations would often be precluded by heavy seas, particularly in winter, the ability to continue producing oil between loadings was adopted as a significant design objective, calling for on-site storage capability.

Figures 9.3 and 9.4 illustrate the type of platform that was selected. Essential operational functions to be performed by the facility were well drilling, production processing, emergency gas flaring, oil storage, and tanker loading. In addition, provisions were needed for personnel accommodation as well as for injection of gas and water into the subsurface oil reservoir. In shallower waters, this multiplicity of functions would normally lead to the use of several platforms, but the depth and foreseen costs strongly urged that the number be kept to a minimum.

With the foregoing criteria, the "Condeep" concept of a single drilling and processing platform mounted on its own storage facility, with a nearby tanker mooring, was selected for initial development. The platform allows the drilling of slanted wells within a circle over 4 mi in diameter. Productive areas beyond this reach can be developed either from satellite drilling platforms or by the use of subsea well completions.

9.5 PRODUCTION PROCESSING AND STORAGE

The crude oil in its virgin reservoir condition some 10,000 ft under the seabottom is a liquid and exists in porous sandstone at a natural pressure of 5000 psi and a temperature of 200°F. Under these conditions, the liquid oil has natural gases dissolved in it.

Three major design elements of a North Sea platform are the following:

Gas/oil ratio
Water depth
Buoyancy requirements for tow-out

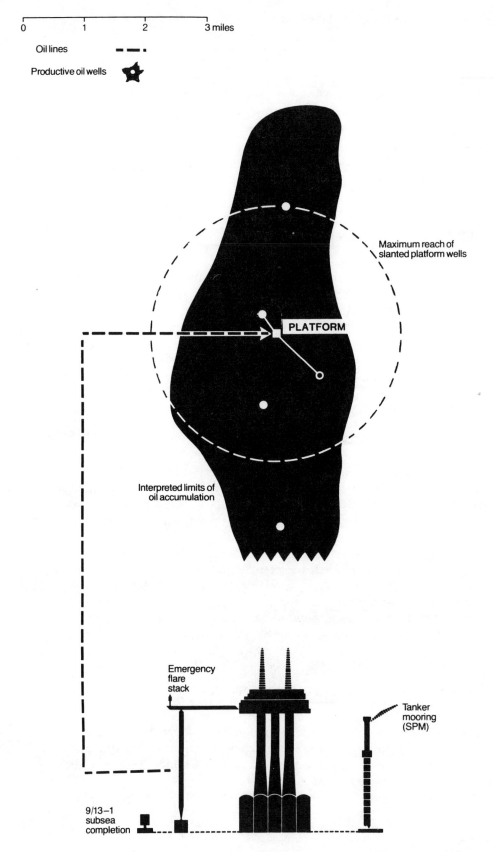

Figure 9.3 Sketch of field and platform.

340

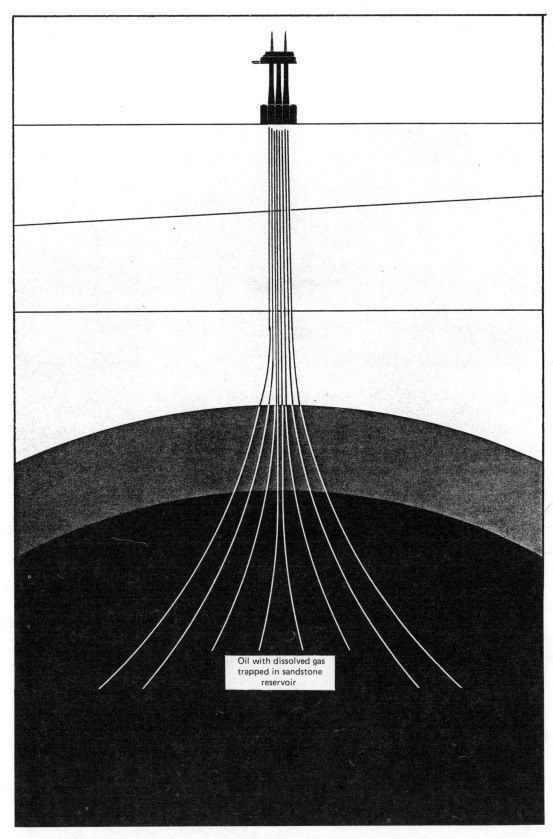

Figure 9.4 Sketch of drilling from platform (slanted drilling).

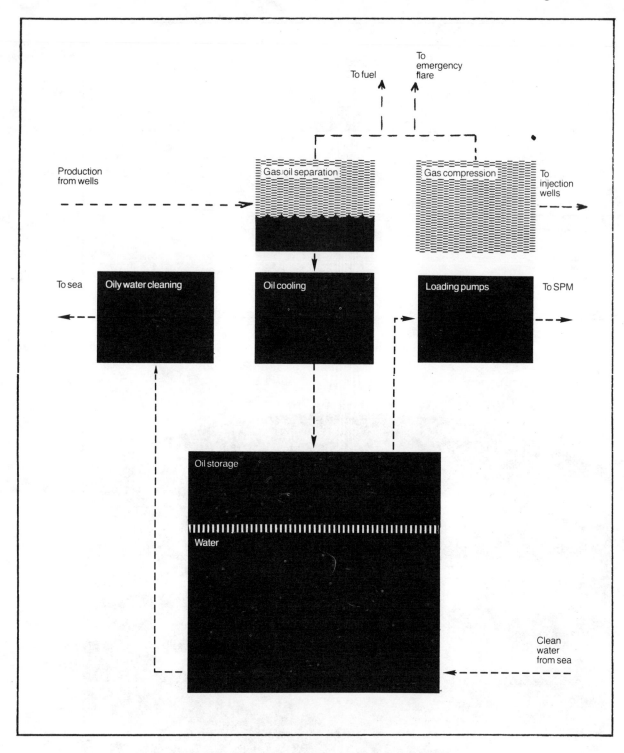

platform processes

Figure 9.5   Block flow of platform processing scheme.

Figure 9.5 illustrates a processing scheme for the platform. The controlled release of natural reservoir pressure in the process of production frees gas from solution and permits the mixture of oil and gas to flow up through the wells to the platform deck. As the mixture leaves the wellhead, its pressure and temperature are about 150 psi and 140°F, respectively.

Oil is piped from the wellheads to large separation vessels for removal of gases. It then flows through coolers, where temperature is reduced to 100°F, before entering the platform's concrete storage cells. The concrete would be overstressed and perhaps crack if the oil were too hot. As oil enters the storage cells, it pushes out seawater which, before being returned to sea, passes through "oily water separators" to assure there is no pollution. During those times when oil is being pumped to tankers, fresh seawater enters the storage cells to replace the oil. There is never airspace in the cells.

Most of the gas removed from the oil in separator vessels will eventually be piped to large compressors to raise its pressure as high as 6000 psi for reinjection through selected wells back into the underground oil reservoir. Until reinjection is commenced, surplus gas will be safely disposed of by burning through the emergency flare system. Reinjection will not only store the gas for possible production and sale at a later time but may also increase the total amount of oil which can be economically recovered from the reservoir over the life of the field. Incidentally, the platform is equipped with pumps to be used for injection of seawater into the reservoir as an added aid to oil recovery efficiency.

Part of the separated gas is used as fuel for turbines driving the platform's electric generators. Electricity powers the drilling rigs, oil pumps, water pumps, some of the gas compressors, and general utility equipment throughout the platform. The power generation equipment has an output capable of supplying electricity to a city of 250,000 people.

As to basic platform functions, the facility initially installed has a daily capacity to process 150,000 barrels of oil production and to inject back into the reservoir 150 million ft^3 of gas and 100,000 barrels of seawater.

9.6   GENERAL DATA OF NORTH SEA PLATFORMS

The following is Norwegian-published data of Stat Oil North Sea platforms.

Figure 9.6 is a sketch of the Beryl A and Statfjord platforms comparing their sizes with well-known buildings in Norway, the United Kingdom, and the United States. Data such as those in Table 9.1 can provide order of magnitude figures for overall scheduling purposes. When specific scheduling data are lacking, quantities as shown in Table 9.1 can be applied to appropriate man-hour units to give an appreciation of the scope or "size" of activity. Durations can then be determined by applying peak-average manpower levels to the task.

Table 9.1

	Beryl A	Statfjord A	Statfjord B
Production capacity (bpd)	150,000	330,000	180,000
Oil storage capacity (barrels)	900,000	1,300,000	1,900,000
Power generating capacity (kW)	75,000	65,000	38,000
Living quarter capacity (beds)	120 (expanded to 200)	200	200
Water depth (m)	120	145	145
Critical wave height (m)	30	30	31
Total height from sea bed to derrick top (m)	209	254	271
Distance between sea & deck (m)	23.5	28	29
Deck height (from cellar deck (CD) floor to helideck (m)	28.3	43.5	30.4
Shaft height above cells (m)	90	106	111
Cell height (m)	50	67	64
Cell inside diameter (m)	19	19	23
Deck cross-sectional area (m × m)	71 × 60	83 × 86	114 × 55
Gravity base structure base area (m^2)	8,200	9,500	18,200
Amount of concrete (m^3)	53,000	87,000	134,000
Deck weight without outfitting (tons)	5,900	9,500	7,500
Dry weight of outfitted dock (metric ton)	19,400	37,300	35,000[a]
Fully outfitted wet deck weight (metric ton)		46,400	49,600
Total weight (metric ton)	350,000	650,000	781,000
Total number of cell structures	19	19	24
Number of shafts	3	3	4

Table 9.1   (Continued)

	Beryl A	Statfjord A	Statfjord B
Number of oil storage cells	16	15	20
Number of wells (m^2)	40	42	42
Number of drilling rigs	2	1	1
Number of deck modules	0	19	10

[a]Estimated as of April 1979.

9.7 PICTORIAL VIEW OF A FIELD DEVELOPMENT PROGRAM

Figure 9.7 is a pictorial view of a single gravity structure platform having drilling, living, and production facilities with a subsea pipeline takeoff to a single-point mooring (SPM) tanker loading facility. An SPM is an alternative method for transporting oil from a platform when connecting shore pipelines are not available.

Large fields may require a multiple-platform arrangement to adequately exploit the total reservoir. In such cases, platforms would not necessarily be identical or even similar. For example, storage supplied by one platform may be adequate for two production platforms in which case the second platform could be supported by a steel jacket structure with no built-in storage capacity. Similarly, an SPM could be designed with enough capacity to support production from two platforms. In both of these cases, interconnecting pipelines between platforms would be required.

Considering differences in production systems, supporting structures, unloading facilities, injection and reinjection schemes, etc., the possible combinations of facilities required to fully develop a large field become almost limitless. The configuration depicted in the pictorial view is one solution to part of a total field development program.

9.8 STEEL PLATFORM

Steel platforms have been built for the Texas-Gulf Coast for many years. These platforms were essentially producing platforms, with crude oil or gas being shipped by pipeline to a shore facility for processing. Water depths were not great, and structural design parameters were comparatively straightforward. The North Sea, with greater water depths and an extremely hostile environment, required much more substantial platforms.

Figure 9.8 shows a typical arrangement of such a steel platform. This sketch shows a steel platform, completely integrated with living quarters, drilling, and producing facilities. As steel platforms do not

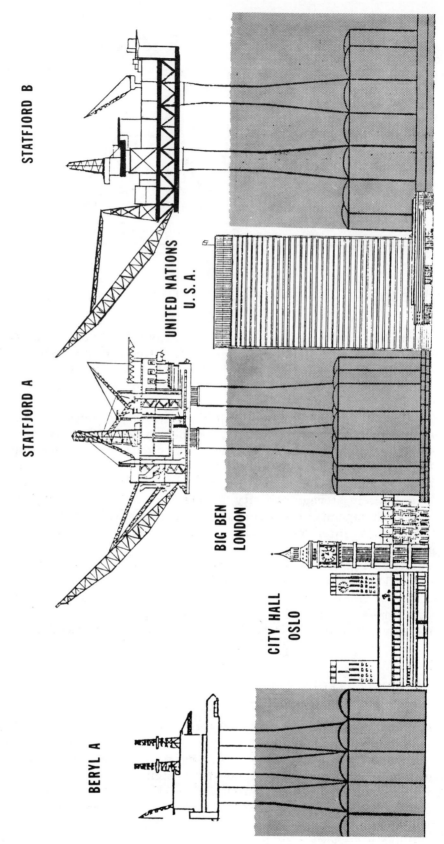

STATFJORD B

STATFJORD A

UNITED NATIONS
U. S. A.

BIG BEN
LONDON

CITY HALL
OSLO

BERYL A

Figure 9.6   Sketch of North Sea platforms.

346

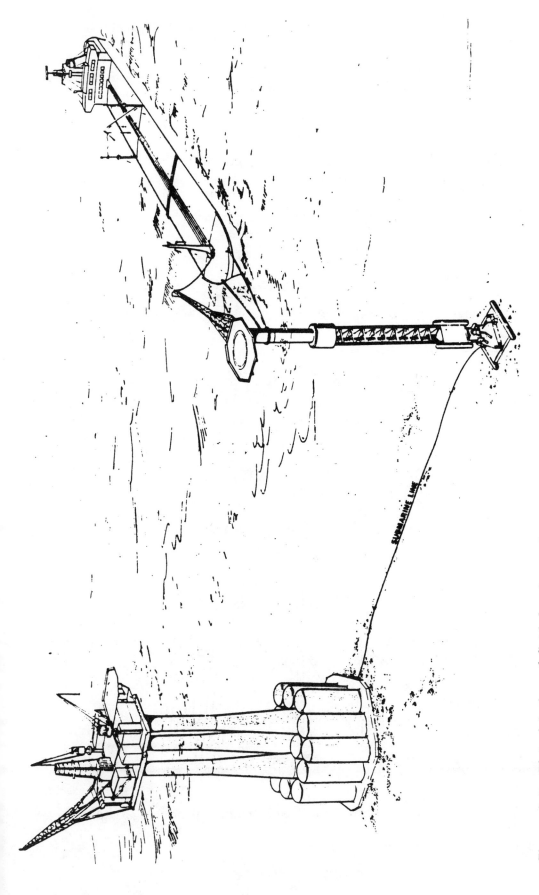

SUBMARINE LINE

Figure 9.7   Pictorial view of field development program.

347

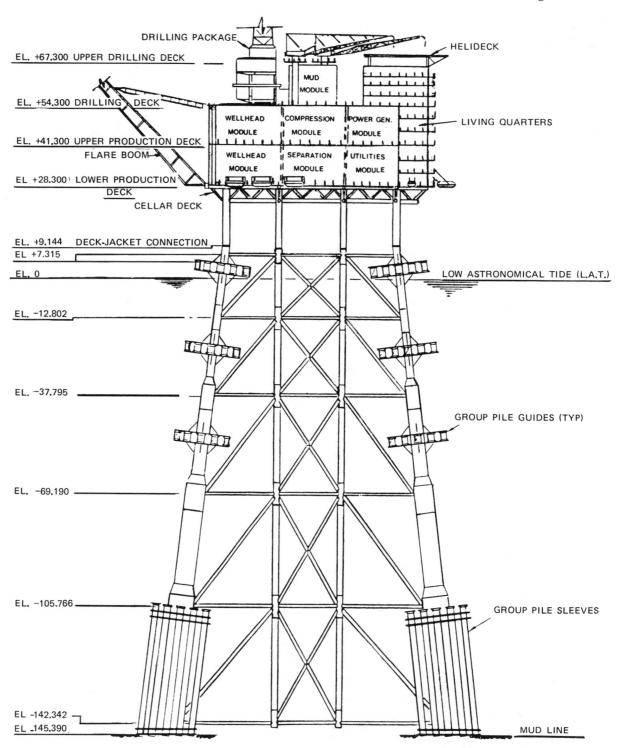

EL. +67.300 UPPER DRILLING DECK

DRILLING PACKAGE

HELIDECK

MUD MODULE

EL. +54.300 DRILLING DECK

WELLHEAD MODULE   COMPRESSION MODULE   POWER GEN. MODULE

LIVING QUARTERS

EL. +41.300 UPPER PRODUCTION DECK
FLARE BOOM

WELLHEAD MODULE   SEPARATION MODULE   UTILITIES MODULE

EL. +28.300 LOWER PRODUCTION DECK
CELLAR DECK

EL. +9.144 DECK-JACKET CONNECTION
EL. +7.315

EL. 0

LOW ASTRONOMICAL TIDE (L.A.T.)

EL. −12.802

EL. −37.795

GROUP PILE GUIDES (TYP)

EL. −69.190

EL. −105.766

GROUP PILE SLEEVES

EL. −142.342
EL. −145.390

MUD LINE

Figure 9.8   Sketch of steel platform: drilling, producing, and living quarters.

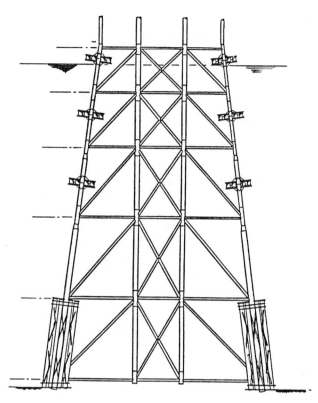

Figure 9.9   Sketch of steel jacket.

generally have a storage facility, they would normally be connected to
a separate storage facility (pipeline to shore--permanently moored
tanker).

The main elements of a steel platform are the following:

Jacket (leg section)
Deck
Modules

9.9 STEEL JACKET

Figure 9.9 is a sketch of a typical steel jacket. This jacket would generally be fabricated on flotation tanks or a barge for future transportation to the field location.

Large platforms can have steel jackets weighing in excess of
20,000 tons. Whereas the simple structures for the Texas-Gulf Coast
can be fabricated for 30 man-hours/ton, these jackets would require an
average of 60-80 man-hours/ton and could take 2 years to complete.
Alignment of pile guides and sleeves is critical, and fabricating the
main connection nodes requires the highest of fitting and welding skills.

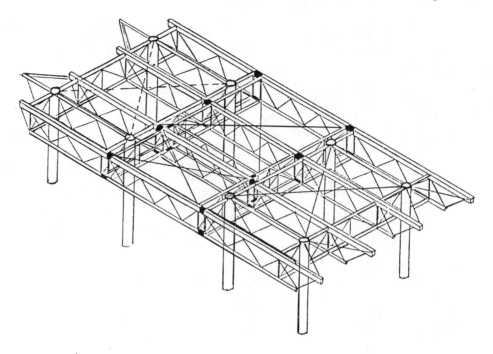

Figure 9.10   Sketch of module support frame (deck).

9.10 DECK-MODULE SUPPORT FRAME

Figure 9.10 is a sketch of a typical deck or module support frame. As illustrated, this is a complex structure from both design and fabrication viewpoints. Apart from structural integrity, major design studies would consider a bare "flat top" for an all-modular platform or an "integrated deck" where some equipment is installed in the deck itself. Modules would contain the remainder of the equipment. For ease of offshore installation (limited by the capacity of lifting vessels), the deck may be fabricated in several pieces.

Such structures can weigh in excess of 5000 tons and require 120-150 man-hours/ton for fabrication. The schedule could be 14-16 months.

9.11 MARINE CONSTRUCTION PROGRAM

Offshore construction could include the following:

Towing, upending, and positioning the jacket
Piling and grouting the jacket
Lifting and welding the deck sections
Lifting and securing the modules
Module hookup and commissioning
Installation and tie-in of the pipeline
Installation of the storage-loading facility

Most of these activities are *weather-dependent*, and the North Sea's hostile environment has a significant bearing. A further consideration is housing construction labor. Experience to date indicates that only about 50% of platform beds can be dedicated to construction labor. Thus, additional beds, on derrick barges and flotels, can shorten offshore schedules.

Figure 9.11 shows the major steps of a steel platform marine construction program. With a 5.1 labor cost ratio of offshore to onshore, it is imperative that onshore construction be maximized. Even so, offshore schedules in excess of 12 months are common.

The increasing sizes of semisubmersible lifting rigs is helping to reduce offshore construction time. Many of the 1970's derrick barges could work effectively only in 3-ft or smaller waves. The "semis," with 2000-3000 tons of capacity, now enable large lifts to be made in 10-ft waves and piling to continue in 15-ft waves.

9.12 PROJECT MASTER SCHEDULE, TYPICAL

Figure 9.12 is a schedule guide for offshore platforms in the North Sea. The schedule shown in based on data and experience from actual offshore platforms. This schedule is based on a concrete support structure, and the schedule should be modified for different support structures.

The latter part of the schedule is on a calendar basis to reflect the weather window sensitivity of some activities, namely, tow to mate, mate, tow-out, install the SPM, and install the subsea pipeline. Durations marked "?" depend on the scope, manpower allocation, shift work program, contracting strategy, work location, and market conditions for delivery of equipment.

Previous experience on North Sea platforms is limited to a handful of projects. Historical schedule data are therefore not as conclusive as for process plants. One major relationship, however, appears to relate as well to offshore platforms as it does to onshore process plants. This is the relationship between engineering completion and the start of mechanical outfitting. For a process plant, historical experience indicates that 75-80% completion of engineering is required prior to the start of field mechanical work in order to adequately support a construction program on a *fast-track approach*. Anything significantly less than this can result in construction delays through lack of engineering drawings. This relationship can also be applied to a platform. The equivalent basis would be 75-80% engineering for the start of the mechanical outfitting of the deck and modules.

A unique element to be considered in platform scheduling is the completion of inshore and offshore work. Some tasks, e.g., towing and mating, can take place only in good weather. The period of the year when conditions are most likely to be favorable for inshore and offshore operations is termed the weather window. Each activity has its own weather window, which is dependent on degree of difficulty, location (inshore, offshore), and financial risk, i.e., mating, February through October; tow-out, May through September; etc. As equipment technology

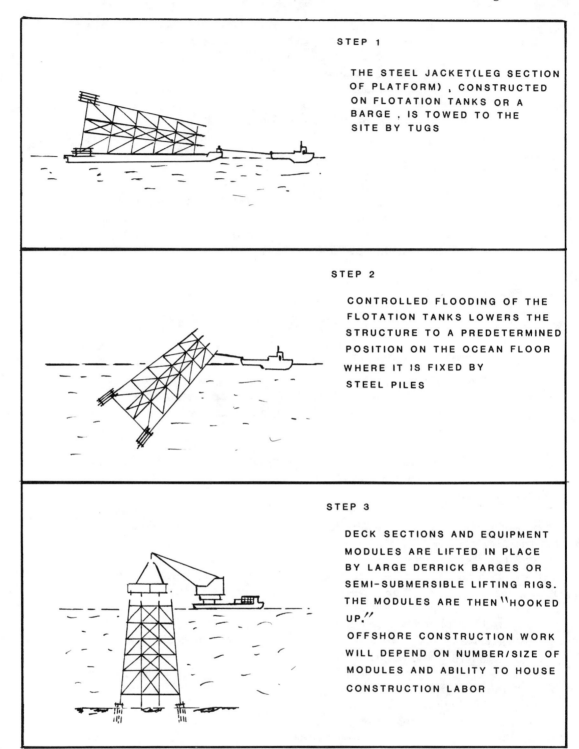

STEP 1

THE STEEL JACKET(LEG SECTION
OF PLATFORM) , CONSTRUCTED
ON FLOTATION TANKS OR A
BARGE , IS TOWED TO THE
SITE BY TUGS

STEP 2

CONTROLLED FLOODING OF THE
FLOTATION TANKS LOWERS THE
STRUCTURE TO A PREDETERMINED
POSITION ON THE OCEAN FLOOR
WHERE IT IS FIXED BY
STEEL PILES

STEP 3

DECK SECTIONS AND EQUIPMENT
MODULES ARE LIFTED IN PLACE
BY LARGE DERRICK BARGES OR
SEMI-SUBMERSIBLE LIFTING RIGS.
THE MODULES ARE THEN "HOOKED
UP."
OFFSHORE CONSTRUCTION WORK
WILL DEPEND ON NUMBER/SIZE OF
MODULES AND ABILITY TO HOUSE
CONSTRUCTION LABOR

Figure 9.11   Steel platform—marine construction program (sketches).

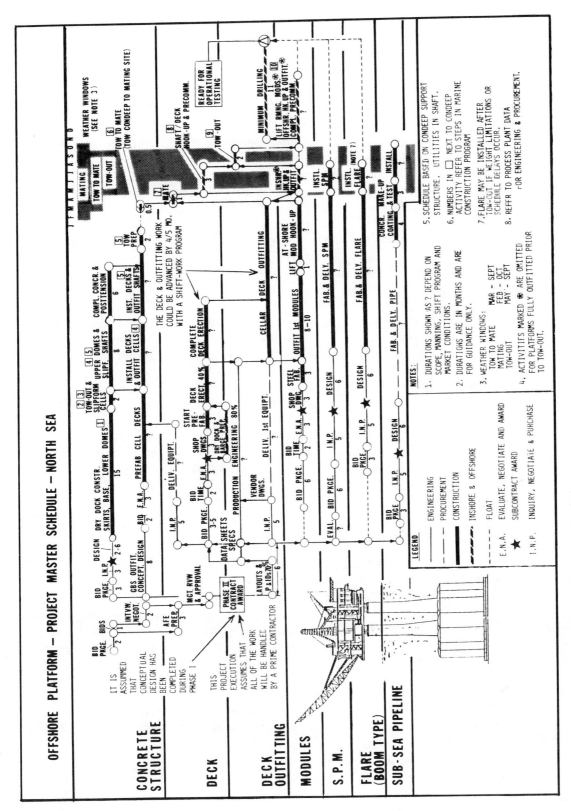

Figure 9.12 Typical project master schedule.

improves, weather windows tend to expand. As an example, with the derrick barges now planned for the early 1980s, offshore piling will be possible during the entire year as compared with a weather window of approximately 9 months in 1978.

Use of "Standard" Schedule

Upon definition of the scope, manpower allocation, shift work program, contracting strategy, and anticipated delivery of equipment, a project master schedule can be completed by evaluating values for the unknown durations. Standard durations should be checked where project strategy or scope differs significantly from previous projects.

Construction durations are calculated and checked by utilizing the trapezoidal calculation method in conjunction with historical percent complete rates, manpower density levels, and/or manpower limitations. Where man-hour estimates are not available, preliminary man-hours could be obtained by utilizing unit rates (man-hours per quantity) to convert estimated quantities into man-hours.

A number of factors inherent in the design and construction of North Sea platforms require an additional allowance to calculated durations. These include new technology, prototype engineering, multiple engineering offices and construction sites, heavy government involvement, and restrictive labor practices. To allow for these factors, an experience factor of 25% should be added to all calculated durations. This is reduced to 15% for offshore construction activities. The following comments relate to the major elements of the work:

Design: Concrete Structure: The duration depends on the amount of design work done prior to contract award and the degree of duplication from previous designs.

Construction: Concrete Structure, General: Use schedules prepared by the concrete contractor when available. This is specialized construction, and historically schedules have been maintained. The durations indicated are for a very large concrete structure ($100,000$-$150,000$ m^3). There will be some variation in the durations depending on the structure size.

Prefabricated Cell Decks: Consider the number and size of the decks, the degree of prefabrication, and the total man-hours.

Install Decks and Outfit Cells and Shafts: Assume a density level, and calculate shaft area and peak manpower. The degree of complexity and effectiveness of labor classify North Sea platforms in the 200-250 ft^2/worker density category. However, due to schedule criticality, a density of 150-200 ft^2/worker is used in practice. The resulting reduction in productivity is "traded off" against an improved schedule achieved with increased manpower. Also consider regulatory guidelines which may restrict the maximum number of workers per shift within the shafts. Assume a shift-work program (with an appropriate efficiency factor) and the availability of shift labor, and calculate the work month (effective man-hours per month). Determine the duration using the trapezoidal method. Shaft outfitting may not be completed prior to tow to mate to meet weather window restrictions. In this case, break the

outfitting activity for tow to mate, and allow demobilization and re-
mobilization time in the overall duration.

Equipment Deliveries: Add a creep factor to standard lead time
duration.

Basic Engineering (Layouts, PIDs, Data Sheets, and Specifications):
Consider the degree of duplication or experience with previous platforms, the number and location of engineering office(s), project organizations, and the magnitude of phase I engineering. The duration may
vary from 4 months for an exact duplicate to 8 months for new concepts.

Production Engineering 80%: Consider process plant experience to
establish the duration. Use the process plant project master schedule
(PMS), and adjust the project duration for the "overseas—U.K." site
by reference to "Add Factors" at the bottom. This will require an add
factor of 30-40% for mechanical-piping work. For example, for a
standard project duration of 33 months and on-site piping of 16 months,
the adjusted duration is

33 months + 40% of 16 months = 40 months

From "Overall Breakdown" (Figure 3.12),

80% engineering occurs at	43% of project time
0% (start) of detailed engineering occurs at	9% of project time
Therefore, 80% of engineering takes	34% of project time

34% of 40 months = 14 months

Add a 25% experience factor to obtain the engineering duration:

14 months × 1.25   17.5 months
Use 18 months.

Deck Fabrication and Erection: Use the trapezoidal evaluation
technique with a density level of 150 ft^2/worker; consider shift work.
Adjust the total hours to take out hours for prefabricated work and
support work completed away from the deck; evaluate the appropriate
manpower buildup and rundown; make allowance for lost time, and
adjust peak manpower if labor is not available. Add a 25% experience
factor to give the activity duration. Concurrent equipment outfitting
will impact on deck fabrication if both activities share the same working
area. Outfitting manpower will build up as deck manpower runs down.
See Figure 9.20 for a composite deck manpower loading analysis.

Deck Outfitting: Use the same method as for deck fabrication.
Where outfitting cannot be completed prior to a mating date, cut off
manpower with a sharp rundown (1-2 months) and "carry over" the
remaining man-hours to inshore-offshore.

Module Outfitting: There are two methods. The first method is to
evaluate the individual module (large and average) area by adding a
10-ft perimeter to the plan dimensions. The application of the density
level (150 ft^2/worker) will determine the peak manpower. Use the
trapezoidal technique to determine the duration. The second method is
to consider the outfitting man-hours of total modules, divide the work
among several or many subcontractors, and, by judgment, determine
the peak manpower for a subcontractor. Then use the trapezoidal

technique to determine the duration. The total hours should be reduced for prefabrication and support work completed away from the module "saturation area." Add a 25% experience factor to give the activity duration. Check the durations against recent module completions. Consider the location of the fabricator (country). Consider the fabrication and delivery of the first modules required for the start of the module hookup activity. For guidance, module fabrication durations are 14-16 months for small modules and 16-18 months for large and/or complex modules. Several modules in the same shop would generally require additional time (15-20%).

Module Hookup: This starts after the first module lift. It may occur at the deck site, inshore after mating, and/or offshore. Use the trapezoidal technique to calculate the durations. The saturation manpower is obtained by assuming that 40% of the module area is available (this varies with the degree of module completion). Apply 150 ft^2/worker. Buildup is short, limited only by the ability to man and plan the work. If work is carried inshore, break the trapezoid abruptly during mating when work ceases—no rundown and buildup for simplicity. Man-hours carried inshore should be adjusted for lower productivity. This also applies to deck outfitting man-hours, which should be combined with hookup man-hours for one calculation. By judgment, assess the manpower level. Man-hours carried offshore require further productivity adjustment. Further reduction may be required for drilling interference (concurrent drilling and construction). Manpower buildup and peak are limited by available accommodations [temporary living quarters (TLQs), flotels, permanent quarters]. The use of high-cost flotels can greatly increase the availability of craft labor and reduce the schedule. The available beds must be discounted for the number of nonconstruction personnel (operational support, drilling, management, catering). Of the total platform beds, about 50% would be available for construction craft labor. The workweek is 7 12-hr days less 5% absenteeism, etc. Module hookup (and outfitting) should be evaluated separately from commissioning as peak manpower cannot be utilized on commissioning work. Use the trapezoidal technique to determine the duration. Add a 25% experience factor to at-shore durations and 15% to inshore and offshore durations.

Mating and Tow-out: Towing of the gravity structure to the mating site, mating, and tow-out are all subject to weather limitations. Weather windows for these activities are as follows:

Tow to mating site: March through September
Mating: February through October
Tow-out: May through September (the latest start of tow-out is the
    first week in August)

To minimize risk, it is desirable not to have all mating and tow-out operations in the same year. It is preferable to schedule tow to mate in the year prior to mating and tow-out. Mating durations of 1 month and tow-out of 2 months include weather contingency.

Minimum Drilling: This is the time required to complete the drilling required for start-up. Eleven months are required to drill three wells, including the conductor driving. Further time will be required to drill all wells for full production.

9.13 GRAVITY BASE STRUCTURE

Figure 9.13 illustrates, in plan and elevation, a typical Condeep gravity base structure (GBS). While a four-legged, 24-cell structure is depicted, GBSs vary in size depending on topside facilities, storage requirements, etc. Condeeps are proprietary products designed and built exclusively by Norcon (Norwegian Consultants). Technology is specialized. Designs are to an extent standardized but require modification to suit each project. Design periods will vary depending on the degree of duplication from previous projects.

The purchase and delivery of steel skirts is critical to the start of construction. Where the GBS is critical, steel skirts can be ordered prior to award of the GBS contract. GBS bid and award time may also be shortened for near-duplicate designs.

9.14 MARINE CONSTRUCTION PROGRAM

Figure 9.14 outlines the steps in the construction of a GBS. The work begins in dry dock with pouring a mud slab. Steel skirts, the base, and lower domes are then constructed. Cell walls are poured to a certain height prior to dry dock flooding, and some outfitting of cells may begin.

The dry dock is filled with water, and the base structure is floated out and anchored at a deep-water site. The base floats on a cushion of air within the skirt walls.

As the slipforming of cell walls proceeds, the structure is ballasted to maintain a working area near the water surface. Concrete is supplied by batch plants located on barges adjacent to the GBS.

Upon completion of cell slipforming, preassembled decks and equipment are installed. Cells are partially filled with ballast sand, and upper domes are then constructed.

Ballasting continues until all but the upper domes are submerged. Slipforming continues on shafts with the upper domes used as a work surface. Installation of decks and equipment and shaft outfitting follow completion of shaft slipforming. Preparation is made for towing. The GBS is complete.

During the weather window (March-September), the GBS is towed to a deep-water site closer to the deck site. The deck (topsides), which is constructed simultaneously with the GBS, is prepared for mating. The deck may be constructed on barges or transferred to barges prior to mating. GBS outfitting may continue at the mating site prior to mating if work is incomplete prior to tow.

At the mating site, the GBS is ballasted until only a few meters of shafts are exposed. The deck, on barges, is moved over the GBS. The mating of the deck and GBS is finalized with the welding and bolting of the deck to shafts.

For partially complete decks, work now commences inshore on completion of outfitting, module lifting, and/or module hookup. A minimum

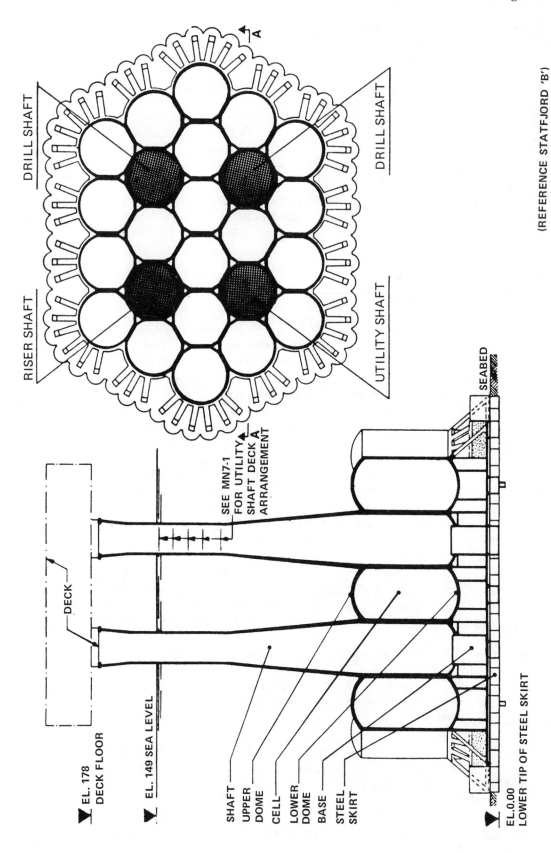

Figure 9.13   Gravity base structure.

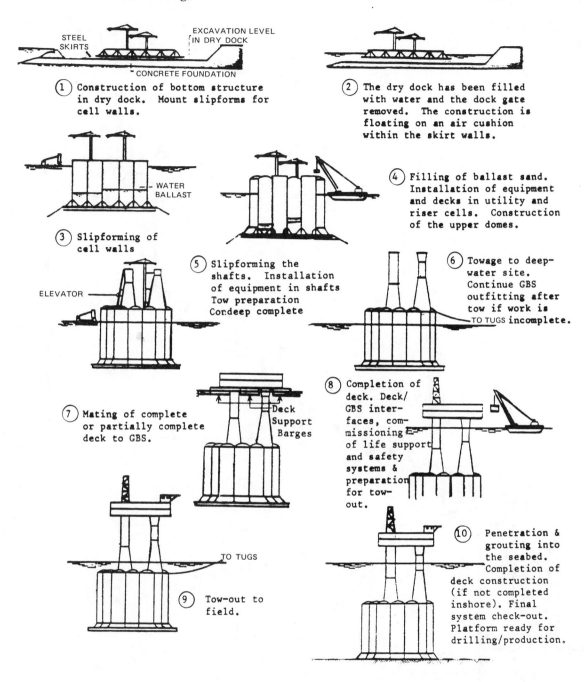

Figure 9.14   Sketch and flow chart of marine construction program.

of 3 months is needed inshore to complete the deck to GBS interfaces, commissioning of the life support and safety systems, and preparation for tow-out.

The GBS is towed to the final location in the North Sea and ballasted to the ocean floor. Steel skirts penetrate the seabed to hold the structure in its permanent location, and concrete grout is pumped

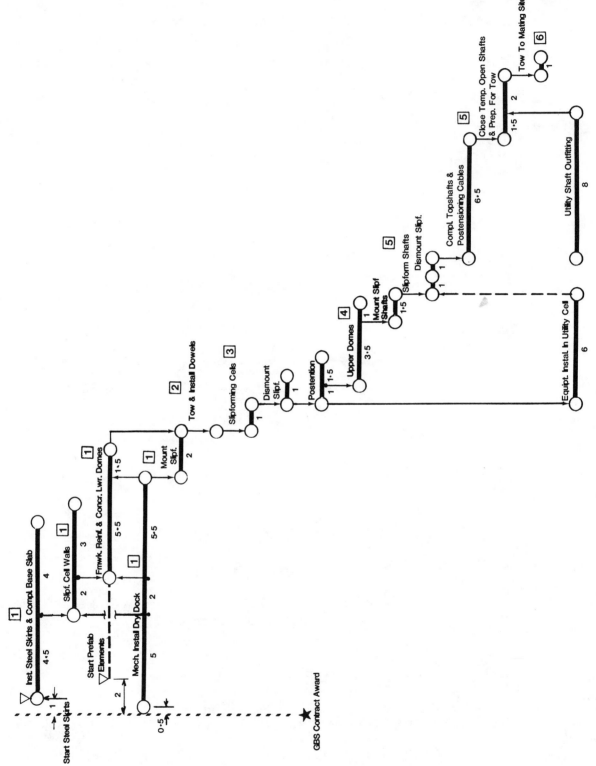

Figure 9.15 Schedule of GBS construction: duration in months.

into the base voids. Any outfitting or hookup work remaining is completed offshore.

Figure 9.15 is a summary bar chart of the GBS construction phase. This overall schedule of 36 months is for a very large GBS (100,000-150,000 m^3).

9.15 DETAILED ENGINEERING SCHEDULE

The detailed engineering schedule is based on a topsides having an integrated cellar deck and two levels of modules.

Figure 9.16 outlines major areas of engineering and shows typical activity durations. The project contracting strategy impacts heavily on logic and durations as does a tight tow-out date, which may "force" engineering work. The schedule shown is based on actual experience.

Deck construction is often critical and may require prepurchase of steel. The deck is usually a lump sum contract. Since the deck and deck outfitting are usually done by one fabricator, the decision on contracting strategy for outfitting can influence the timing of the bidding and contract award. Reimbursable deck outfitting results in earlier contract award and start of construction. Unit price or lump sum contracts require much greater engineering definition, and hence there is a later contract award.

Deck outfitting is always critical. Three major paths through engineering are piping-isometrics, equipment purchasing, and overall engineering progress (70-80%). Process flow diagrams and PIDs restrain general engineering and require special attention and control. Purchasing criticality stems from vendor drawing supply as well as equipment supply. Overall engineering progress of 75-80% is required to support an efficient construction program for deck outfitting.

The GBS outfitting strategy depicted entails completion of production engineering by the fabricator. The contract could be on a lump sum basis.

9.16 UTILITY SHAFT

Figure 9.17 shows the relative elevations of the decks in a utility cell and shaft of a concrete gravity structure. This layout shows a total of 14 decks, which results in a very complicated construction program. The work must be properly sequenced so as to minimize congestion. Decks U01-7 could be prefabricated and outfitted as deck units and installed prior to the concrete slipforming of the utility shaft. If not practicable, then piece-small installation is the normal method. Whichever construction method is used, the resulting scheduling evaluation should ensure that prefabrication and package units are utilized to the fullest extent possible to minimize craft labor inside shafts.

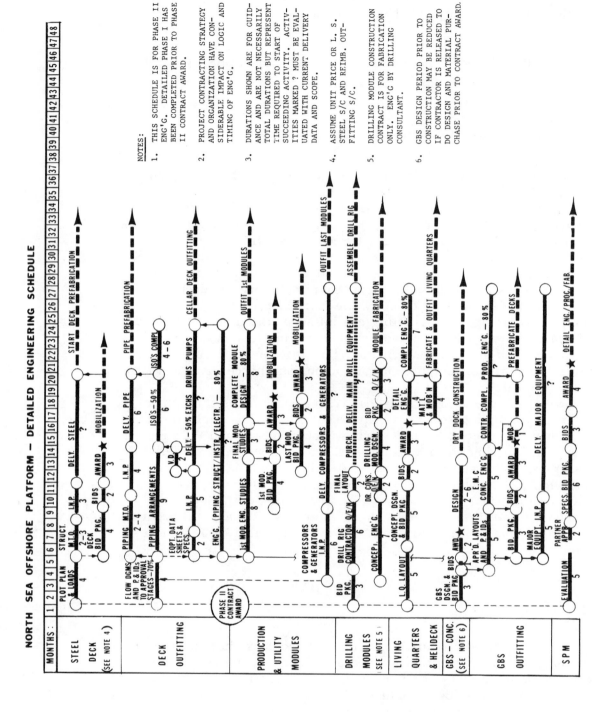

Figure 9.16   Detailed engineering schedule.

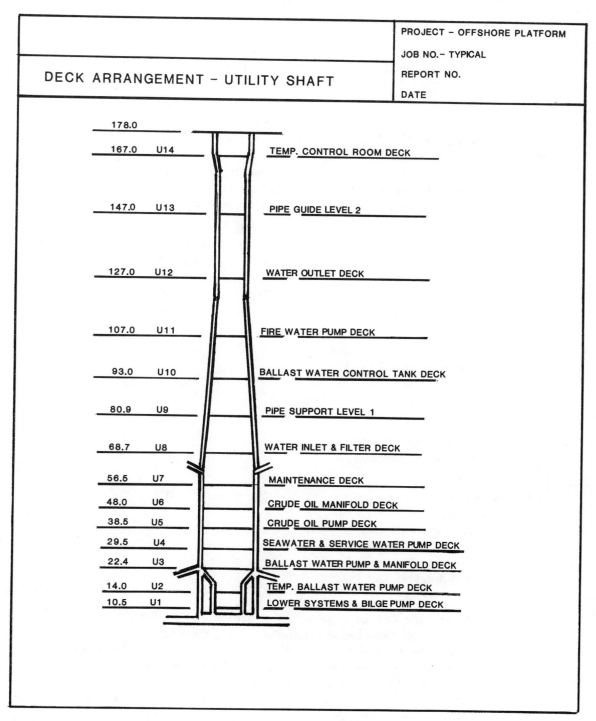

		PROJECT – OFFSHORE PLATFORM
		JOB NO.– TYPICAL
DECK ARRANGEMENT – UTILITY SHAFT		REPORT NO.
		DATE

178.0

167.0   U14   TEMP. CONTROL ROOM DECK

147.0   U13   PIPE GUIDE LEVEL 2

127.0   U12   WATER OUTLET DECK

107.0   U11   FIRE WATER PUMP DECK

93.0   U10   BALLAST WATER CONTROL TANK DECK

80.9   U9   PIPE SUPPORT LEVEL 1

68.7   U8   WATER INLET & FILTER DECK

56.5   U7   MAINTENANCE DECK

48.0   U6   CRUDE OIL MANIFOLD DECK

38.5   U5   CRUDE OIL PUMP DECK

29.5   U4   SEAWATER & SERVICE WATER PUMP DECK

22.4   U3   BALLAST WATER PUMP & MANIFOLD DECK

14.0   U2   TEMP. BALLAST WATER PUMP DECK

10.5   U1   LOWER SYSTEMS & BILGE PUMP DECK

Figure 9.17   Utility shaft.

9.17 GBS OUTFITTING SCHEDULE

Figure 9.18 illustrates a schedule for GBS outfitting. General guidelines for preparing the schedule are as follows:

1. For the duration calculation, consider only the utility shaft since the outfitting of other shafts is not critical.
2. Consider the degree of prefabrication and preassembly. Since final assembly is on the critical path, preassembly may improve the schedule. The extent of preassembly can vary. The following table provides a general guide to determining the split of direct man-hours between off-site and on-site locations for various levels of preassembly:

	Off-site Man-hours	On-site Man-hours	Additional Man-hours
Piece-small (prefabrication only; no pre-assembly)	25%	75%	0
Skids (two or more pieces of equipment mounted together prior to installation)	30%	70%	2%
Pancakes (equipment and piping preassembled on a floor and installed as a unit)	45%	55%	10%
Modules (maximum pre-assembly of an area within a structural framework with only interface piping, etc., remaining)	70%	30%	18%

3. Determine the work area in the utility shaft from the number of decks and the average diameter. By judgment, determine the maximum number of decks that can be worked simultaneously. Calculate the number of workers per shift using 150 ft^2 as a maximum density level. Check regulations which limit the maximum number of workers per shift due to limited access to fire escape routes within the shaft.
4. Assume two shifts per day, 5 days per week, and 4.3 weeks per month. If there is a scarcity of labor for the second shift, discount the second shift accordingly. Subtract 10% to allow for absenteeism, etc.
5. Allow 3 months for buildup and 1 month for rundown, and use the trapezoid method to calculate the duration of the utility shaft outfitting installation. Add a 25% experience factor to give the activity

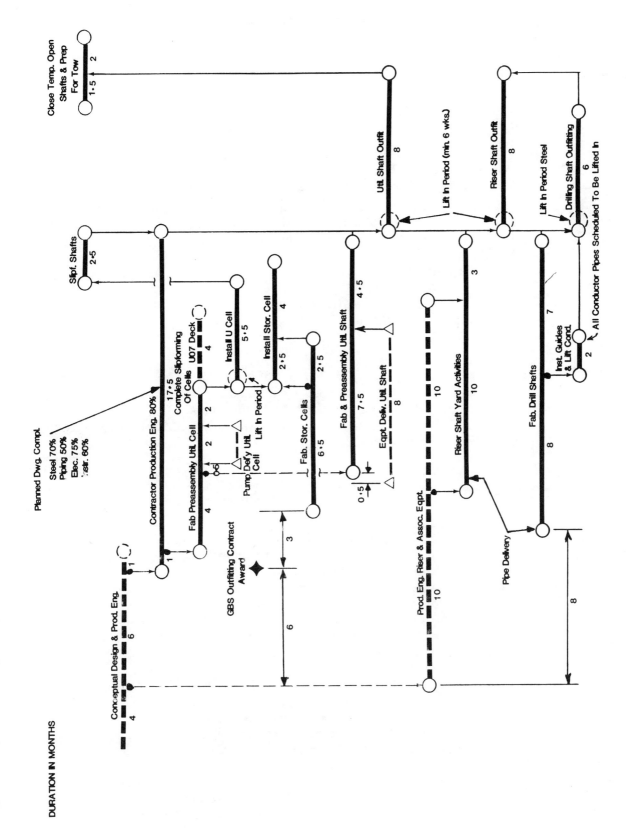

Figure 9.19   Typical topside construction schedule for deck and outfitting.

duration. Approximately 40% of this duration is in the utility cell and 60% in the utility shaft.

6. Installation in the other shafts can occur concurrently with installation in the utility shaft.

9.18 TOPSIDE CONSTRUCTION SCHEDULE

Figure 9.19 illustrates a master schedule for construction of a topside with a truss deck. Activities fall under the following:

1. Deck fabrication (trusses, rings, infill pieces, and floors)
2. Prefabrication of deck outfitting
3. Fabrication of preassemblies and modules
4. Deck assembly
5. Deck outfitting
6. Hookup of preassemblies in the cellar deck
7. Hookup of modules in the module deck
8. Inshore completion
9. Offshore completion

The first three activities are carried out off site (away from the deck assembly site). The next four are carried out on site. As such, these four should be considered simultaneously and a composite manpower loading compared against saturation levels. This schedule is used in conjunction with the manpower histograms. Exhibits that follow go into greater detail.

9.19 TOPSIDE CONSTRUCTION MANPOWER

Figure 9.20 illustrates a composite manpower loading for off-site and on-site activities associated with the previous topsides construction schedule. Two saturation levels are evaluated. One corresponds to a two-shift operation. The other is based on the assumption that only 50% of the workers are available for the second shift. Under a short labor supply for the second shift, the peak manpower requirement exceeds the saturation level. This can result in productivity deterioration due to oversaturation on the first shift or schedule extension due to the nonavailability of labor.

Trapezoids 1, 2, and 3 represent histograms corresponding to the fabrication of trusses, rings, infills, and floors. Trapezoid 4 represents prefabrication of the deck outfitting and preassembly fabrication. Since these four activities occur at an off-deck location, they are excluded from on-deck labor saturation considerations. Trapezoids 5-8 represent total on-deck labor.

The manpower rundown depicted by this example is considerably faster than that dictated by an efficient construction program. For planning purposes, a rundown of 6-8 months would be desirable for a major construction effort. This diagram reflects the result of front end

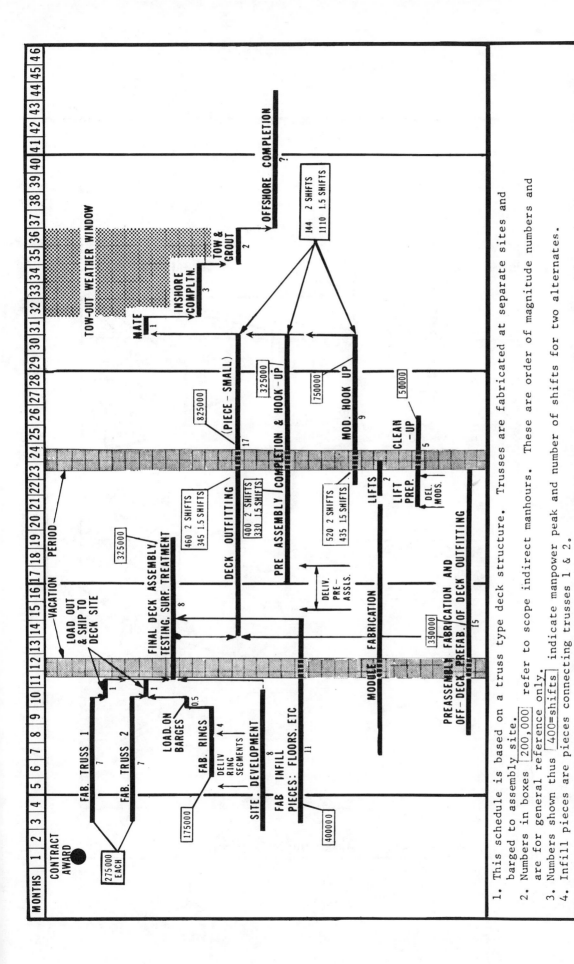

Figure 9.18   GBS outfitting schedule duration in months.

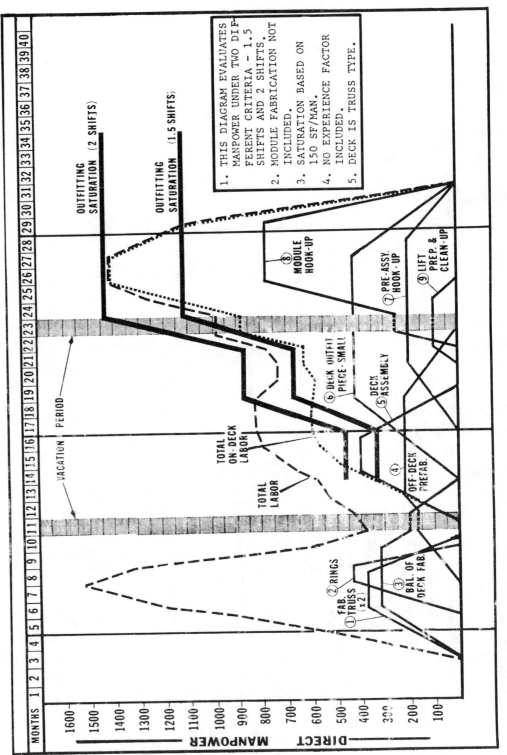

Figure 9.20   Typical topside construction manpower histogram.

slippage and an immovable completion date dictated by weather window considerations (see Figure 9.19). The results are higher manpower peaks, heavier shift work requirements, fast rundown which may prove unattainable, and the elimination of the experience factor.

9.20 DECK CONSTRUCTION: TRUSS TYPE

Figure 9.21 illustrates the frame of a truss deck. The following describes one method of fabrication and assembling a truss deck.

Truss decks are made up of the following components:

Box sections
Nodes
Subassemblies
Box trusses
Infill pieces
Rings

Box sections are main structural elements. They are rectangular sections approximately 3 × 6 ft made of steel plate 1-2 in. thick. Box sections intersect at nodes. A number of box sections and nodes assembled prior to placement at a final box truss assembly point are termed subassemblies. Subassembly size is limited by the crane capacity of the fabrication shop. Subassemblies are connected to form a box truss which consists of two vertical trusses connected by longitudinal box sections.

Dimensional control at all stages is crucial.

The box truss is skidded from the final assembly point to a barge by use of hydraulic jacks. Each box truss may weigh up to 3000 tons.

At the deck assembly site, support rings are assembled and placed on concrete supports. Box trusses are barged to the site, positioned over rings, and lowered onto rings by ballasting. Each box truss is supported by two rings. Infill pieces may be installed after one box truss is in place.

The area between the top and bottom chords of trusses is the cellar deck. Cellar deck floors are installed subsequent to deck assembly and do not form an integral part of the deck structure. Preassemblies are lowered into the cellar deck and usually include the cellar deck floor as well as preassembled equipment and bulks. Modules are supported on the top truss chords. Theoretically, outfitting can start after the first box truss is positioned, but deflection control prior to final weld-out limits this activity. Very large-bore pipe, floors, steel outfitting, and fireproofing may be installed at this time.

One feature of truss decks is free access between cellar deck areas. Fabrication is complex, particularly with the level of dimensional control required and the handling of large subassemblies and box trusses. Mechanical outfitting effectively starts later than with plate girder decks because it is impractical to start prior to final assembly.

For progress and productivity control on fabrication, measure the weld volume deposited.

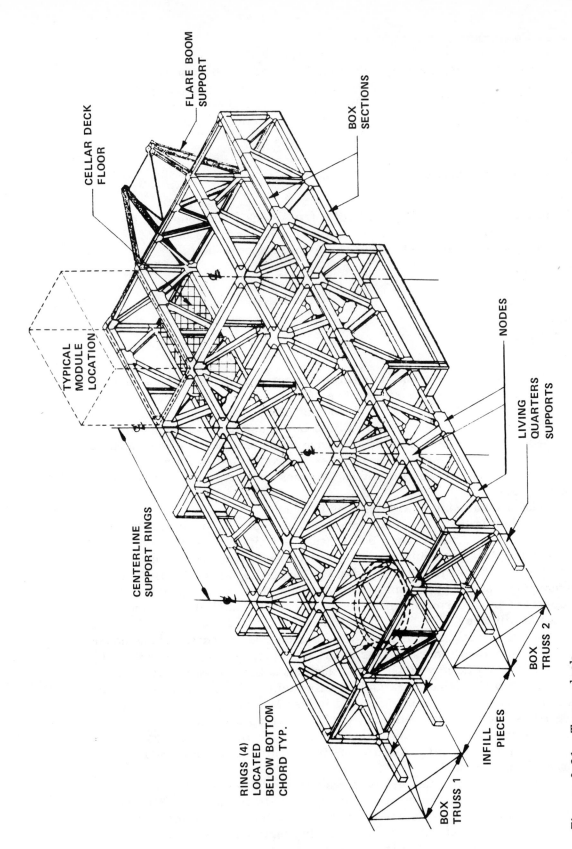

FLARE BOOM SUPPORT

BOX SECTIONS

CELLAR DECK FLOOR

NODES

TYPICAL MODULE LOCATION

LIVING QUARTERS SUPPORTS

CENTERLINE SUPPORT RINGS

BOX TRUSS 2

RINGS (4) LOCATED BELOW BOTTOM CHORD TYP.

INFILL PIECES

BOX TRUSS 1

Figure 9.21 Truss deck.

370

9.21 DECK CONSTRUCTION SCHEDULE

Figure 9.22 illustrates a schedule for prefabrication and assembly of a truss deck. The following steps constitute some guidelines for the preparation of a schedule; check all values supplied below with the latest project data available:

1. If man-hours are not available from the estimating department, determine the total scope (i.e., prefabrication and assembly manhours) from the weight of the deck excluding the deck outfitting. Use 150 man-hours/ton.
2. Assume that prefabrication constitutes 75% of the total scope and assembly 25%.
3. Distribute prefabrication man-hours over the three major components (a) trusses, (b) rings, and (c) remaining items such as infill pieces, floors, etc., in the ratio of 50, 15, and 35%, respectively.
4. Distribute the total prefabrication work among four subcontractors as follows: (a) two subcontractors for two tursses, each constituting 25% of the total man-hours, (b) one for rings, and (c) one for the remaining items. At each site, assume 200 workers per shift and a two-shift operation—8 hr/shift and 5 days/week. If there is a labor shortage for the second shift, discount it accordingly.
5. At each site, use 4 months for buildup and 2 months for rundown, and calculate the fabrication duration using the trapezoidal method. Add a 25% experience factor.
6. To determine the duration of deck assembly, calculate the area of the deck, and use 150 ft^2/worker to determine the maximum number of workers to be employed per shift. The additional area at the top chord is offset by a loss of area away from the truss centerlines. Assume a two-shift operation—8 hr/shift and 5 days/week. Allow 3 months for buildup and 3 months for rundown, and calculate the duration using the trapezoidal method. Add a 25% experience factor.

9.22 MODULE LAYOUT

An arrangement of modules on a truss deck is illustrated in Figure 9.23. Modular construction consists of designing and building all or part of the topside facilities in prefabricated segments which are then assembled on a deck and connected (hooked up) together. This differs from integrated construction where the installation of equipment is performed piece-small into the deck.

The primary reason for modular construction is to spread the work among many fabricators in order to obtain a schedule advantage compared with completing work in one yard. Modular construction is generally thought to be more costly, however, due to additional material and labor.

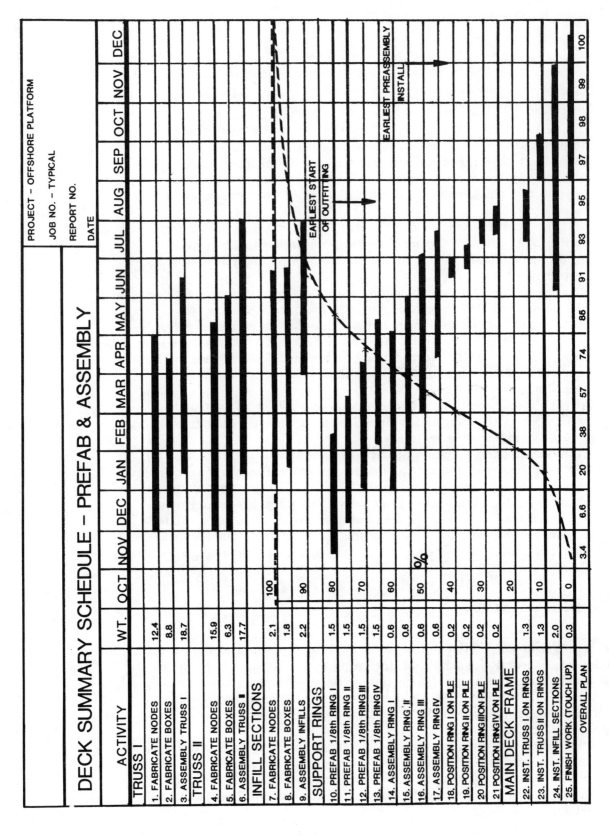

Figure 9.22   Deck construction schedule.

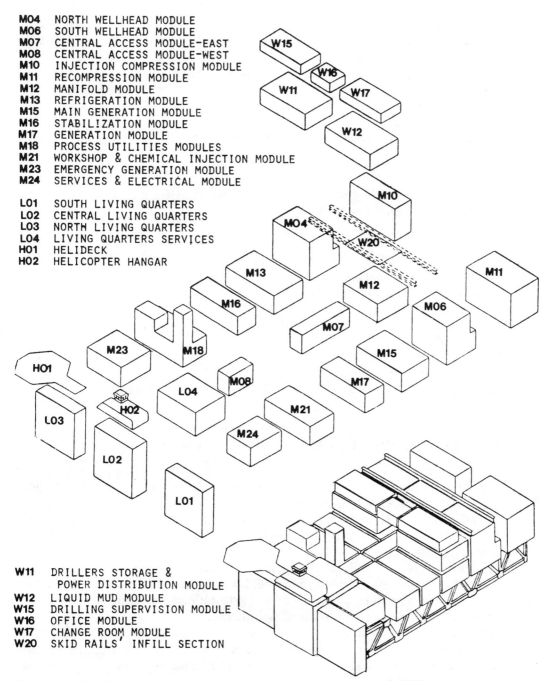

M04   NORTH WELLHEAD MODULE
M06   SOUTH WELLHEAD MODULE
M07   CENTRAL ACCESS MODULE-EAST
M08   CENTRAL ACCESS MODULE-WEST
M10   INJECTION COMPRESSION MODULE
M11   RECOMPRESSION MODULE
M12   MANIFOLD MODULE
M13   REFRIGERATION MODULE
M15   MAIN GENERATION MODULE
M16   STABILIZATION MODULE
M17   GENERATION MODULE
M18   PROCESS UTILITIES MODULES
M21   WORKSHOP & CHEMICAL INJECTION MODULE
M23   EMERGENCY GENERATION MODULE
M24   SERVICES & ELECTRICAL MODULE

L01   SOUTH LIVING QUARTERS
L02   CENTRAL LIVING QUARTERS
L03   NORTH LIVING QUARTERS
L04   LIVING QUARTERS SERVICES
H01   HELIDECK
H02   HELICOPTER HANGAR

W11   DRILLERS STORAGE &
      POWER DISTRIBUTION MODULE
W12   LIQUID MUD MODULE
W15   DRILLING SUPERVISION MODULE
W16   OFFICE MODULE
W17   CHANGE ROOM MODULE
W20   SKID RAILS' INFILL SECTION

Figure 9.23   Module layout.

Generally, engineering is performed by the prime contractor and
design drawings are supplied to the module fabricator. The fabricator
will then prepare shop drawings and fabrication details. For some
modules—living quarters, drilling, etc.—it is preferable to have the
fabricator do detailed engineering as well as fabrication. In this case,
contract award will be earlier since less definition is required prior to
requesting proposals.

Modular construction is done in two stages: module fabrication and hookup. The man-hour split is approximately 70% fabrication and 30% hookup, but will largely depend on the schedule. Design drawings define the limits of fabrication and hookup. When the fabrication schedule slips, extensions may not be possible, resulting in incomplete modules. This reduces the fabrication scope but increases the scope at the assembly site.

The following are modular construction schedule advantages:

It spreads construction work over many sites.
It minimizes peak manpower levels at each site.
Fabrication proceeds concurrently with the deck fabrication.
There is an overall schedule advantage.

Disadvantages include the following:

It is more difficult to control many sites; a larger task force and
    engineering management effort are required.
Additional weight for module steel.
Additional man-hours.
Engineering is more difficult; interface drawings are required at all
    module faces.
Module hookup scope is dependent on the degree of module completion;
    it is difficult to determine—requires tight control.
Heavy lift barges are required to lift the modules on deck.

9.23 TYPICAL MODULE FABRICATION SCHEDULE

Figure 9.24 illustrates a typical fabrication schedule for a refrigeration module. This is a relatively simple module. The total duration, contract award to load out, is 13 months. Nearly half that time is spent in mobilization and structural framework erection. Equipment installation and outfitting start in month 7.

For proper control, it is essential to measure progress in terms of quantities installed. This should yield a realistic status as well as provide an accurate determination of work to be completed after load out. Previous experience shows some modules will be shipped out prior to completion in order to meet overall project schedule requirements. When this occurs, an accurate knowledge of quantities installed at the module fabrication yard is essential to assess the remaining work which has to be transferred.

9.24 TYPICAL DECK OUTFITTING SCHEDULE

See the deck outfitting schedule in Figure 9.25 and refer to Figures 9.19 and 9.20 for the overall calculation of deck outfitting, the module hookup duration, and composite manpower histograms.

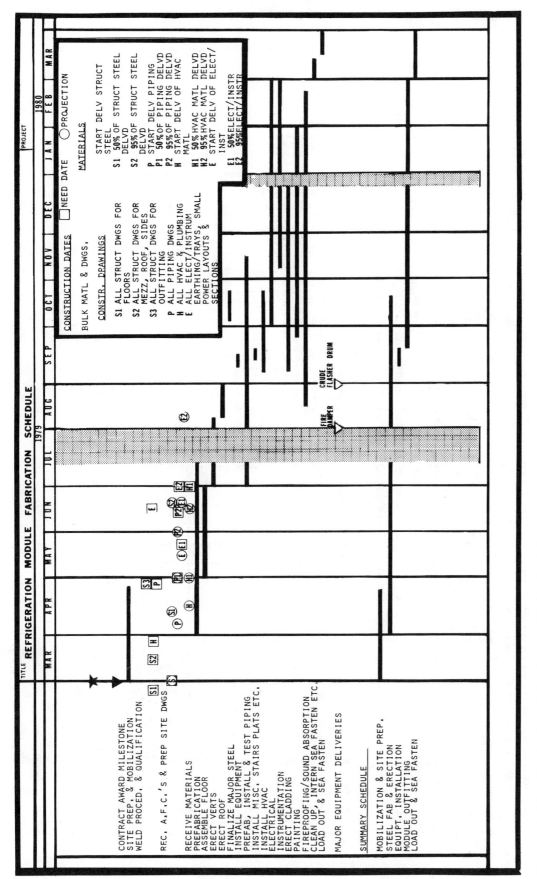

Figure 9.24 Typical module fabrication schedule.

375

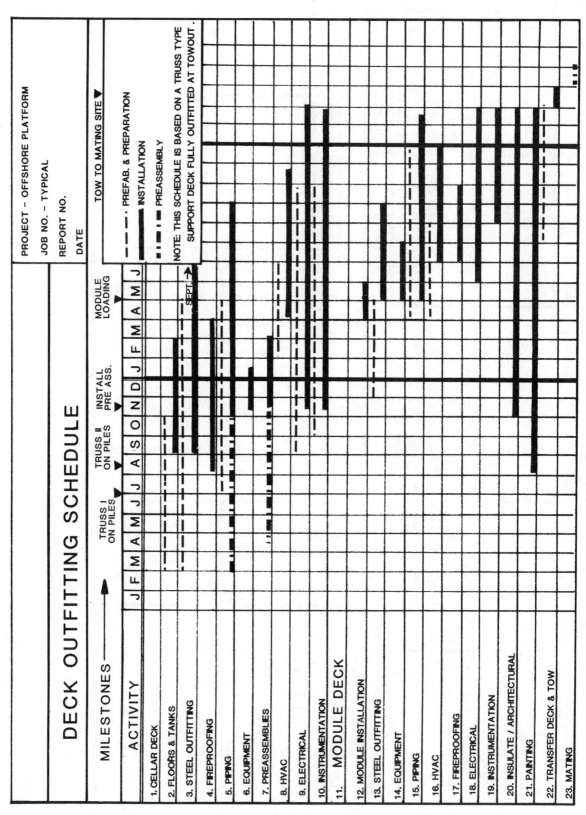

Figure 9.25 Typical deck outfitting schedule.

In this section we shall provide a typical example of a more detailed calculation of deck outfitting durations and manpower levels. Three main activities are considered: piece-small outfitting, preassembly outfitting, and module hookup. Since these activities all overlap, a composite manpower analysis is necessary.

1. Obtain at-shore man-hours for piece-small outfitting, preassembly outfitting, and module hookup from the estimating department. Where formal estimates have not been provided, apply unit man-hour rates to estimated weights. The percentage of man-hours in each of these activities will depend on the project strategy for the contracting of modules and preassemblies. (See Figure 9.24 for prefabricated versus piece-small percentages.) Also consider precommissioning man-hours and, if predictable, module carry-over.

2. Determine the starting dates for each activity based on the completion of the deck assembly and the anticipated delivery dates of the modules and preassemblies.

3. Determine the areas available for each activity from detailed engineering drawings. If drawings are not available, make assumptions as to the area split. For instance, assume that 50% of the cellar deck area is available for piece-small outfitting and 25% for preassembly outfitting. The remaining 25% will be for deck welding and some module hookup. Assume that 50% of the module deck area is available for module hookup. This is to account for the fact that the majority of outfitting work is completed prior to hookup and hence that much of the area is not available for work.

4. Determine the manpower peaks based on 150 ft^2/worker. Use 1.5-2.0 shifts depending on labor availability. Calculate the workweek based on current practice.

5. Assume buildup rates, i.e., piece-small, 5 months; preassembly, 4 months; and hookup, 3 months. For corresponding rundown rates, assume 4, 3, and 2 months, respectively.

6. Use the trapezoidal technique to determine the duration of each activity. If the durations exceed the time available, some work must be moved from at-shore to inshore. Add a 25% experience factor to the calculated duration.

7. Where a fully outfitted tow-out must be achieved in a specified weather window, use the trapezoidal technique to calculate the manpower peaks required to meet the activity durations dictated by the mating and tow-out dates. Discount the available time by a 25% experience factor; i.e., with a given time remaining of 15 months, to calculate the manpower peak, use a duration of 15 ÷ 1.25 = 12 months. If saturation is exceeded, equate the manpower levels to saturation productivity losses (see Figure 3.17), add man-hours, and recalculate. Perform this iterative procedure until an acceptable distribution is obtained. Additional man-hours due to oversaturation must be recognized in the cost estimate as well as in the schedule.

9.25 MATING AND TOW-OUT

Mating and tow-out activities are depicted in Figure 9.26. Prior to towing, the GBS must have its ballasting system and towage instrumentation operational. The tow to site duration is dependent on the location of the mating site. At the mating site, the GBS is ballasted and submerged to within 6 m of the tops of the shafts. Concurrently the deck is transferred to mating barges (two or three) and floated to the mating site.

The deck is positioned and the GBS deballasted to accomplish mating of the deck to the structure. Mating takes only a few days, but 2 weeks is allowed for weather contingencies. Further deballasting is performed prior to commencement of the shaft to deck hookup and essential system commissioning. It is desirable to have life support and safety systems commissioned prior to tow-out to allow occupancy of permanent living quarters immediately after tow-out. If these systems are not operational, offshore completion must be done using flotels to accommodate construction and commissioning personnel with a resultant loss of productivity and an increase in cost. Although flotels may be used eventually, the loss of permanent quarters for the first few months would be significant.

The 3 months allowed for the shaft to deck hookup and commissioning was the time used for U.K. platforms. For Norwegian platforms, with increased safety requirements and facility complexity, this may be tight. The following should be considered during this period:

Bolt up and grouting the deck to the structure
Uncoupling and recoupling equipment drives and pipe flanges due to
     reverse deck deflection
Reinstating temporary facilities removed for mating
Deck crack detection and repair program and painting
Electrical, piping, instrumentation, heating, ventilation, and air-
     conditioning (HVAC) hookup between the deck and shafts
Completion of the outfitting and hookup of safety and life support
     systems
Commissioning of safety and life support systems
Preparation for tow-out
Transportation time for workers to and from the platform

An ideal tow-out date is April 1. Tow-out, penetration, and grouting take less than 1 month. Two months are allowed for weather contingencies.

9.26 OFFSHORE CONSTRUCTION AND PRECOMMISSIONING

Offshore work may consist of any or all of the following:

Module hookup
Integrated deck outfitting
Module installation

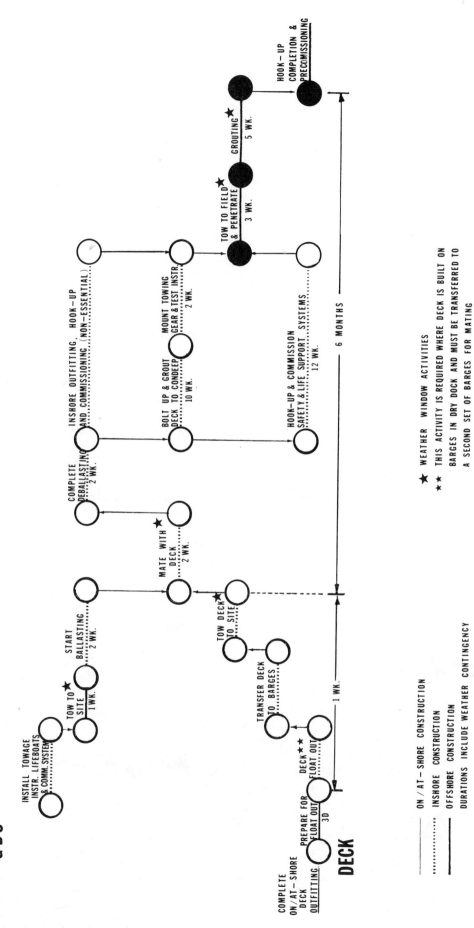

Figure 9.26 Standard mating and tow-out schedule.

Rework
Precommissioning
Commissioning and start-up
Drilling

Due to higher costs and lower efficiencies, offshore work should be kept to a minimum. Slippages in engineering, topsides construction, and an immovable tow-out date often increase this work to significant proportions. Some work (commissioning, start-up, and drilling) must be done offshore.

9.27 OFFSHORE CONSTRUCTION, TYPICAL

The following duration calculations (inshore and offshore) assume a minimum of inshore and offshore work:

1. Calculate the man-hours remaining from onshore and at-shore activities. Convert to inshort and offshore man-hours by adjusting for the difference in productivity.
2. Assume a fast buildup and rundown—1 month. For short periods of work, assume a limited work force—say 200—due to transportation limitations. Where the period is longer, i.e., greater than 3 months, a higher manpower peak may be assumed but must be supported by related assumptions on accommodations. This may require reassessment of the productivity multiplier. Also, buildup and rundown times may have to be increased.
3. Calculate the man-hours expended inshore using the trapezoidal technique. Divide the duration by 1.25 (25% experience factor) prior to calculation.
4. The remaining man-hours are adjusted for offshore by multiplying by the ratio of offshore and inshore productivities. Keep commissioning man-hours separate since manpower is limited on this activity.
5. Indirect labor offshore can be as high as 70% of direct labor (40% of the total).
6. Once drilling starts, additional productivity losses may be incurred. Increase the man-hours expended after the start of drilling by 25% for drilling interference. Also, additional bed spaces are required by drilling personnel (approximately 60) once drilling commences.
7. Consider special work rules imposed by local governments which may be included in productivity multipliers. (For Norway, a 25% increase in man-hours should be assumed due to special offshore work rules.)
8. Manpower and beds utilization (major offshore work): Figure 9.27 is based on an offshore program using the platform permanent quarters, temporary living quarters, and two flotels. Figure 9.27 assumes the following: a large offshore work content and a maximum buildup of 100 men/month. Logistical problems of recruiting and establishing a rotational work force; setting up flotels, permanent living quarters, and temporary living quarters; and managing and

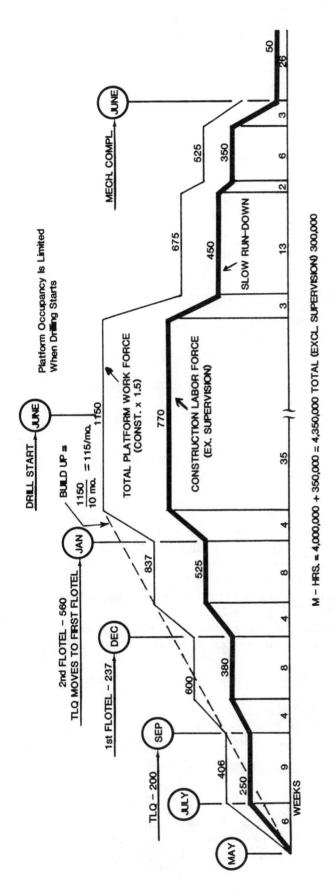

Figure 9.27 Typical offshore labor histogram.

381

supervising an offshore labor force and support personnel make
100 men/month a practical limit.

9.   Use the trapezoidal method. Limit the commissioning peak to 200.
     The peak for the remaining work is dependent on accommodation.
     The practical maximum, with two flotels, is about 1400 beds. Of
     these, approximately $\frac{1}{2}$ - $\frac{2}{3}$ are for construction labor. Assume a
     practical maximum for construction labor of 800. The workweek is
     7 × 12 = 84 hrs less 5% for absenteeism or 346 man-hours/month.
     Add a 15% experience factor to calculate the durations.

9.28 OFFSHORE CONSTRUCTION SUMMARY

The scheduling of offshore work is complicated by the following:

Transportation to the work site is difficult.
The work force is limited by accommodation.
Flotels are required; disconnect periods render the work site
     inaccessible.
Rotational assignments cause disruption of the work force and
     construction management and supervision.
Determination of the scope prior to the start of construction is often
     difficult.

Experience to date on significant offshore construction programs
suggests that the following guidelines be used:

Ensure that the offshore scope of the work is accurately assessed in
     terms of the quantities to be installed. Detailed design drawings
     marked up with partly completed work are essential. If this has
     not been completed prior to tow-out, it should be a top priority
     immediately after tow-out. The marked-up drawings should show
     the work status in the cellar deck and modules.
Schedule the work by area until the systems are near completion.
     Then schedule by system for punch list items.
The overall network is limited by 3000 activities, maintained onshore.
     Use a manual weekly work program for detailed scheduling on the
     platform.
Instruct construction supervision on planning system, objectives and
     requirements.
Report the weekly status and productivity.
Overall system priorities are usually the following:
     1.   Safety (including lifeboats)
     2.   Life support
     3.   Winterization
     4.   Drilling
     5.   Production
Determine the scope of each of the preceding early, and obtain
concurrence by all parties. Where there is a large offshore work
content, it is difficult to develop a logical network for the
production facilities. There can be few dependencies between

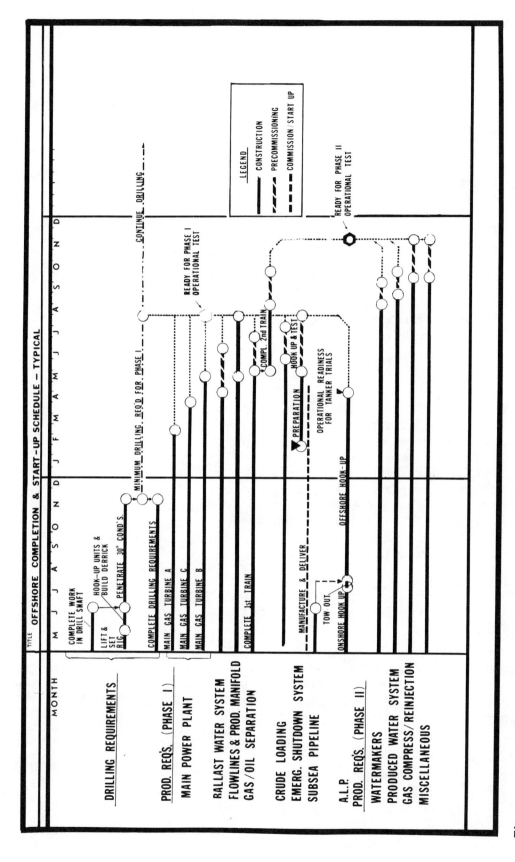

Figure 9.28 Offshore construction summary schedule.

the many systems, and the sequence of completion can simply
be a matter of preference. Production facilities are generally the
major part of offshore work.

Figure 9.28 illustrates a typical summary-level schedule. Note that
there are very few interdependencies between systems. Safety, life
support, and winterization priorities have been completed, and drilling
and production remain.

Confusion often exists with the terms testing, precommissioning,
commissioning, and start-up. They can mean different things to different groups and have differing connotations. For this schedule, the
following is intended:

Precommissioning (testing): completing all operational tests and checkout prior to the introduction of the process fluid (crude oil). After
a system has been precommissioned, it is ready for operational
testing.

Commissioning (start-up): operational testing subsequent to introduction of process fluid.

To start commissioning, a minimum flow of oil is required to enable
the systems to operate properly. This throughput will vary with each
platform, and hence the number of wells required to supply it may
vary. The number of wells required determines the *minimum drilling*
duration which restrains the *ready for operational testing* milestone.
(Generally, three wells are required for minimum drilling; the drilling
duration is estimated to be 11 months.)

If minimum drilling is to be completed in advance of production
facilities, then the system completion sequence should follow the
commissioning sequence. When minimum drilling is to complete after
construction, the system completion sequence has little importance.

Information relative to drilling and commissioning is generally
supplied by operating personnel.

9.29 DESIGN ALTERNATIVES

Figure 9.29 shows pictorial views of platforms other than concrete-
based ones. The fixed platform (steel) and guyed tower rest on the
seabed. The floating platforms are more suitable for water depths in
excess of 600 ft. The next generation of deep-water platforms is expected to employ the tension leg design, supported by subsea well-
gathering systems.

9.30 TENSION LEG PLATFORMS

The decision to pioneer a floating tension leg platform (TLP) for production at the North Sea's Hutton oilfield is a fittingly dramatic start to

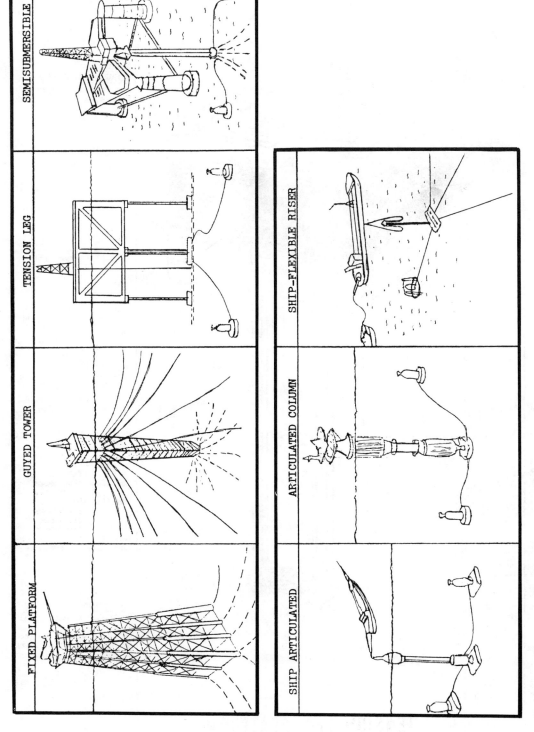

Figure 9.29 Platform design alternatives.

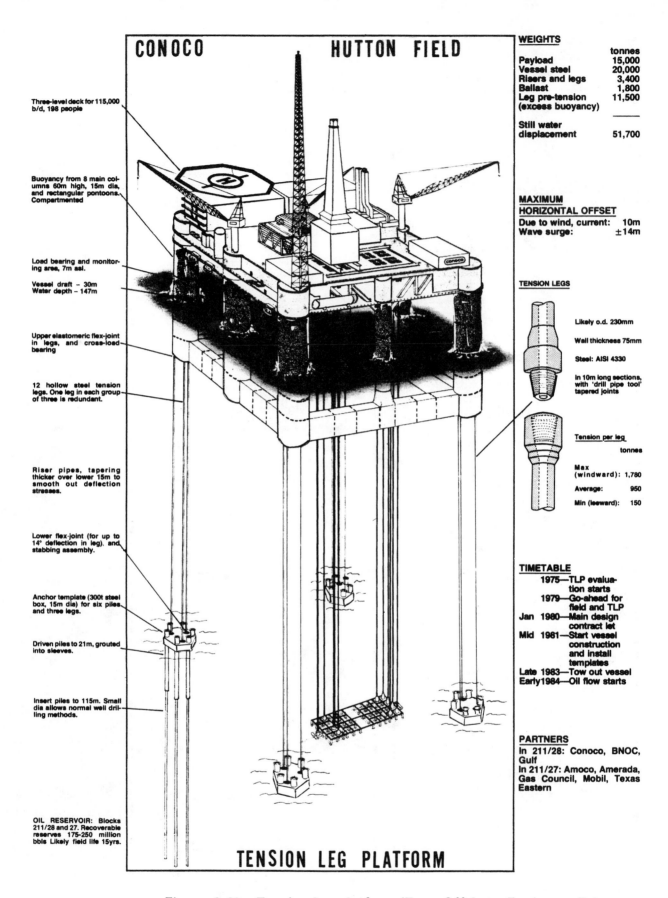

CONOCO   **HUTTON FIELD**

WEIGHTS	tonnes
Payload	15,000
Vessel steel	20,000
Risers and legs	3,400
Ballast	1,800
Leg pre-tension (excess buoyancy)	11,500
Still water displacement	51,700

MAXIMUM HORIZONTAL OFFSET
Due to wind, current: 10m
Wave surge: ±14m

TENSION LEGS

Likely o.d. 230mm

Wall thickness 75mm

Steel: AISI 4330

In 10m long sections, with 'drill pipe tool' tapered joints

Tension per leg	tonnes
Max (windward):	1,780
Average:	950
Min (leeward):	150

Three-level deck for 115,000 b/d, 198 people

Buoyancy from 8 main columns 60m high, 15m dia, and rectangular pontoons. Compartmented

Load bearing and monitoring area, 7m asl.

Vessel draft – 30m
Water depth – 147m

Upper elastomeric flex-joint in legs, and cross-load bearing

12 hollow steel tension legs. One leg in each group of three is redundant.

Riser pipes, tapering thicker over lower 15m to smooth out deflection stresses.

Lower flex-joint (for up to 14° deflection in leg), and stabbing assembly.

Anchor template (300t steel box, 15m dia) for six piles and three legs.

Driven piles to 21m, grouted into sleeves.

Insert piles to 115m. Small dia allows normal well drilling methods.

OIL RESERVOIR: Blocks 211/28 and 27. Recoverable reserves 175-250 million bbls Likely field life 15yrs.

TIMETABLE
1975—TLP evaluation starts
1979—Go-ahead for field and TLP
Jan 1980—Main design contract let
Mid 1981—Start vessel construction and install templates
Late 1983—Tow out vessel
Early 1984—Oil flow starts

PARTNERS
In 211/28: Conoco, BNOC, Gulf
In 211/27: Amoco, Amerada, Gas Council, Mobil, Texas Eastern

TENSION LEG PLATFORM

Figure 9.30   Tension leg platform (From *Offshore Engineer*, Feb., 1980).

the offshore 1980s. This first commercial application of the concept is one of the most important technological steps ever taken by the industry.

At a stroke, it extends the ability to exploit reserves into areas beneath 600 m or more of water as well as introduces the possibility of the portable platform, easily removed from one location and floated to another.

Figure 9.30 illustrates an overall design of this type of platform. The mooring tethers will be "gunbarrel technology" vertical steel tubes. There will be 12 of these *tension legs* holding the vessel 10 m lower in the water than it would float naturally and so giving it an effective displacement of 51,700 tons.

The tension legs will be pinned to the seabed by a combination of driven and drilled piles, following exhaustive studies of soil behavior under cyclic loading in tension.

The TLP is designed to operate continuously, exactly like a fixed platform, for a probable 15-year life at the field, and it is claimed that motion will be imperceptible for 90% of the time.

Tension legs will be grouped in threes at each platform corner. In still water, the total uplift they will resist is 11,500 ton, an average of 950 tons/leg. Under dynamic loading, individual leg tensions will range from 150 up to 1780 tons under maximum design conditions. Tension in each tether can be read out on the platform at all times.

The heavy-walled tubes will probably be of high-tensile AISI 4330 steel. The outside diameter is likely to be 230-250 mm and the wall thickness a massive 75 mm. Extension of the 150-m-long tension legs over their 1630-ton extreme operating range is put at 150 mm, although everyday extensions will be only a millimeter or so.

Fatigue studies indicate the legs will last as long as the platform. They will be strung in 10-m-long sections using threaded tapered joints with shoulders, similar to drill pipe tool joints.

Adoption of traditional industry practices is also apparent in the anchors which hold down the tension legs. Each group of three locks into one of four 15-m-diameter anchor templates pinned to the seafloor by six piles.

The main elements resisting load in the foundation are 115-m-long insert piles, probably 500 mm (20-in.) in diameter, grouted into a pre-drilled hole. This small diameter of pile allows use of normal exploration well drilling techniques.

An underwater hammer will probably be used to drive the 140-mm-(54-in.) diameter piles to the top of the first main sand layer, at 21 m, and the upper 8-m of these piles will be grouted into sleeves in the anchor template.

A major influence on the overall feasibility of the TLP concept is how the seabed soil around anchor piles will perform under constant cyclic loading in tension. It is also an area where there are few precedents, which is what makes Hutton such an important development.

The first piece of hardware into the seabed will be the template through which a semisub will later drill the first nine production wells while the platform is being built. Next, the same rig will place the four 300-ton self-floating anchor templates in 3-m-diameter target circles (and within 2° orientation). Then pile installation and well drilling go ahead.

Two years later, when the main platform is to be installed, procedures will again be based on practices familiar to drillers. Tension legs (stored in the corner columns before float out) will be placed by equipment permanently based on the platform, so that a mooring can be retrieved for inspection at any time during its life.

When the TLP arrives on location, it will be ballasted down to "somewhat less than the final installed draft," and one tension leg from each corner will be connected to its anchor.

The hydraulic tensioning system will pull the TLP nearly 2 m deeper in the water, and deballasting then puts about 800-ton tension in each leg. Using a combination of hydraulics and deballasting to maintain tension around this level, the remaining legs are installed and locked into the load block on the platform's mooring flat.

Design loading criteria are as follows: 30-m-high waves of 17-sec period, a 1-min mean wind speed of 44 m/sec, and a surface current of 1/13 m/sec.

The design flow rate is 115,000 bpd from a dozen production wells. Another dozen of the 32 slots available will go to water injection wells.

10

GENERAL DATA

This chapter comprises general data for formulating project plans, schedules, and cost trends.

The range of data covers the following:

Overall project cost breakdown
Typical home office man-hour breakdown
Construction man-hour and craft breakdowns
Material breakdowns
Labor efficiency versus extended overtime
Construction indirects

These data can provide guidance in quantifying schedules, manpower levels, and cost trends with statistical relationships. However, specific project circumstances should be used to temper the use of general data.

Typical cost and man-hour breakdowns can be useful in breaking down overall numbers.

10.1 OVERALL COST BREAKDOWN

Figure 10.1, an overall breakdown of project cost, is based on historical data for projects built in the United States on a direct-hire basis during the period 1955-1975.

Application

When only an overall cost is known, this breakdown can be useful in providing overall data for a quick evaluation of engineering and construction schedules.

Example

Assume that a project has an estimated overall cost of $100 million.

1. From the diagram, home office costs are roughly 13% or $13 million. By a further assumption that the contractor home office all-in cost is $30/hr, we can derive a total number of home office man-hours:

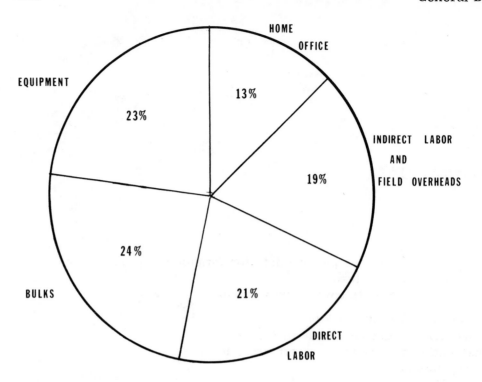

Figure 10.1   Pie chart of project cost breakdown.

No. of man-hours = $\dfrac{13,000,000}{30}$ = 433,000

Thus, a gross schedule and manpower evaluation can now be made.
2. From the chart, direct field labor costs are roughly 21% or
$21 million. By a further assumption that the direct field labor payroll
cost is $10/hr;

No. of man-hours = $\dfrac{21,000,000}{10}$ = 2,100,000

Applying known and historical relationships, allow gross evaluations
for engineering and construction durations to be made. These in turn
can be used to prepare manpower histograms and progress curves.

Note: For larger projects, the percent of home office and field overheads increases.

10.2 TYPICAL HOME OFFICE MAN-HOUR BREAKDOWN

Table 10.1 is a typical breakdown of total home office man-hours for a
full-scope project. It is based on historical data for small- to medium-
sized projects engineered on a reimbursable basis and executed during
the period 1955-1975.

Table 10.1

Description		% Man-hours
Design & Drafting	*Full-Scope (%)*	
Civil & structural	25.00	10.000
Vessels	7.50	3.000
Electrical	15.00	6.000
Plant design (piping)	41.00	16.400
Piping engineering	5.25	2.100
Bill of material	5.25	2.100
Model	1.00	0.400
	100.00	40.000
Administration—indirect drafting		
Engineering		
Instrument (engineering & drafting)		3.000
Mechanical (rotating machinery, plant utilities, metallurgy, etc.)		3.000
Mechanical (consultants)		0.200
Project management		7.500
Project engineering		6.000
Project (operating expenses, services administration)		0.200
Process design		3.000
Process technology services		0.100
Project services	67%	*Engineering*
Estimating & cost control		4.000
Proposals		—
Computer control		—
Computer systems		1.000
Initial operations—office		0.200
Technical information		0.200
Scheduling		2.000
Procurement		
Purchasing		5.000
Inspection and Expediting		5.000
General office		
Stenographic		4.500
Accounting		7.000
Office services		2.000
Labor relations		0.100
Construction (office)		2.000
	Total	100.000

392

General Data

Application

This information can be used to check a contractor proposal of home office man-hours. It can be used for early evaluations of home office manpower and schedules when only total costs or man-hours are available.

Example

1. For a typical project we can assess the percent piping man-hours. This is derived by summing the hours required for piping engineering activities (plant design, 16.4%; piping engineering, 2.1%; bill of materials, 2.1%; and model, 0.4%, of a total of 21%).
2. As a percent of engineering only, piping becomes 21%/0.67 = 32%.

As overall engineering and piping design are often on the critical path, individual evaluations are frequently required. Where information is lacking, use the following:

Engineering man-hours as a percent of total home office: 65%
Piping man-hours as a percent of engineering: 35%

10.3 MATERIAL COST BREAKDOWN

The following is a breakdown cost of equipment and material:

	Typical Refinery (%)	Crude Unit (%)
Structural steel	4.76	3.84
Heaters	5.08	14.52
Exchangers	9.34	19.89
Reactors	6.38	–
Pressure vessels	8.54	19.10
Pumps + driver	15.91	6.47
Compressors	1.73	–
Mechanical equipment	3.46	1.04
Piping	27.24	21.60
Electrical	9.78	5.67
Instruments	4.86	4.82
Insulation	2.92	3.05
	100.00	100.00

Application

This percent breakdown cost of equipment and material can be useful when only the overall cost is known. The typical percentages can provide scopes of classes of equipment and materials for schedule and cost evaluations. Applications of man-hour units per dollar of material can provide labor man-hours for installation.

This statistical breakdown can also be used to check an overall budget estimate.

10.4 CONSTRUCTION MAN-HOUR BREAKDOWN

Prime Account	Total Construction Man-hours (%)
Earth moving	10 (see note in text)
Civil	12
Structural steel	5
Buildings	2
Equipment	10
Piping (erection only)	35
Electrical	11
Instruments	6
Painting	4
Insulation	5
	100

This is a typical overall breakdown by prime account based on historical data for small- to medium-sized grass roots process plant projects.

Application

This exhibit can be used to provide a breakdown of construction when only the total man-hours are available. The data are based on pipe spool fabrication as a material supply. If significant pipe fabrication is carried out at the job site, the 35% for piping will increase.

Example

Assume that a project has 2 million construction man-hours. By using the preceding breakdown, we can determine that 35% (or 700,000) of these hours are for piping erection and 10% (or 200,000) of the total labor hours are used for equipment installation.

Note: The amount of earthwork varies from project to project. It will normally be a higher percentage on large grass roots projects compared to small projects containing a single process unit.

10.5 LABOR EFFICIENCY FOR EXTENDED OVERTIME

There are many occasions when a project is placed on extended overtime
to shorten the schedule. In many cases productivity will be reduced,
and costs will increase. If this condition was not part of the original
estimate, an assessment of the increased cost, as well as the schedule
advantage, should be made. The schedule evaluation should recognize
increased man-hours in the duration calculation. It is also possible that
absenteeism will increase, sometimes to an extent that there is no
schedule advantage for the increased workweek.

Figure 10.2 presents data compiled from the sources indicated on
the chart. It plots labor efficiency against overtime hours worked based
on 5-, 6-, and 7-day workweeks. These data apply only to long-term
extended workweeks. Occasional overtime can be very productive with
no loss of efficiency. Figure 10.2 shows a recommended range of productivity loss by project size (small-large).

Application

This chart can be useful in an overall evaluation of the impact of overtime hours on schedule and cost. It can establish an increase in total
labor hours required for a loss in efficiency due to an extended workweek. However, judgment should be used on an individual location basis.
Some areas, particularly less developed countries (LDCs), work 60-hr
weeks which are as productive as 40-hr weeks.

Example

Assume that a project has a total construction scope of 1 million man-
hours and is based on a 5-day, 40-hr workweek. If the same workweek
were increased by 8 hr to 48 hr, look to the chart for 8 hr of overtime,
and using the (NECA) 5-day (large-project) curve, read across to an
efficiency of 90%. This indicates that 10% more hours will be required to
accomplish the same amount of work due to a loss in efficiency. Thus,
we estimate that the total man-hours will be 1 million × 1.10 = 1,100,000
man-hours. Schedule and cost evaluations can now be made for an
additional 100,000 man-hours but at an increased level of work. Obviously, there is a schedule advantage.

Note: These curves do not include efficiency losses for a second shift.

10.6 CONSTRUCTION INDIRECT MAN-HOURS-PROGRESS

The data for Figure 10.3 have been compiled from actual experience.
They reflect the historical experience of construction indirect labor on
a large project. The curve shows that indirect man-hour usage is

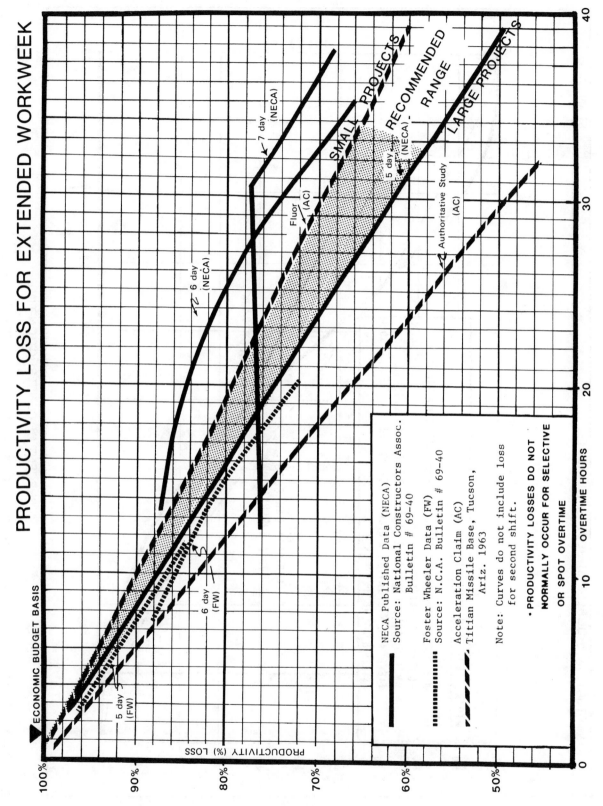

Figure 10.2 Chart of labor efficiency vs. extended overtime.

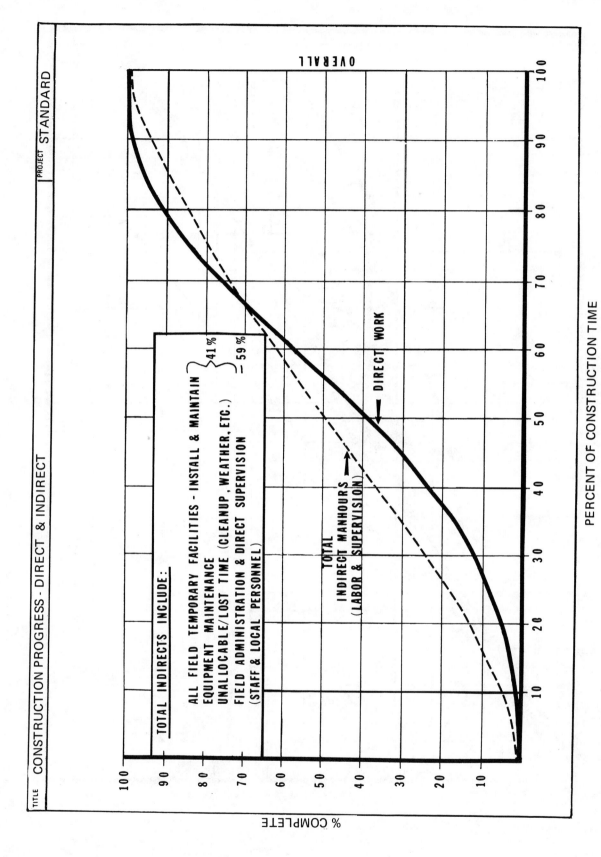

Figure 10.3   Chart of construction indirect man-hours-progress curve.

essentially constant throughout the life of a project. Early buildup for installing temporary facilities is matched by a late buildup for final cleanup and demobilization. The indirect labor represented in this graph includes craft labor for the following:

1. All field temporary facilities (install and maintain)
2. Equipment maintenance
3. Unallocable and lost time (cleanup, weather, etc.)

Field administration and direct supervision are not included in the curve but are covered in Figure 10.4.

Application

The purpose of this exhibit is to illustrate a typical relationship between *direct work* and *indirects*.

Direct work progress is a measure of physical quantities installed, and as shown, the direct work curve is identical to the historical construction curve included in the owner scheduling section.

Indirect construction progress cannot be assessed by measuring physical quantities and is usually measured in man-hours. This typical curve shows the rate at which these man-hours would normally be expended.

Indirect and direct construction curves for a project could be compared with the curves in this exhibit. During construction, actual performance should be compared with these profiles. This can provide an early warning that the expenditure of man-hours is deviating from the "norm."

Figure 10.4 is similar to Figure 10.3 but includes an additional curve for field administration and direct supervision and additional information relating to indirect man-hours. These curves should be used to assess initial planning as well as actual performance.

The percentage breakdowns for craft indirects and field administration and direct supervision can be used to check estimates and performances of individual categories.

On jumbo projects, individual control curves could be developed for individual categories.

10.7 CRAFT MIX

The data in Table 10.2 through 10.4 have been gathered from contractors.

Application

Craft mix is a useful tool for calculating manpower requirements for specific classes of work.

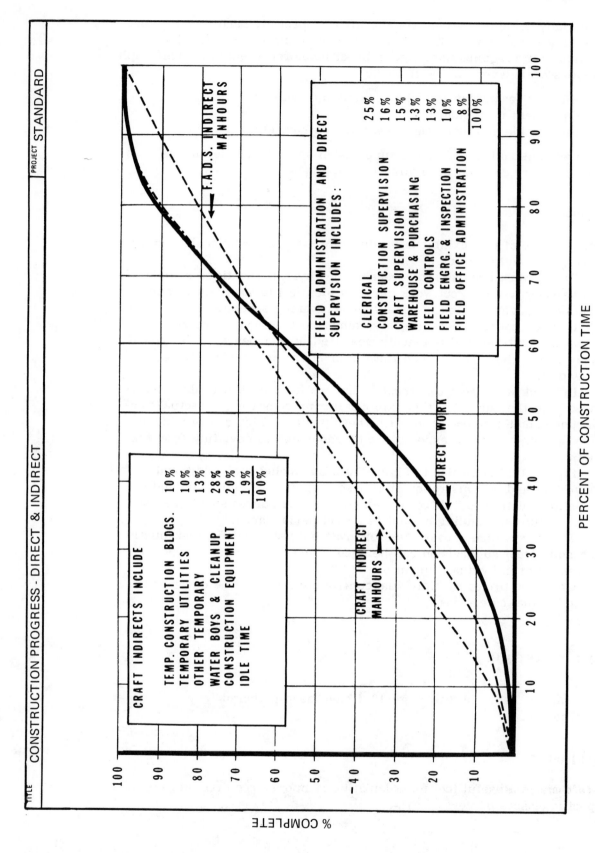

Figure 10.4 Chart of construction indirects—craft and staff.

Table 10.2

Suggested Craft Mix (%)

Craft	Standard (also for grass roots refinery)	FCC Unit	Alkylation Unit	Polypro- pylene Unit	Crude Unit	Nuclear Fuel Unit	Ammonia Plant
Boilermakers	4.2	4.6	6.7	2.9	5.6	2.5	12.2
Carpenters	8.2	8.6	7.2	8.1	7.0	13.3	5.8
Cement masons	1.1	1.1	1.7	2.4	0.9	2.1	0.6
Electricians	10.2	12.1	11.3	18.8	10.9	6.1	5.6
Ironworkers	6.2	5.5	3.4	4.4	3.8	7.8	4.7
Laborers	12.8	15.0	15.3	13.7	13.4	15.1	9.8
Millwrights	1.7	1.4	1.4	1.8	1.4	1.8	2.2
Operating engineers	7.6	6.0	4.1	4.8	6.3	3.2	6.4
Pipe fitters	40.9	42.5	45.5	39.7	46.2	32.7	49.2
Teamsters	4.6	2.0	2.5	2.6	2.7	2.4	1.6
Others	2.6	1.2	0.9	1.8	1.8	13.0	1.9

Table 10.3

Craft	Suggested Craft Mix (%)						
	Sulfur	Hydro-cracker	Gas Plant	Cat Reformer	Isomeri-zation	Pharma-ceutical	Pulp and Paper
Boilermakers	6.2	4.6	6.0	6.2	4.8	—	1.3
Carpenters	7.7	5.3	8.2	5.3	12.5	7.8	10.9
Cement masons	1.6	0.7	1.0	1.3	1.5	16.8	2.5
Electricians	10.4	8.8	13.8	12.0	15.9	2.0	20.2
Ironworkers	5.0	4.9	5.3	4.4	5.1	10.3	7.0
Laborers	13.5	9.4	13.8	8.5	15.6	18.4	17.6
Millwrights	1.5	2.1	2.7	2.4	2.3	5.9	5.1
Operating engineers	7.4	4.0	5.6	6.5	4.7	2.6	4.2
Pipe fitters	43.1	53.4	38.7	50.0	33.4	30.2	25.5
Teamsters	2.6	4.1	2.7	2.0	2.4	3.3	2.3
Others	1.0	2.7	2.2	1.4	1.8	2.7	3.4

Table 10.4

| Craft | Suggested Craft Mix (%) | | |
	Hydrogen Plant	Hydro-desulfurizer	Surface Coal Mine
Boilermakers	6.2	4.6	0.3
Carpenters	2.6	3.9	17.8
Cement masons	1.4	2.2	4.4 (cement finisher)
Electricians	16.9	17.2	11.9
Ironworkers	2.0	1.8	18.3
Laborers	10.5	8.0	18.9
Millwrights	3.9	1.7	4.2
Operating engineers	4.3	5.0	17.1
Pipe fitters	50.1	48.2	5.2
Teamsters	1.1	5.1	1.3
Others	1.0	2.3	0.6

When only the overall project cost is available, the direct field labor payroll can be calculated and converted to man-hours, as previously illustrated. Using the field labor man-hours and the appropriate craft mix, man-hours can be calculated for the various crafts.

10.8 COST CONTROL REPORTS

The following lists major reports required for a large project and shows typical monthly man-hours for developing the reports:

Overall	*Man-hours Per Month*

1. *Monthly cost report:* by account, by area, by total—actual costs and predictions — 80
2. *Trend reports* (plus engineering change log): weekly; potential and firm trends — 160
3. *Total home office cost report* (curves); Man-hour cost, burdens, overheads, fees, monthly report of commitments and expenditures — 80

	Man-hours Per Month

4. *Total home office man-hour and rate curves:* development of budget man-hours and rate against time with the actual man-hours plotted weekly-monthly — 20

5. *Contingency and overall cost tracking curves:* issued monthly — 20

6. *Cash flow curves:* cash payments related to physical progress of project; issued every 3 months and updated monthly — 40

Engineering

1. *Discipline man-hour curves:* estimated plot of man-hours against time; actual man-hours expended plotted weekly-monthly — 20

2. *Man-hour rate curves:* estimated development of budget hourly rate against time with actual rate plotted weekly-monthly — 20

3. *Quantity reports:* analysis of engineering development quantities versus budget estimate basis — 60

Procurement

1. *Material commitment report:* record of current commitments versus budget value — 80

2. *Material exception report* (rundown control): separates budget for last 20% material and controls separately from overall commitment control — 20

3. *Backcharge register:* tracks actual costs and predicts cost recovery — 40

4. *Material cost curves:* by prime account and overall — 40

Construction

1. *Monthly field cost report:* all accounts—cost to date and final forecast — 320

2. *Monthly subcontract report:* cost to date and final forecast for all subcontracts — 320

3. *Subcontract performance report:* monthly analysis of field cost per labor man-hour for major and critical subcontractors — 40

4. *Weekly field man-hour report* (curves): craft man-hours only; no supervision; actual man-hours plotted against estimated expenditure curves — 320

5. *Craft productivity report:* weekly; analyzes current level and forecasts final productivity — 160

		Man-hours Per Month

6. *Craft average rate report:* weekly-monthly, actual plotted against planned curve for key crafts — 80

7. *Unit cost report:* weekly-monthly; labor man-hour cost to install standard units and quantities; actual plotted against budget or historical base — 60

8. *Field man-hour exception report* (rundown control): last 20% budgeted and controlled separately; curves developed, and actual plotted — 40

9. *Field indirect cost curves and reports:* curves developed for all major accounts; actual plotted monthly — 240

10. *Field purchase order report:* monthly issue — 20

Total per month — 2240

The preceding is based on 160 hr/man-month = 14 workers.

Note: On a total construction subcontract job, there could be additional quantity surveyors for measuring the quantities of work accomplished.

10.9 TYPICAL DATA POINTS

The following are typical data points for evaluating estimating levels or monitoring project performance. These data apply to large U.S. process plants. Adjustments should be made for overseas locations and for small projects.

I. *Engineering*
   A. Man-hours per drawing (total drawings) — 150-160
   B. Man-hours per piece of equipment — 1000-1200
   C. Man-hours per piping isometric — 8-10
   D. Man-hours per PID — 400-500
   E. Man-hours per plot plan — 200-300
   F. Man-hours per material requisition — 8-10

II. *Construction:* The following rates do not include scaffolding, testing, or rework.
   A. *Civil*
      1. Site strip: man-hours per square yard — 0.2
      2. Machine excavation: man-hours per cubic yard — 0.5
      3. Hand excavation: man-hours per cubic yard — 2.0

4.	Underground carbon steel pipe: man-hours per foot (2-10 in.)	1.0
5.	Underground plastic pipe: man-hours per foot (1-10 in.)	0.5
6.	Concrete foundations (including formwork, rebar, etc.): man-hours per cubic yard	20-25

B. *Structural steel*

1.	Erect heavy steel (100 lb/ft): man-hours per ton	12
2.	Erect light steel (20 lb/ft): man-hours per ton	36
3.	Install platforms, ladders, etc.: man-hours per ton	40

C. *Equipment*

1.	Install pumps (0-10 hp): man-hours per each	20
2.	Install pumps (10-100 hp): man-hours per each	45
3.	Install compressors (large): man-hours per ton	20
4.	Install exchangers [shell and tube (S & T)]: man-hours per each	6
	man-hours per ton	0.7
5.	Install towers and vessels: man-hours per ton	2
6.	Install vessel internals: man-hours per ton	120

D. *Piping* (including pipe supports and testing)

1.	Prefabricate—all sizes: man-hours per ton	80-100
2.	Erect piping (0-2½ in.): man-hours per foot	0.6-1.0
3.	Erect piping (3-8 in.): man-hours per foot	1.5
4.	Erect piping (10-20 in.): man-hours per foot	2.0
5.	Erect piping (3-8 in.): man-hours per ton	200
6.	Erect piping (10-20 in.): man-hours per ton	250

Even though these are typical numbers for the United States, there are individual areas where adjustments would be required to reflect poor productivity.

These numbers can give some guidance as they do generally reflect current conditions; however, development of one's own set of data points is recommended.

INDEX